Electronic Product I

TUTORIAL GUIDES IN ELECTRONIC ENGINEERING

Series editors
Professor G.G. Bloodworth, *University of York*
Professor A.P. Dorey, *University of Lancaster*
Professor J.K. Fidler, *University of York*

This series is aimed at first- and second-year undergraduate courses. Each text is complete in itself, although linked with others in the series. Where possible, the trend towards a 'systems' approach is acknowledged, but classical fundamental areas of the study have not been excluded. Worked examples feature prominently and indicate, where appropriate, a number of approaches to the same problem.

A format providing marginal notes has been adopted to allow the authors to include ideas and material to support the main text. These notes include references to standard mainstream texts and commentary on the applicability of solution methods, aimed particularly at covering points normally found difficult. Graded problems are provided at the end of each chapter, with answers at the end of the book

Transistor Circuit Techniques: discrete and integrated (3rd edition) – G.J. Ritchie
Telecommunication principles – J.J. O'Reilly
Digital Logic Techniques: principles and practice (3rd edition) – T.J. Stonham
Signals and Systems:
  models and behaviour (2nd edition) – M.L. Meade and C.R. Dillon
Electromagnetism for Electronic Engineers (2nd edition) – R.G. Carter
Power Electronics (2nd edition) – D.A. Bradley
Semiconductor Devices: how they work (2nd edition) – J.J. Sparkes
Electronic Components and Technology (2nd edition) – S.J. Sangwine
Control Engineering (2nd edition) – C. Bissell
Electronic Product Design – A.E. Ward and J.A.S. Angus

Electronic Product Design

A.E. Ward
Lecturer in Engineering Management
University of York
UK

and

J.A.S. Angus
Senior Lecturer in Electronic Engineering
University of York
UK

CHAPMAN & HALL
London · Weinheim · New York · Tokyo · Melbourne · Madras

Published by Chapman & Hall, 2–6 Boundary Row, London SE1 8HN, UK

Chapman & Hall, 2–6 Boundary Row, London SE1 8HN, UK

Chapman & Hall GmbH, Pappelallee 3, 69469 Weinheim, Germany

Chapman & Hall USA, 115 Fifth Avenue, New York, NY 10003, USA

Chapman & Hall Japan, ITP-Japan, Kyowa Building, 3F, 2-2-1 Hirakawacho, Chiyoda-ku, Tokyo 102, Japan

Chapman & Hall Australia, 102 Dodds Street, South Melbourne, Victoria 3205, Australia

Chapman & Hall India, R. Seshadri, 32 Second Main Road, CIT East, Madras 600 035, India

First edition 1996

© 1996 A.E. Ward and J.A.S. Angus

Printed in Great Britain by Alden Press, Oxford

ISBN 0 412 63200 4

A catalogue record for this book is available from the British Library

∞ Printed on permanent acid-free text paper, manufactured in accordance with ANSI/NISO Z39.48-1992 and ANSI/NISO Z39.48-1984 (Permanence of paper)

Contents

Preface

This is a book that has been crying out to be written. Engineering is all about applying science in order to improve people's lives. In fact the word engineer is formed from the Latin word meaning genius or clever device. Therefore designing new electronic products is surely a core aspect of the discipline. Yet as engineers we are often guilty of focusing on a small, possibly intellectually very stimulating, technical part of the product. We are more comfortable with calculations that give right, or wrong, answers. Unfortunately real electronic products involve a variety of aspects which are less amenable to rigorous calculation, such as: what does the user actually want; or, can the product be made at a price the customer will pay. The history of engineering is littered with examples of excellent ideas and real ingenuity, which have failed in the marketplace because they have failed to address the needs of the customer or production. Even more galling is the fact that many of these products have subsequently been re-engineered by others who then go on to make a lot of money because they have addressed the needs of the customer and the production process.

Perhaps the problem is one of education. By and large our engineering courses, quite rightly, focus on rigorous, often mathematical, methods of analysis and modelling of electronic devices, techniques and systems. These are essential to the understanding and detailed design of electronic products and also are amenable to the production of examination questions with correct answers. However, it is possible to lose sight of the fact that there are aspects of electronic product design which, although they are less amenable to calculation, are nevertheless important. This is because we find 'soft' results difficult to cope with, we want a definite yes or no rather than a definite maybe!

Yet many aspects of real product design involve dealing with 'soft' information such as: how big, how much, what facilities, how reliable and so on. There are also the harder considerations to do with making lots of anything. Answering the question, 'Can we make a lot of the product and sell it at a profit?' requires a careful analysis of the production process, preferably before you mortgage your home. Thus electronic product design is like a very large juggling act with a combination of art, finance, hard sums and science and in many cases there is not a single correct answer. Instead there is a balance of compromises, which are an expression of the creativity of the team or individual responsible. When it works well it is exhilarating. Getting it together in electronic product design is what this book is about.

This book, uniquely, covers electronic product design from the perspective of the electronic designer. It assumes that the reader is familiar with the basics of electronics normally encountered in the first year of an undergraduate programme and deals with how electronic functionality is implemented in a wide range of products. In particular it covers the areas of: what should one be designing and what design goals one should aim for? How can one approach designing the system? How can one determine how much a product will cost to develop, make and distribute and how will that relate to the selling price? How can one design a product to be easy to manufacture with a good yield and at a low cost? How can one design a product to ensure it works well and reliably in different environments and how can one calculate and measure these aspects before the customer does it for you?

In all of this our core philosophy is that if you design an electronic product from the outset to take account of the needs of both the customer and production then it is more likely to be successful than if you do not. We also believe that to do so is not only at the heart of our discipline but is also intellectually challenging, emotionally satisfying, financially rewarding and generally fun!

We would also like to thank Jackie and Kate for their tremendous support and our families for putting up with our antisocial behaviour during the gestation of this book.

Electronic product design : an introduction   1

Objectives

At the end of this chapter you will be able to:

- Explain the basic product development process
- Demonstrate the difference between sequential and concurrent product development
- Define the difference between product and process development
- Indicate the risks associated with product development

The process of electronic product design requires a logical progression from a functional specification to the finished product. The functional specification comes from an analysis of the needs and expectations of the product, these being expressed as a set of design parameters, usually, but not solely, numeric. As a first example consider the design of an audio amplifier. Given a specification similar to that shown in Table 1.1, most electronic engineers could design a suitable amplifier. Would the product work? If so, would it meet the customer's expectations? Would it still be working in a year's time? How rugged is it? Will it still work in a very hot or very cold spell of weather? Can it be manufactured? If so, for how much?

Table 1.1 Outline specification for an audio power amplifier

• frequency range	10Hz - 20kHz
• input signal	700mV p/p
• input impedance	1 kΩ
• output power	100W p/p
• output impedance	8Ω
• total harmonic distortion	<0.001%
• mains powered	

There is insufficient information in the specification to answer the questions posed above. The specification is purely electronic with no statement of the environment within which the product will be required to function, the required reliability, quality of build or whether it is to be a mass produced or a high specification one-off.

What then does the designer set out to design when faced with the above electronic specification? The design may end up as a breadboard or at best a design based on what the designer thinks might be appropriate answers to some of the above questions. The end product is likely to be an amplifier that needs redesigns later when the full extent of the specification emerges.

The design of a circuit to perform a specified function, such as the amplifier above, usually requires very specific skills, a lot of flair and creativity and careful attention to detail. To say such an activity is easy would be an understatement of what is involved. However it is only one part of the design of a complete electronic product. This book explores some of the other issues involved and puts 'electronic' design into context with 'product' design.

Design in reality is the balancing of a number of conflicting requirements and constraints to produce a product that meets the expectations of everybody who comes into contact with it. We once had a long debate with a colleague, a purest designer, who argued that design in this sense is a compromise. Electronic design theory, as taught in most classical undergraduate courses, seeks to find the optimal solution for a given set of conditions. So why is the best design not the right one? What is the best design? The design with the most gain, the design with the most bandwidth, the design with the most power added efficiency, the most robust design? All of these answers might be correct for one particular design, none is right for all designs in general. The best design is the design which best fits all the requirements.

The specification shown in Table 1.1 does not, for example, define anything related to:

- the manufacturing process to be used to produce it;
- the physical environment within which the product will be operated;
- the reliability required of it;
- the cost to develop it and cost to produce it.

These, and many others, are defined constraints which strongly influence the design process. In this first chapter the context of design will be set. The general process followed and the options open to designing products will be explored. This will set the scene for a number of chapters that follow which will consider some of the other design aspects, such as design for manufacture, cost and the physical environment as well as designing for real components (tolerance design). All these constraints must be known at the start of the project if the most effective development programme is the be achieved.

In these days of increasing business competitiveness there is little time to take multiple iterations at designing products. The time from idea to production needs to be as short as possible. The need to become better at understanding the whole design problem is key to achieving these objectives and it is this area this book starts to address. To start with a short review of the general product development process might be appropriate.

The basic product development process

Product development is a process within organisations. As a process it takes a series of inputs and, within a given set of constraints, produces a set of outputs. Fig. 1.1 depicts this general process form. The inputs can be in the form of raw materials, components, people skills, time, money and so on. These basic inputs are transformed by the process which operates with a set of constraints which would include the company procedures and practices, the quality system, the human resources system, and so on. The end result is the output, the final product, the service provided, or whatever the process output happens to be.

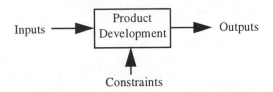

Fig. 1.1 The general product development process.

Also, being a process, it requires a defined start and end. The start may be the signing-off of a project authorisation form or simply the instruction to go. Whatever the organisational form, it is necessary to have, at the outset, a statement of the target for the development. This target is usually the specification, or a set of documents which, together, form an overall requirement specification. The specification needs, as a minimum, to embrace the:

- electrical specification;
- 'Ilities
- product process(s);
- production unit cost;
- production documentation package;
- product approval requirements;
- production volume;
- quantity of prototypes.

The 'Ilities address the suitability of the product for its intended purpose and include:

- manufacturability;
- environmental compatibility;
- reliability;
- safety;
- testability;
- serviceability;
- liability.

Product developments take place in the organisational environment present at the time. This necessarily imposes constraints on the development. Some of these constraints are:

- available budget;
- company development practices and procedures;
- the quality system;
- available development time;
- reporting requirements;
- available resources.

It might be argued that adherence to the company quality system is not a constraint but an input. How it is considered is less important than recognising the need to produce a good quality product through good quality practices. This book stresses the need to achieve this through good and thorough general design practices and by considering all the required factors at the most appropriate time.

The simple product development process model in Fig. 1.1 shows only the outline of the model. In order to turn the idea for a product into the product itself a more detailed model is required. The model shown in Fig. 1.2, with some words of caution, will be used as a more detailed model.

Whilst Fig. 1.2 is shown as a sequential series of process steps, it still needs expanding in order to reflect what happens in practice. Before expanding on this it is useful to define the meaning of each of the process steps.

3

Design

The objective of the design stage is to take the requirements and from them produce an overall product requirement statement. This overall requirement can then be used as the basis of a top-down structured decomposition of the problem into more manageable parts. Take as an example a point-to-point communications system. The need is to communicate low speed (less than 1000 baud) data from a control room to an outstation a mile away. The outpost is in line of sight of the control room.

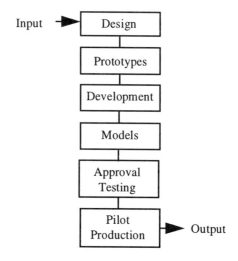

Fig. 1.2 The product development process.

The design stage would take the overall requirement and break it down into its major parts. Some questions immediately arise, such as will the link be a wire link or a radio link. If the latter, what frequency will be used and what modulation technique? The design at this stage has many unknowns and many technical risks. The design stage is there to consider these questions and carry out studies to provide answers. In this way the design stage is the technical risk reduction phase of the project. Clarity is brought to the approach to be taken.

The output of the design stage must be an agreed approach to the problem and a definition of performance requirements of the individual components that will come together to form the overall product. The design stage must, therefore, result in the specification of the communications approach to be used in the communications system example above, a specification for the transmitter and receiver, antenna specifications (assuming a radio link) and the communications protocol. In some cases it will be appropriate for the design stage to look inside modules to produce detailed sub-system designs with module specifications.

Using these specifications, residual technical risks, those that cannot be dealt with by theory alone, can be identified. These risks can be addressed by construction of prototypes.

Prototypes

Prototypes are trial circuits constructed to prove whether the basic design ideas will work. The form of the prototype need not be representative of the required final form. The key objective of the prototypes is to reduce the technical risk of the overall design and to show that the design principles will work. Once these have been achieved full development can go ahead.

Development

The development stage is where the product is turned into something that will meet all the overall requirements. During development a full set of product drawings and specifications will be produced. The fine detail of the production process will be decided and all required jigs and fixtures will be produced to allow production to take place.

Models

The full drawing package will be used to produce a number of models that are fully representative of the final product. Some of these will be used in the formal product approval testing

Approval testing

Approval testing, sometimes referred to as 'type approval testing', is the formal testing of the product to the specification. This will normally involve environmental testing, testing for compliance with national or international regulations, such as Electromagnetic Compatibility (EMC) and safety testing. Certification to these requirements is normally required before product sales can take place.

Pilot production

To verify that the developed design can be manufactured it would be normal to produce a small initial or trial batch on a pilot production line. Pilot production is there to verify both the product design and the manufacturing process design, to ensure the product can be assembled and tested with designed-for production costs and yields.

Serial or parallel activity management

The activities shown in Fig. 1.2 are shown as sequential. This is not implying an 'over-the-wall' product development approach. In over-the-wall product development one team performs a specific task and then passes the design onto another group who do the next stage. For example, in the audio amplifier case, there would be a team of designers who would design the circuit diagram and verify it using a computer aided design and verification package. The design team would then pass the design information onto a separate team who would produce and test a specified number of prototypes. The results of the prototypes would be passed to a development team who would develop the product into a form suitable for the customers needs and for production. Samples, in the form of representative models are produced which demonstrate that the product has been successfully developed. Some of these samples are passed to an approval team who test the samples against the formally required approval specifications such as the European Electromagnetic Compatibility specification and the Health and Safety standard for mains powered devices. Models and the development information package are also passed to a pilot production team who produce a pilot batch of the amplifiers to demonstrate that the design meets the required production time standards, that it can be made for an acceptable cost and that the manufacturing process has an acceptable yield.

The approach just described has involved six different teams and five occasions where hand-over of information occurs. At each hand-over there is an opportunity for one team to say their part of the product development is finished and for the other party to disagree. Each hand-over presents the opportunity for one team to say that a particular part of the overall product development is their responsibility and the other to say it is not. Clearly there is scope for conflict and holes into which essential tasks can fall where nobody will accept responsibility. The whole methodology is slow, cumbersome and inefficient.

This approach of working has now been superseded, at least in terms of a management model that can be adopted by organisations who are prepared to accept change, with a more parallel approach. There is considerable debate over the title of the alternative approach and of the various variations of it. The two most commonly heard names are 'concurrent engineering' and 'simultaneous engineering'. Without entering into the politics of the difference in name, both approaches aim to ensure all activities, and especially all parties, are involved in the project at all stages starting on day one.

To produce a product in an efficient and effective way everybody who will come into contact with the product ought to be involved from the outset. Such an approach makes it essential to establish a project team from the outset and to ensure good and open communications take place. Take for example the audio amplifier again, a product which will be manufactured in volume. An inefficient way of designing and developing the product would be to give it to an electronic design engineer to produce a prototype and demonstrate that it works, then to pass it on to a development engineer who redesigns it to make it compatible with the company production process and preferred components. A far more efficient way would be to assign a representative of the production process to the project team and ensure the electronic designer produces a design which is compatible with the company production process and preferred components.

This argument can be easily extended to include sales, marketing, quality, service, purchasing and so on. Few parts of an organisation are not touched when a new product is introduced. Even the telephone switchboard operators, and that is not to be taken as belittling the one part of the organisation that is regularly the first point of contact of customers and clients, need to be aware of new product introductions so that calls can be routed in a knowledgeable fashion. By involving everybody in the project team, from the outset, each task has the greatest potential of only needing to be completed once. If everybody has a say at each stage there is the highest probability that the result will be correct.

Allowing everybody to have a say in every task has the potential of being an organisational nightmare. Imagine a team of 50 people designing a large, complex product. Should all fifty people be gathered into a single room for a debate on whether the power supply should be fixed to the chassis by nuts and bolts or by bolts into threaded inserts riveted to the chassis? If this approach is adopted decisions will take an enormous length of time, if they are reached at all.

To get everybody together is unnecessary. However, there are a sub-set of the team who ought to be given the opportunity to have an input to the decision. The choice of who should have an input depends on the impact the decision has. In the case of how the power supply is attached to the chassis, Production will be affected because they will be making large quantities of the end result and

Mechanical Design are affected because the attachment method affects the strength of the joint and how well it will withstand the rigours of the environmental specification. Any decisions will affect Purchasing and Finance, although in this case in a way that is simple enough for either the manufacturing or design representative to bear in mind. The project manager may need to be present to ensure the reasons for the decision are recorded and all options or design considerations are borne in mind. The decision may also impact the time taken to design the joint and hence may impact the project timescales, costs or risks.

There can be no general rules for the ideal project team other than that every affected discipline should be represented to ensure the best decision possible is reached. The nearest constituency of a complete product development team would be one that comprised members who can:

- manage the project;
- carry out mechanical design;
- carry out tolerance analyses;
- carry out electronic design;
- represent the quality needs;

- represent the needs of formal testing;
- carry out reliability analyses and testing;
- represent the needs of purchasing and production;
- represent the views of the customer;
- represent the purse holders (accounts).

Some of these inputs can be made by the same people; in other cases a resident or external expert in the field will be more appropriate. In large projects there may be several people in each area. There may also, by virtue of the company organisation structure, be representatives of the documentation control system, the drawing office, the thermal design, mechanical stress, electromagnetic compatibility, safety, product liability. The general picture should be one of involvement rather than exclusion.

The team at the outset should establish a method of communication to ensure no member is left out of any decision or deprived of any information relevant to their input or area. Information should be made freely available rather than picketed for private use.

For a project to be completed successfully and to time and budget there needs to be a total commitment to the project by everybody, especially management. Management enables the allocation of resources and the right type of resources. The allocation of poor physical resources or inadequately trained human resources will add risk to the project. The allocation of personnel unfamiliar with the particular requirements of the project or lacking the skills required to carry out their particular job will involve training or learning and will be less efficient than using somebody with the skills already developed.

How then do people develop and grow? Experience gained on new projects is a valuable part of this staff development. However if this involves the learning of new tools or techniques then it will be inefficient. A more efficient approach would be to consider the introduction of the new tool or technique as a valuable general skill and provide the training in such a way as it does not impact upon product development timescales and hence add risk to current projects. Such training is then said to be off-line.

The important first project steps

Two important first steps have so far been described, the need for a defined specification and the establishment of a project team. These are two of the three keys to a successful project. The keys are summarised in Fig. 1.3. For completeness the first two will be summarised before expanding on the third key.

The specification

A complete statement of the needs of the product is required if the project target is to be achieved. Any aspect of the specification that is undefined or ambiguous is one that has the scope for causing delays or confusion in the future. All such issues should be resolved at the outset.

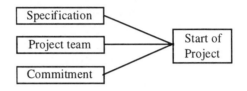

Fig. 1.3 The starting keys to a successful project development.

Project team

Team size is important. Too large a team and the management task becomes difficult. Too small a team results in resource shortages, overload and sometimes mistakes.

No project should be started without a defined project team. The team should comprise the main resources required and representatives of functions that need to have an input to the product design and development.

Management commitment

Without management commitment to and understanding of the needs of the project, time and money can easily be lost. Take for example an internal company rule that says all purchases have to be authorised by the line director, a rule we have experienced. What happens when the individual is unavailable, perhaps for days on end. The delays introduced cannot easily be planned for. Most project plan reviewers would object to an activity called 'wait for director to sign purchase order'. There must be the commitment, perhaps through delegation of signing authority in this case, to the project and its attendant needs.

The project, to start, will need some form of authorisation. This can range from the formal signing of a project authorisation document to the verbal command from a manager. Whatever form the authorisation takes it must be seen to have been made by the project team because it should start a train of activities that will commit money.

Product development management

There are two aspects to product development management. Firstly, there is the management of each product development, that is each project. This task is referred to as 'project management'. Secondly, there is the management of the product development process as a whole within the organisation. This, too, is referred to as 'process management'. These two management tasks are very different for a number of reasons.

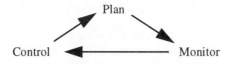

Fig. 1.4. The project management cycle.

Project management

Project management is concerned with the whole process illustrated in Fig. 1.1, that is the transformation of the inputs, bearing in mind any and all constraints, into the desired outputs. The output could be an audio amplifier, a computer controlled house central heating controller, a computer installation, a piece of software, a book, anything that has a definable output. The key objective of project management is to ensure that every task that needs to be completed to achieve a good quality output product on time and within the prescribed costs, is completed. In anything other than trivially simple projects, project management requires the use of some formal planning methods that enable a project plan to be drawn up and used to manage the project. There are three stages to project management, as shown in Fig. 1.4, planning, monitoring and controlling. These three stages are generally iterative in that the original plan often requires modifying during the development of a product to reflect changes that may occur. Two of the basic tools of project management are described in chapter 4.

The creation of a project plan and the identification of all the activities required during the product development is a small part of project management. As the product specification becomes clearer and the route to the end product more visible, project management becomes the task of motivating the staff to achieve outputs by due dates, of managing costs, and of managing the risks associated with the project. There are three types of risk associated with product development:

The management of the Channel Tunnel project was not simply the management of the people; the machines that bored the hole and the provision of the tunnel services. The safety risk of personnel and the risk of the two holes not joining in the middle had to be very carefully managed.

- target, or specification risk;
- technical risk;
- programme risk.

Target or specification risk. At the start of the project there should be a specification, the specification defines the 'what', that is, what the end product must look like, or must do, if it is to meet the customer's needs and expectations. If the 'what' is not very clearly defined there will be a risk that the target aimed at throughout the product development process is not the target the customer is expecting. This risk must be minimised if time and money are not to be wasted developing a product that does not match the need.

Consider, for example, the specification given in Table 1.1. The specification has already been shown to be inadequate in that it does not define the environmental requirements, the required reliability, the quality of build and so on. If this specification is all you were given, the end product could, and almost certainly would, not meet the customer's needs and expectations. It could fail to meet the needs on the grounds of size, weight, inability to withstand the environment, and so on. A clear and complete specification is needed to avoid target specific risks.

An important point to remember about target risks is that they will not materialise until the end product is delivered to the customer, or the customer is invited to see prototypes. A significant part of the product development process has taken place by this time, a significant amount of time will have elapsed and a significant amount of money will be spent. A serious specification omission will result in rework, redesigns, more time and more money.

Technical risk.   As soon as common agreement has been reached over the target the next consideration is the 'how'. How will the product be developed? Does the product require some new circuitry, a new approach to doing something, or a new process? There is very likely to be a technical risk associated with the product. This technical risk will be greatest at the start of the project and must, again through project management, be reduced quickly to enable full development to go ahead.

Consider the amplifier example again. If the customer requires the amplifier to be able to take the output of the latest standard in digitally recorded music, a new equalisation circuit might be required. Perhaps nobody within the organisation has designed such a circuit before. Perhaps the standard must first be obtained before the output is really understood. There is a risk that the circuit will prove harder to design than is anticipated or, even worse, cannot be designed with the present state of technology in general. The success of the whole project relies on the elimination of this technical risk and the design and development of the input circuit. Project management must address such technical risks very early on so that if there is an insurmountable technical risk, the minimum time and money is spent.

Programme risk.   With all the target and specification risks under control there is the risk that one or more project activities will take longer than planned, that a key resource will not be available exactly when it is required, that a supplier or sub-contractor takes longer than planned to produce what is expected of them, that a communication goes wrong and somebody does the wrong thing, and so on. There is a multitude of different things that can go wrong, and regularly do, in the management of a real project. The role of the project manager is to maintain control of the project plan and to look forward to ensure that required resources are going to be available at the date required, that the resources are of adequate calibre to perform the task in the planned time and that the support equipment is going to be present and will be in a fully working state.

The role of the project manager, as far as the management of programme risk is concerned, is one of problem anticipator. Problems will occur, but which ones and when are unknown. However, by looking at the future plan the question what happens if ... can be asked. What happens if the printed circuit board layout engineer is away sick when the circuit needs to be laid out? What happens if the design computer breaks down? What happens if the prototype parts are delivered late by the supplier? The answers to all these questions, and what can will be done if the eventuality happens, are called 'contingency' plans. Contingency planning is an important part of the successful project manager's job.

The main objective of process management is to ensure that the organisational environment is such that products can be developed in a fast and efficient manner. The competition in the electronics industry is getting progressively more efficient at developing new products. We see more and more products coming onto the market with shorter and shorter product lives. Consider, for example, the development of the personal computer. From the days of a physically large machine, such as the Apple I or II, with memory measurable in the hundreds of kilobytes and no internal permanent storage, through the days of the evolving personal computer, the XT, AT, 286, 386, 486 to the Pentium chip and so on. The processor speed, available working storage, so called Random Access Memory, and internal more permanent storage, the hard disk, have all increased. We have seen the introduction of CD ROMs, optical rewriteable disks, multimedia systems, voice recognition systems; the list goes on. All these have appeared over a very small number of years. Computers and add-ons appear in the computer magazines one month and may be gone within a couple.

It is interesting to note that in a typical 286 system there was typically 512kbytes of Random Access Memory. Modern Pentium systems require 16Mbytes or more.

If an organisation cannot match, or set the standard for, the speed of new product developments it is likely to have a tough time staying in the business. Not only do new products need to be introduced quickly but quality and cost need to be fully under control. The good name of the company is exposed every time a new product is launched onto the market. A bad product can result in the boycott of future products. A product that costs too much to develop or is not cheap enough to manufacture in volume can result in heavy losses for the company and bankruptcy.

A robust and effective product development process is one of the keys to the overall success of a company. The management of the product development process should therefore be a key management objective. The product development process, as shown in Fig 1.1, has inputs, constraints and a process. The management of the process is concerned with ensuring that the procedures, practices and culture within the organisation are appropriate and supportive of the process. A procedure that requires every purchase to be approved by a senior manager who is busy and out of the office most of the time, is likely to result in delays at key times. A very hierarchical organisation that complicates team level communications is likely to be slow and inefficient. Everything needs to be geared to ensuring the maximum competitive advantage can be gained from new product development.

Process management can only be achieved by reviewing what is happening within specific product developments. Reviewing whether the current procedures and practices are supporting or hindering product developments will reveal areas for improvement, new technologies that can be introduced to overcome serious bottlenecks or technical problems, changes to the organisation structure that will improve communications, and so on. Regular reviews and responses are requires if the organisation is to remain flexible and responsive to market opportunities and the treats provided by the competition.

Summary

In this chapter we have introduced the product development process and some of the common terminology used to describe some of the main ways in which products are developed. In principle product development can be described in a simple input - process - output type of model where inputs are acted upon and turned into the finished product. In reality the situation is vastly more complicated. To develop a product successfully attention must be paid to both the management of the project itself, and in particular of the risks associated at each stage in the product development, and of the company's approach to product development as a whole.

The major objective of the chapter has been to lay a foundation of understanding of the whole process of product development that can be developed in subsequent chapters. It should be remembered that there is no single approach to product development and no single set of terminology used to describe what happens within the process. Every organisation will have its own variant of the process, its own terminology to describe project stages and project documentation and its own set of procedures and practices. The process adopted and set of terminology used within this book is one example and is a fairly simplistic and top level view. There will, in most cases, be other models and approaches, all based on the general model describe in this book, that are used in practice.

Problems

1.1   What are the risks associated with the development of a new, flat screen display suitable for portable computers?

1.2   You are required to form a team to develop a new, flat screen display suitable for portable computing products. The display needs to be taken to final product form such that it will interface directly with a specified type of portable computer. What skills would you need in the development project and what resources would you look for in the formation of a project team?

1.3   Produce a preliminary list of the areas relevant to the development of the flat screen display described above, which need to be specified to form an outline product specification.

1.4   Explain the main purposes for producing models representative of the final form of a product.

Establishing needs and specifications

2

At the end of this chapter you will be able to:

- Define the sources of new product ideas
- Interpret a customer problem and translate it into a product specification
- Be able to state the importance of the product, price, promotion and place in the marketing of a product
- State the options open to gaining a product competitive advantage
- Produce a specification based upon the organisational needs and expectations associated with new product development
- State the major contents of a product specification
- Develop checklists to help ensure all aspects of a product specification are included

Before any product development can start there must be a clear specification for the end product. Basically the rules need to be fixed. Who creates the specification and what it contains is the subject of this chapter. There is no universal correct person, or group of people, in the best position to create a specification. There are many routes to a specification with a number of starting points. The first part of the chapter considers these routes and their starting points. The second part explores the contents of a specification and the types of things that need to be specified. A good specification is a broad, all-embracing document or set of documents. A general set of checklists will be used to help ensure the breadth of coverage of specifications you might encounter or be asked to produce in the future.

Routes to a specification

The need or idea for a product can come from four different areas. These are:

- customer need or problem;
- idea generated by an individual;
- new technology;
- legislation.

Customer need or problem

Some of the best products result from a problem or need. A customer or individual realises there is a problem that can be overcome; or the need, or desire, for a product that will do something to add value to living or working. Products that fulfil a real purpose or overcome a real problem create good products, as illustrated by the following example.

In 1990 there was a large amount of concern for the quality of fresh food and its storage. In particular, several well publicised incidents of food poisoning had resulted in public concern over the possibility of salmonella and listeria micro-organisms being present and reproducing in stored food. Several areas for improvement were identified, the main ones involving the quality of food production and storage in the home. In the light of this a need was identified for some way of monitoring the quality of refrigerated food storage in the home. In particular two areas for monitoring were identified.

- refrigerator or freezer temperature, in order to ensure that it did not rise above the maximum safe level for food storage;
- inadvertently leaving the door open, which would ultimately result in the first condition.

In addition the product had the following additional requirements :

- memory of a temperature rise incident so that a user would realise that at some point since the last time the fridge/freezer had been used the temperature had risen above the safe level, even if the current temperature was adequate;
- a battery lifetime of at least one year;
- a selling price of between £20 and £30;
- be small, unobtrusive and white.

The last three specifications were determined from a survey of shoppers using a large food supermarket chain.

The requirements implied the need for an extremely inexpensive product with a minimum of parts. In particular, the power system was identified as a key area because normal batteries have significantly reduced capacities at low and subzero temperatures.

A block diagram of the final system is shown in Fig. 2.1. And the features of the design that helped it meet the specification are as follows:

The wake-up timer is, in this example, an electronic circuit that produces a short pulse every 30 seconds, that switches the power switch to energise the rest of the circuitry for a period that is just long enough to perform its required function.

• **Pulsed battery operation**: All of the circuitry, except for the wake-up oscillator, was powered up for a only a few milliseconds in every 30 seconds. This significantly extended the battery life, in fact at normal room temperature the system would work for over five years! As this exceeded the shelf life of the battery it was a little irrelevant. However if the alarm went on the alarm circuitry operated continuously.

• **Alarm lock**: Once the alarm was set it could be switched off only via the use of a manual reset. This meant that the user would hear it the next time the fridge was opened.

• **Dual environment sensing**: As well as temperature, the product sensed light level. This allowed the fridge-alarm to sense either the fridge light or the ambient light level in order to detect the presence of an open door.

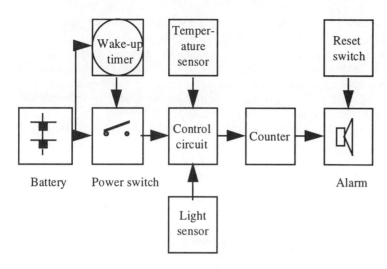

Fig. 2.1 Block diagram of the fridge alarm.

• **False alarm protection**: The temperature and light level had to be present for four wake-up periods (two minutes) in order to operate the alarm. This gave protection against occasional glitches and allowed the user to open the fridge for normal use.

• **Low cost**: The circuitry required was kept as simple as possible and the number of external controls minimised. The only control was the reset switch, and there was no on-off switch. In addition, two separate versions were created; the fridge-alarm for the fridge and the freeze-alarm for the freezer. The freeze-alarm was black in order to differentiate it from the fridge-alarm. This reduced both the cost and the possibility of the product being set wrongly.

The idea for a product can come from an individual customer as a specific request for a product such as one where the item may solve a specific problem the customer has. In such cases, there is likely to be a clearly describable target from which the establishment of a specification can commence. Figure 2.2 shows a flow chart representation of the route to the specification in this case.

In Fig. 2.2 the starting point for the specification is a statement of the customer specific problem. This statement is evolved into a problem statement which can be used as the basis for an investigation into possible solutions. The possible solutions can then be tested against a set of customer defined selection criteria from which a single solution should emerge. This solution, in conjunction with company specific needs and needs introduced by the competitive environment within which the product will be sold, forms the basis of the product specification.

Idea generated by an individual

Another source of new product ideas is an individuals idea for a product. Again the idea can be for a product to solve a specific problem or to fill a need or perceived need. In the case of a product to fill a need there is likely to be a clear definition of the need but a rather less clear view on the product to meet the need. It is also possible, if not probable, that different potential users will perceive the need slightly differently. To ensure the product will have wide appeal it might be necessary to survey prospective customers seeking their views, in other words carry out a market survey. Figure 2.3 shows the route to a specification where a market survey is included as a source of information. An example of a product that has been developed following an idea by an individual is the Sony Walkman. The brief story of the origin of the Walkman is given below.

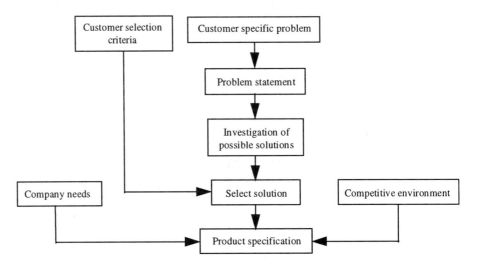

Fig. 2.2 Customer specific problem.

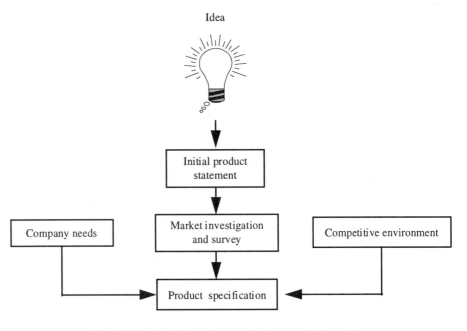

Fig. 2.3 Product idea using market survey information.

The Sony Walkman began its life when Akio Morita, the then head of the Sony Corporation, realised that the weight of the current portable stereo tape player and headphones was too much. The discussion that followed centred around the problem experienced by Ibuka, namely that of wishing to listen to music but not to disturb others while doing so. At that time listening to personal radios held against the ear whilst walking down the street or on the train, was the popular pastime of the young.

As the idea developed in his mind, Morita ordered one of his engineers to modify the company's existing, and well proven small cassette tape recorders, Pressman, to remove the recording circuitry and speaker and introduce a stereo amplifier. He also described the lightweight headphones he wanted to complement the new product.

The popular view, within Sony, of this new product was that it would not sell without a recording facility. Not put off by the comments Mr Morita persisted, even dictating the selling price of 30 000 yen, only 60% of the then selling price of the Pressman product. The product was developed and launched and proved a huge success.

The Sony Walkman is a slightly unusual example in that, in the early days, little or no market survey was performed. The product was driven by an individual with the authority to drive the product through design and development into production and into the market place. The Sony Walkman is a good example of a product that created its own market. Once the targeted customer group experienced the product it became desirable with the result that it created its own market. There is a very significant risk in developments of this kind. The cost of developing a product can cost from hundreds of thousands to millions of pounds. If such a development is carried out and no market exists for the output and one is not created by the introduction of the new product, no sales will result, no profits will be made and the money spent in development will all have been wasted.

By creating its own market the Sony Walkman has paved the way for a large number of competitive products, all similar in features and performance. The competition has resulted in the progressive reduction in selling price, a characteristic of a developing product market. To date millions of portable stereo tape players have been sold worldwide.

New technology

The proving, or making possible, of a new technology, or new way of doing something can create new products or whole new categories of products. The invention of the semiconductor junction was the cornerstone of all current electronic products. Without the semiconductor junction the transistor would not exist and without the transistor, integrated circuits would not exist.

New technologies can also make possible alternative ways of solving problems for which solutions, in the form of products, already exist and are being sold. The name for products that are produced as a result of a completely different way of solving a problem are called substitute products. Figure 2.4 shows the route to a product specification from a technological development.

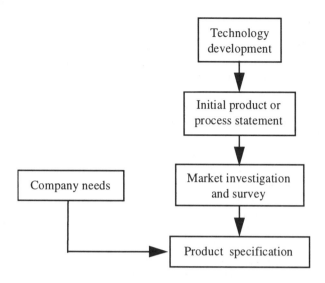

Fig. 2.4 Product specification from technological development.

Legislation

Changes in existing laws or the introduction of new legislation is a potential creator of new products. With a change in the law the affected group are required to do something new or different from how they have previously carried it out. With this change comes the opportunity to create a new product that will make life easier for those affected. The harmonisation of the European Community has created a very significant number of new standards which have, through individual country legislation, become mandatory if products made in one European country are to be sold in any of the other countries. The following list shows some areas in which standards have been introduced as part of the European harmonisation programme.

- Active medical devices
- Health and safety at work
- Food labelling
- Data protection
- Marine safety

- Electromagnetic Compatibility (EMC)
- Implantable electromedical devices
- Transportation
- Environmental monitoring

The IMO is the International Maritime Organisation. It is the organisation that sets the standards for maritime matters worldwide.

Each directive has the scope for creating the need and market for a product. Take, as an example, the worldwide issue of maritime safety. To help to ensure the safety of lives at sea the IMO has introduced the need for all ships greater than a defined size to carry electronic safety equipment. An example of a piece of such equipment is the Electronics Position Indicating Radio-Beacon (EPIRB). One type of EPIRB is a beacon which is mounted in a bracket on an exposed part of the vessel. If the vessel gets into difficulty and capsizes or sinks the EPIRB is automatically released and activated by coming into contact with sea water. Once activated the EPIRB emits signals on two of the internationally recognised distress frequencies and through them the emergency rescue services are alerted. The recognised distress frequencies are:

- Amplitude Modulated 121.5MHz continuous carrier signal;
- Phase Modulated 406.025Mhz intermittent carrier signal. The phase modulation carries information to identify the vessel and indicate the nature of the distress.

Figure 2.5 shows the route to a specification with legislation providing the impetus for the new product or the creation of the opportunity for a new product.

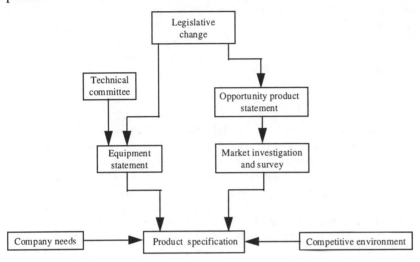

Fig. 2.5 Product specification from legislative change.

In all of the above cases, the cost of developing the new product will be born either directly or indirectly by the customer. If the product is specifically requested by a customer, as would be the case for a bespoke solution to a problem, the design and development cost would be charged to the customer in return for the delivered 'solution' to the problem. In all other cases the design and development cost will need to be considered as an opportunistic investment to be recovered on sales to a number of different customers, that is, from the market place into which the product will be sold. The exploitation of the marketing opportunity is an important part of being able to create an effective new product specification.

Exploiting the market opportunity

If a proposed new product is to sell such that it recovers the design and development investment and provides profit for the organisation it must be launched in an appropriate way and an appropriate price and with an appropriate availability. There are four key considerations in marketing a product, generally referred to as the four Ps, Product, Price, Promotion, Place.

Product

Customers never buy just the product you are developing or have just developed. What is bought is the benefi, the product gives the owner. Take as an example the simple drill bit. Do people purchase drill bits because they wish to own drill bits or because a drill bit will allow them to produce holes. The customer has the need to drill holes, hence needs the product called a drill bit. Needless to say, a drill bit is not the only way of solving the customer's problem, but is likely to be one of the cheapest.

The appearance and capability of the product are a means to an end of providing the customer with something that will be of benefit. A successful product must, therefore, meet the needs and expectations of the customers and provide them with a benefit. Expectations are important because, with the benefit there will be some things that are unwritten and taken for granted. For example, a product that meets the technical needs but which constantly fails to work or regularly breaks will not meet the customer's expectations and will be branded a poor product. Any product suffering from poor quality due to manufacture or design will not be received well by customers and will usually not sell as well as expected.

Price

The pricing of a product relative to competitive products and alternative ways the customer can gain the benefit, is an important factor in the sales success. Pricing a product too low may result in the perception of a low quality product, pricing it too high may result in customers choosing to buy a cheaper alternative. The pricing of a product is closely associated with the product capability and features relative to the competition and of its quality. Similarly pricing the product above that which would allow the customer to switch to an alternative way of gaining the benefit could also result in loss of sale. One alternative way of producing a hole is to use a laser. This is a very expensive method unless the customer happens to have one lying about in the garage for some other reason!

Promotion

Customers may not be aware of products that are not promoted and may therefore not even consider it when faced with a choice. Promoting a product is a vital part of the marketing campaign for any product. The important considerations in promotion are to ensure that the promotion reaches the target audience and that the message creates an appeal in the minds of the audience. It would be, for example, a waste of money advertising a children's toy on television after midnight!

With any form of promotion the method of advertising must be appropriate for the audience, for example, placing advertisements in magazines read by the target customers.

Place

The locations from which customers can purchase the product is an important consideration. If the product is of a type that customers expect to be able to walk into a shop and purchase, making it available only by mail order is likely to result in lower sales. The availability of the product must be appropriate for the outlets from which it can be purchased and for the product itself.

Selling in a competitive environment

Products generally have competition. Products created from new ideas will be new to the market and will have a monopoly for a while. New products that are seen to offer good sales potential will be seized upon by competitors resulting in a competitive selling situation. In some cases protection, through patents, can be gained to prevent competition in the short term, although patent protection cannot be obtained for everything!

Where there is a competitive selling situation the competition needs to be taken into account in the formulation of the product specification. You have to sell more products than the competition or, if a product is being introduced into an existing market, sales will need to be taken away from an existing producer. Consider for example, the organisation that sees money to be made by developing a product competitive to the Sony Walkman. To steal sales away from the companies that are already manufacturing personal audio tape recorders, they will have to create a product that customers will want to purchase in preference to those already on the market. What options are there open to entice customers over to the new product? The list below shows some of the possible answers to this question.

- Unique new features
- Better quality
- Marketing appeal
- Lower price
- Greater availability
- Accesses a different customer set.

Unique new features

Adding new features to the product that existing products do not have, and which customers are likely to want, is one way of gaining customers. The addition of a radio receiver to the basic tape player is an example of a feature addition. An alternative is the creation of a compact disc player version, offering improved playback sound quality.

The progressive addition of new features and facilities to an existing product is an example of product evolution and is a common marketing approach.

Lower price

Price is a pivotal feature of a product. A customer, with no manufacturer preference, faced with two products with identical functional and aesthetic specifications, made by companies with high quality reputations might choose the cheaper product. There are many conditions within this statement and no guarantee at the end of the day. A common consequence of introducing a product substantially below the price of the established competition, is that the product will be of inferior quality or lacking in features. Price alone is unlikely to result in the significant capture of sales. If the market did suddenly switch to the new product the existing competition is likely to react by reducing prices, if they can, resulting in a price war situation. Competing on price alone is a very risky business strategy unless the organisation can produce and get the product to the customers significantly more cheaply than the competition.

Better quality

A product that offers a better quality than existing products will sell provided there is a perceived value in the improved quality. If, for example, all the personal stereo systems currently on sale were known to fail after a year, the introduction of a product that lasted five years would offer customers a clear benefit. If however all of the current products have a reliability such that they do not fail within five years, the introduction of a product that has a life of 10 years is unlikely to sell significantly more than the existing products. The average ownership period of a personal stereo player is shorter than the expected life. Improvements in this area therefore offer no advantage to the customer.

The improvement in quality must be visible and of use to the customer if it is to confer a competitive advantage on the product.

Greater availability

Producing a product that is available where and when the customer wishes to make the purchase will have an advantage over a product which needs to be ordered because it is in short supply. However, if all the competitive products are readily available, then there is little scope to gain competitive advantage through improved availability.

Marketing appeal

Marketing the new product through a media advertising campaign can influence prospective customers and persuade them to purchase one product in preference to another. Television advertising is an example of such influencing. There are regular advertising campaigns for certain types of household commodities with evidence to show increased sales during the advertising campaign. Media advertising campaigns aim to raise the awareness and appeal for a specific product in the minds of prospective customers. Large scale advertising campaigns are expensive and, to be cost effective, must generate sufficient additional sales to cover the cost of the campaign.

Accesses a different customer set

The exception in the list given in Table 2.4 of ways of gaining sales in a competitive product market is to create a new market, that is to open the product up to a new group of customers. New groups of customers can be found in new geographic locations such as by exporting, or to new sociological groups such as selling a product currently targeted at children, to adults; or selling a product currently aimed at industrial customers, to the general public.

There is scope in any of the areas listed in Table 2.4 to develop the product or the market to increase sales or create a market for a competitive product. In all cases, a good knowledge of the position of all the competitors is a vital ingredient in the generation of a product specification.

So far it has been established that to produce a product specification requires knowledge of the customer's needs and expectations and the current state of the competitive environment. The third contributor to the specification is the needs and expectations of the company itself. Figure 2.6 shows these three sets of contributing factors.

Fig. 2.6 Major groups of contributing factors to a product specification.

Company needs and expectations

The primary objective of any manufacturing organisation is to create profit. Shareholders invest money in organisations with the expectation that the investment will provide them with an annual return in the form of share dividends and in the longer term in the form of capital growth. In organisations where manufacturing is the end result of the product design and development process, it is this manufacturing that is the only activity that creates significant sales and hence profit. Some organisations make substantial amounts from other activities, some of which are listed below.

- Return from financial investments
- Income from provision of a service
- Income for hiring out facilities or people

For the purposes of this chapter we will assume that the primary method of creating income for the organisation, is the sale of manufactured products. The profit generated by the sale of any individual product is the amount it is sold for less the amount it cost to manufacture. The selling price is affected, as was shown above, by the market place. The design and development process does not directly impact selling price.

The design and development process does, however, directly affect the cost of manufacturing it and hence the process directly affects the profit potential of the product and the scope for price reductions in the event of product competition. The cost to manufacture an individual product is therefore an important parameter in the product specification.

It is proposed to develop a new portable cassette player. The shop selling price of competitive products ranges from £75 to £95. It is decided that a selling price for the new product will be £80. If the shops are to be supplied directly from the manufacturing organisation, resulting in a distribution cost of £1.50 per player, and the shops require a 40% profit on each product, how much must the manufacturer produce each product if they need to achieve £15.50 profit on each player?

Worked Example 2.3

The shop selling price is	£80.00
Shop profit of 40% is	£32.00
The price the shop buys the product is therefore	£48.00
The cost of distribution is	£ 1.50
The cost of the product as it leaves the manufacturer is therefore	£46.50
The manufacturer requires a profit of	£15.50
The required cost of manufacture is therefore	£31.00

If the player cannot be made for £31.00 one of the above numbers will need to change. That is, the profit gained by the company will need to fall or the selling price to the shop will need to rise. The former will result in a direct loss of profit. The latter might result in the shop passing on the price rise to the ultimate customer which will make the product less attractive to customers resulting in lower sales. The consequence of this is a reduced number of products required to be made and a reduced overall profit.

23

Either course of action is likely to result in a reduced profit for the organisation. Since the primary objective of the organisation is to make profit, either is therefore likely to result in an unhappy management.

The above worked example has determined the required manufacturing cost to maintain a happy financial situation through the product supply chain. It has made no allowance for price changes due to changes in the competition. If, as a result of the introduction of the new product the other manufacturers decide to reduce their prices, again the new manufacturer suffers reduced profits because there is no slack in the financial model. It is preferable for the manufacturer to aim for a manufacturing cost that is below the required figure of £31.00 to allow for future price reductions. It is also important to realise that this required manufacturing cost is the total cost to convert all the constituent components and raw materials into the product as it is when it leaves the manufacturer. The product will have been manufactured, tested and packaged ready for sale on the shop counter. There will be both material and labour components in this overall manufacturing cost. How to produce the manufacturing cost of the product is dealt with in chapter 4.

The required manufacturing cost is one of the key internal product parameters which needs to be included in the product specification at the outset. It is, however, not the only manufacturing related parameter that is important. It would, for example, be extremely expensive to establish an entire production line to produce one player. Unless a significant number of players are to be produced the establishment of any kind of production line would not be cost-effective. Would it be cost effective to produce a fully automated production facility to produce 10 players per week? The answer is likely to be no. However if production were 10 000 per week the answer is likely to be yes. The number of products that need to be manufactured and the rate at which they need to be produced are therefore also important specification parameters.

The manufacturing part of the organisation will be expected to produce the products. The capability of the manufacturing part of the organisation needs, therefore, to be known at the outset of product design and development. As is shown in chapter 8 not all the process steps required to produce a product need be carried out by the manufacturer; some can be sub-contracted to other, more specialist, organisations. The overall manufacturing capability accessible to the organisation must, however, be known to ensure that a manufacturable product is developed.

Finally, the quality of the delivered product must be considered and specified. The required quality comes in part from customer expectations and in part from the quality convention within the organisation. The organisation might have a very high quality standard and a reputation based on past performance. Any new product would, quite reasonably, be expected to maintain or even enhance this quality reputation in the minds of the customers. The way the product is manufactured and tested, the quality of the raw materials used, the quality of the labour and methods used, will all need to conform to the organisations standards. Such standards will normally be laid down in the company quality manual which all employees are expected to work to.

The contents of a specification

Having established that there is more to a specification than a statement of what the product will do technically, we can start to create some general lists of areas that need to be considered and what are the important aspects as them. Using

Figure 2.6 as a starting point, the overall product specification results from needs and requirements from three broad areas.

Customer needs and expectations

The basic product aspect that needs to be specified for the customer is the basic functional and visual specification of the product, what it does and what it looks like. Looks affect sales, especially when alternative products are available to choose between. Additionally there are considerations including the physical environment in which the customers will use the product and in which the product is expected to survive. The reliability of the product is an important longer term consideration to the customer as is the cost of maintaining it and having it serviced when it does fail. Finally, once the product has been introduced into the market there will need to be a customer support system established to deal with product enquiries, complaints, service and maintenance needs, and so on. The list below summarises the areas that need to be specified.

- product technical specification
- product aesthetics
- physical environment
- reliability
- ease of maintenance and service
- customer support.

Product technical specification. The technical specification for a product is the most obvious part of the product specification. Without a statement of what the product is expected to do any product specification is clearly meaningless. The product specification is also the most difficult to generalise because of the vast range of different possible products. A general approach to technically defining a product is progressively to break-down the requirement based on the operation of a general product. Figure 2.7 shows the functional operation of a general product.

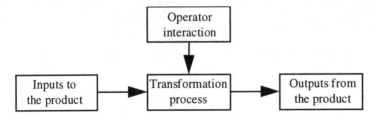

Fig. 2.7 Functional operation of a general product.

Products take one or more inputs, perform some operation on these inputs depending on the state of the product or upon operator interaction, to produce one or more outputs. A general approach to producing a product specification for any product is therefore to start by listing the inputs, listing the outputs and listing the allowable operator interactions. The outputs can then be related to the inputs and operator interactions to allow the product transformation process or processes to be specified. A simple general checklist for the technical specification of a product can be created as follows:

- list the inputs to the product;
- list the outputs of the product;
- list the allowable operator interactions;
- define the transformation process performed by the product on the inputs for the operator interactions.

Worked Example 2.4

For a portable stereo player, produce a list of product attributes that would need to be specified in order to produce an initial product technical specification.

- Step 1: List the inputs to the product
  The inputs to the player are:
  Source of music to be played.
  Battery to power the player.

- Step 2: List the outputs of the product
  The outputs of the player are:
  Audio output signal to headphones.

- Step 3: List the allowable operator interactions
  The allowed operator interactions are:
  On/off control.
  Load and eject source of music.
  Fast search facility to find desired music.
  Volume control.

- Step 4: Define the transformation process performed by the product on the inputs for the operator interactions.
  The transformation process is as follows:
  The signal from the sensor for the music source is amplified, with a mechanism for varying the amplification, to a level appropriate for listening through headphones. Additional facilities are included to allow the player to be turned on and off and for the music source to be loaded and ejected without damaging the player or the music source.

Product aesthetics. Product looks and ease of operation generally have a significant impact on the sales potential. Product design can also affect the ultimate portability, safety and general usability. It is important to ensure that the developed product has a good chance of being sold against the competition. A carefully constructed specification of the aesthetic design of the product is necessary, if only in general form, if a competitive product is to result. The main aspects of the aesthetic design of a product are:

- size;
- weight and weight distribution;
- position and type of handles;
- position and type of operator controls;
- position and nature of labels;
- location and type of any user interfaces.

The impact most of the above items have on the general usability of the product is obvious. The position of the user interfaces is perhaps one that requires some expansion. User interfaces are connections that need to be made to the product to allow it to do what it is designed to do. The most common example of a user interface is the power supply connection. Many products are mains powered, the mains connector being the user interface. Test equipment is an example of a type of product that also has one or more connectors which are used to connect electrically to the item to be tested, these connectors being also user interfaces. The physical location of these user interfaces affects the usability of the product and hence affects product sales.

For the portable stereo player, produce a list of product aesthetic design attributes that would need to be specified in order to produce an initial product specification.   **Worked Example 2.5**

- Step 1: Size
  The size of the player must be such that it can be carried in the jacket or coat pocket.
- Step 2: Weight and weight distribution
  The weight of the player must be such that it can be carried in a jacket or coat pocket without distorting the clothing or being inconvenient to the wearer. The weight distribution must be approximately even throughout the entire player.
- Step 3: Position and type of handles
  The player must be provided with an eyelet suitable for the attachment of a carrying strap. The strap must be strong enough to support the weight of the player with music source loaded into it. The strap must be large enough so that a hand can comfortably be passed through it.
- Step 4: Position and type of operator controls
  The on/off control must be integral with the volume control. This combined control must be a thumb-wheel variable control cited on the top face of the player in such a way that the accessible part of the wheel is proud of the top face and can be operated by the user easily. The wheel must have a serrated edge to provide grip and prevent the operator's finger from sliding over the control. The serration must not be sharp enough to cause injury to the operator. A battery compartment with removable lid accessible from the back of the player must be provided.
- Step 5: Position and nature of labels
  The combined on/off and volume control must be labelled with the internationally accepted volume control symbol as must the headphone socket. The operator must be provided with instructions on the music source loading cover on how to load and eject the music source; and on how to load and replace the batteries required to power the player. The inside of

the battery compartment must be labelled to indicate the type and quantity of batteries required.

- Step 6: Location and type of any user interfaces
  The headphone socket must be a miniature stereo socket compatible with existing commercially available miniature headphones. The socket is to be located on one side of the player close to the bottom face. The battery compartment lid should be on the rear face at the bottom of the player. The lid must be a snap fit that does not require any screws or other fixings to hold it in place. It must be easy for the operator to remove and replace the compartment lid. The music source load and eject location must be on the front face of the player.

Physical environment. The physical environment is the environment within which the product will be operated by customers either intentionally or by virtue of moving the product from one place to another. The physical environment can be divided into three main parts, the environment within which the user will operate the product, the environment likely to be encountered during transportation at any time and user physical abuse.

The major categories of physical environment are listed below. Each of these categories can be sub-divided into appropriate parts and quantified for the particular product and target environment.

- temperature
- humidity
- electrical

- vibration
- contamination
- survival.

Worked Example 2.6

A personal stereo player is to be developed for sales in Europe and the Middle East. How can the thermal environment of the product be defined?

In Europe the normal outside temperature range could range from 35C or above on the beach in a hot climate to sub-zero during winter. In the Middle East the temperatures often climb to above 40C in exposed situations. It is reasonable to expect the product to operate over a fairly wide temperature range of perhaps -15C to +40C. It might also be reasonable to expect the player to actually survive temperatures in a greater range, possibly -20C to +55C. Operation will not be needed over this extended range but the product should not suffer any permanent damage when exposed to or stored within this range.

The final type of thermal specification, which is not really applicable in this product case, is thermal shock. Thermal shock is where the product must survive a very rapid change of temperature.

The overall thermal specification for the product could therefore be as shown below:

Operating temperature range	-15C to +40C
Storage temperature range	-20C to +55C
Thermal shock	not applicable

By adding in a not applicable requirement in the above case we have used a generic list to test the product against. The list of thermal parameters consists of operating range, storage range and thermal shock. This list can form the starting point of a general product environmental parameter checklist which can be used in the formulation of any new product specification to ensure all environmental parameters are considered. The use of checklists helps to take the chance of missing a requirement out of product specification writing.

In exactly the same way, lists of the detailed requirements for all of the environmental areas listed above can be produced. Below is an outline checklist covering the major environmental requirements. The detail of these environmental characteristics are explained in chapter 6.

• Temperature	Operating temperature range, storage temperature range, thermal shock
• Vibration	Sinusoidal, random, resonances, shock, bump, drop
• Humidity	Waterproofing
• Contamination	Chemical, sand and dust, salt spray, fungal growth
• Electrical	Electromagnetic compatibility
• Survival	Crush resistance, fire resistance.

This outline checklist can be used to ensure that the operational environment is fully specified. The list can also be used to ensure the environment that is likely to be encountered during transportation is also fully specified. One the worst environments that is commonly encountered by products is that of transportation and in particular the vibration, bump and shocks encountered when a product is carried on the floor of a lorry driven over rough ground.

The final area of the physical environment that deserves mention is user abuse. To design a product that will withstand any amount of user abuse is likely to result in totally impractical products. However, a level of user abuse should be expected and allowed for during design and development. As far as the product specification is concerned this may result in a safety margin being added to appropriate specification items. In all cases it is important that, whilst formulating the product specification, the level of expected, or allowable user abuse be considered and allowed for.

Reliability. The reliability of the product will impact the longer term success of the product and of the organisation as a whole. An organisation that launches a product that proves to be unreliable in that it fails very quickly or very regularly will gain the reputation of a poor quality producer. Not only does such a reputation affect sales of the product, but affects sales of other products manufactured by the organisation in the future.

There are various ways of specifying reliability. These methods and design considerations regarding reliability are addressed in chapter 7.

Ease of maintenance and service. The speed with which maintenance and repair can be made on the product will again affect the longer term perception of the organisation as a quality supplier. An organisation that produces products that can be maintained easily and can be repaired and returned to the customer quickly will earn a better reputation than one from which products take a very long time to repair.

Customers have long memories. It can take a manufacturer a considerable time and a lot of effort to recover from bad maintenance and service performance.

Customer support. The support offered in response to customer enquiries again affects the view customers have on the quality of the organisation. An organisation that is rude to customers that contact them, or fail to respond at all, will gain a reputation for poor customer support, which will affect sales.

It is perhaps unnecessary for a product specification to state specifically how customer support will be provided. It is more likely that the new product will be supported by the existing customer support system. The only impact of the new product will be a resourcing impact. Additional support staff might be required to increase capability sufficient to deal with the expected increase in enquiries. A major new product might require a completely new customer support system. The provision of the new, or supplements to the old, system will need to be put into place before product launch. The activities therefore become part of the wider project plan.

Competitive environment

As has already been stated, most products are sold into an existing competitive environment or into an environment that will become competitive as new companies develop competitive products. Wherever there is a competitive product situation information about the other products is vital to ensure the product being developed can be sold. The key pieces of information that can be fed into the product design and development process to enable a competitive advantage to be developed are selling price; competitive product features and the competitiveness of the distribution chain.

Selling price positions the product in the minds of customers as far as quality and features is concerned. If the product or organisation do not match up to these expectations, sales will be lost. The price also sets the baseline for the determination of the required cost of manufacturing as has already been illustrated.

The features of the competitive products establish the benchmark against which the features of the product being developed will be compared. An equally priced product with fewer features would not expect to sell as well.

Finally, the distribution chain to be used to get the products from the place of manufacture to the point where the customers make the purchase, is an important consideration for a number of reasons.

Firstly, the distribution chain costs money; the more complex the chain the more cost is likely to involved. The cost of distributing each product is taken from the available profit. It is therefore desirable to make the distribution process as efficient as possible. Products with a shelf life need to be moved relatively quickly from the place of manufacture to the point of sale.

Secondly packaging needs to be considered. It is normal for products to be placed in the packaging in which it will be sold at the end of the manufacturing process. For small products this final packaging may itself be small. To avoid moving a large number of small boxes, the small boxes will normally be packed into larger, plain cardboard, boxes. These larger boxes may also be packed onto pallets for movement in bulk. The number of intermediate boxes is dependant on the proposed distribution method. Since the boxes need to be planned for and possibly designed, they become part of the product development process.

Finally the distribution process involves product being transported between the place of manufacture and the various points of sale. The form of transportation used can affect the design of the packaging used to transport the product. Consider the movement of pieces of electronic equipment with large Lithium based batteries. Lithium is considered by carriers as a dangerous material. Some carriers, including some airlines, will not carry products containing such batteries under any circumstances. Others will carry them provided the total amount of Lithium in all the products they carry, is below a certain limit. In all cases the product packaging must carry specific labels and warning symbols to indicate that it contains Lithium batteries. The addition of these labels and symbols must be planned for and dealt with as part of the product development process if last-minute problems are to be avoided. The form of transportation also affects the strength and support that needs to be given to the product by the transportation packaging. Clearly, rough handling during transportation requires stronger and more supportive packaging.

Company needs, expectations and constraints

The final categories of needs and expectations that need to be considered when producing a product specification are those of the design, developing and manufacturing organisation itself. The more important inputs are:

- manufacturing cost;
- manufacturing capability;
- quality requirements;
- available resources;
- manufacturing volume and rate;
- preferred suppliers and sub-contractors;
- company finance and accounting.

Manufacturing cost. We have already seen that, given the proposed selling price and details of the distribution chain and any required margin of safety, the required manufacturing cost can be calculated. This figure is referred to as the target unit production cost or target UPC. Unless the product can be repeatably manufactured for the target UPC or less, the desired profit cannot be realised.

> UPC is the unit production cost, that is, the cost or producing a single product.

Manufacturing volume and rate. Closely associated with the target UPC is the manufacturing volume and rate. Is the market requirement to be met with a single production volume over a very short period of time, or spread at a low rate over a longer period of time? Will the product be manufactured in batches or on a continuously operating production line? The proposed total volume and rate of production will affect the required production tools, jigs and fixtures and will therefore affect the cost of establishing the production line. The total volume and rate will also affect how some parts, such as moulded parts, are fabricated; a high volume will require a more robust and more expensive mould tool.

> Volume rate is the number of products manufactured per unit of time. The unit of time can be day, week, month or year.

Manufacturing volume and rate also affect who will carry out the manufacture. High volume might require more operators; the more operators that are required the lower the skill that needs to be present in the job or the higher the amount and cost of training required to achieve a consistent quality output. Both alternatives cost money and need to be planned if there is not to be last-minute panics as product manufacture commences.

Manufacturing capability. The current manufacturing capability is the starting point for the range of processes that the new product can use. The current capability can be developed and extended to include new processes demanded by the new product; alternatively they can be sub-contracted to a third party. Again, in either case there are cost implications. To ensure a quality result from any process the people or sub-contractor completing the process must be quality-assessed and, where necessary, provided with necessary training.

In the case of a radically new process that needs to be introduced into the company's capability, new equipment or specially trained personnel may need to be acquired. Both the cost of acquisition and any training required, and the time required to bring the new resources to the point where quality outputs can be achieved, need to be catered for in the overall product plan.

Where the required processes are within the current technical capability, there may be a throughput limitation. For example, if the new product will require printed circuit board assembly, a process that is within the current capability, can the current assembly equipment and personnel handle in the increased load that the new product will introduce? Will new equipment be required? Will extra personnel be required? Will additional shifts have to be worked? There are cost and time implications to all of these issues and, again, they should not be left to the last minute to be resolved.

Companies can develop mutually beneficial relationships with suppliers and sub-contractors.

Preferred suppliers and sub-contractors. The organisation is likely to have a preferred list of suppliers and sub-contractors, that is those suppliers and sub-contractors in whom the company has confidence that a quality product will be supplied. These suppliers and sub-contractors will have just as the company itself has, a current capability. If a process is required that cannot be catered for within the current list of approved suppliers or sub-contractors a new one will need to be added to the list. The quality approval of a new supplier can take a considerable amount of effort spread over a number of months. It would be normal for the new supplier or sub-contractor to be used to produce development samples of product pieceparts. The required supplier or sub-contractor quality-approval should be carried out as part of the development task and hence included in the project plan.

Quality requirements. The overall quality requirements of the product have a component dictated by the customer, in the form of expectation or stated requirements, and a component dictated by the company quality practices and procedures. The quality practices and procedures, usually in the form of the quality manual, state the procedures to be followed when certain tasks are carried out. The range of tasks varies from organisation to organisation however there are many that are common such as how engineering changes, hardware, software and document issue control are dealt with. The quality manual is, in our experience, viewed by many as a constraint rather than a resource to be used. Quality is considered in depth in chapter 10.

The quality requirements also include the nature and extent of the design proving, design for tolerance and reliability required of the new product. Where the customer or legislative change does not demand specific approval requirements, it would be normal to resort to the company's good engineering practice rules. These rules can normally be found in the quality manual.

Available resources. The available resources that can be called on during design and development is an important input to the product during the planning stage. If the anticipated effort and specialist skills exist within the company and access can be assured the planning of the project should be relatively straightforward. If, however, specialist resources are required to be hired in from an external consultancy or specialist, the cost, availability and quality of resource will all need to be assessed before an accurate project plan can be produced.

The available physical assets are also important, in particular the computer-aided engineering equipment. If the new product requires a new software capability, such as finite element analysis, for the assessment of the mechanical strength of the product, or a thermal analysis program, the software, host hardware and staff will all need to be investigated, selected and introduced.

Personnel training will be needed in the software which requires both cost and time.

Staff training can be very costly and requires careful planning if the full benefit is to be gained.

Company finance and accounting. For the company to be able to develop the new product it must be able to fund the design, development and launch of the new product. These costs represent an investment now and in the near future, for a financial return in the medium to longer future. If the company has a surplus of cash available to invest in itself, the funding is not a major issue. If, however, external funding is required, the cost of acquiring the capital is a key input to the overall financial profitability of the project.

To enable the project development cost to be determined, the direct labour rates, the overhead rates and expected raw material costs are all required at the project planning stage. Once the total cost of the project has been determined and the projected income incorporated, a full development cost plan, DCP, results. This DCP can be compared with the company expectations in terms of payback requirements, to enable a decision as to whether to develop the product or not. Project costs and payback are covered in more detail in chapter 4.

Checklists

In the description of some of the sources of inputs to the product specification stated above, a basic checklist approach has been adopted. A checklist is a general set of questions or statements that can be used to tease out aspects to be included in the specification which might otherwise be overlooked. A specific example is the outline environmental checklist discussed earlier in this chapter. The checklist is, in the form shown, a simple list of the environmental requirements. To be of real use as a checklist it should develop each of the stated items to include the units and any required tolerances. For example the first section of the environmental checklist is temperature. Three types of temperature are noted: operating, storage and thermal shock. As stated, these are not specifications, they are memory joggers. To turn them into usable outlines for inclusion in a specification, values need to be added.

For operating and storage temperature range there needs to be an upper and lower temperature limit specified. For thermal shock there needs to be a temperature change, rate of change and direction of change specified. How the temperature section can be turned into a usable outline for a more complete product specification is shown below.

Temperature
- Operating temperature range:
  Upper operating temperature   C
  Lower operating temperature   C
- Storage temperature range:
  Upper storage temperature   C
  Lower storage temperature   C
- Thermal shock
  Temperature change   C
  Rate of change   ....   C/sec
  Direction of temperature change   from cold to hot for example

Checklists can be developed for the whole range of sources of specification inputs noted above. The end result will be a checklist that will ensure a very detailed and all embracing technical specification results. The assumption is made that answers to all the blanks in the checklist can be given. In many cases it is quite possible that the requirement is unclear in some areas. In such cases either the requirement should be clarified or an assumption should be made. If any assumptions are made they should be recorded so that they can be referred to at a future date for periodic checking for appropriateness and validity.

The subject of checklists is revisited in chapter 10 where quality is considered.

Summary

In this chapter the routes to a product specification have been explored and used to introduce the need to consider customer needs and expectations, the competitive environment and the company's needs and expectations in the formation of a product specification. A specification is not complete unless all three of these areas are given close attention and thoroughly analysed.

Structured approaches, such as the use of checklists, can help to improve the completeness of specifications by providing a generic set of pointers to the content of the document and of the way to specify individual aspects. The need to start the product development process with a clearly defined specification is a central theme throughout this book. Without such a statement of development target, it is argued that the target cannot be reached in an optimal fashion. In some situations a clear definition of the specification cannot be made available at the start of the 'project'. In such cases the specification needs to be documented as far as can reasonably be stated and steps put in place to fill the gaps as quickly as possible.

Problems

2.1   Produce an outline specification for a remotely controllable room light dimmer.

2.2   Produce a list of the current European product specifications. A technical library is a good starting point for the search.

2.3   In what ways could you improve the competitiveness of a laptop computer?

2.4   Without referring to chapter 6, develop a more detailed environmental requirement checklist for vibration.

2.5   Produce a description, in specification format, for the aesthetic design of a television.

System design
3

At the end of this chapter you will be able to:

- Explain the meaning of top-down design and bottom-up build as applied to product development
- Draw the functional block diagram of a product
- Create a physical and functional requirement specification assignment matrix
- Draw a structure chart for the modules of a product
- Explain the meaning of apportionment
- Explain the stages of the general problem solving model and how it relates to system design

To expect a designer or team of designers to design and develop a product from an all embracing specification in one step is a tall order. The outcome is likely to be confusion and a breakdown of order. The development of a complex product requires a systematic, planned approach to both the product structure and the process of development. This chapter introduces and illustrates a few of the many approaches that can be taken to system design. A strong theme through the chapter is the 'top-down design, bottom-up-build' approach, a fundamentally simple but powerful strategy for ensuring a quality product. The other tools and techniques introduced in this chapter are supportive of this approach and enable the development of a basic product development strategy.

Throughout this chapter the example of the development of an audio hi-fi amplifier will be used to illustrate the ideas and concepts that are being discussed.

Top-down design

As was shown in chapter 2, product developments start either with a requirement supplied by the customer directly or as a product idea emanating from one of a number of possible sources including from an individual, resulting from a legislative change or from a technology change. Whatever the source, the requirement, in written form, is the starting point for the specification of the product. At the outset the specification is a large scale product definition. It frequently considers the product as an overall 'black-box', specifying all interfaces but nothing internal.

Detail design cannot sensibly start with this specification except in the case of very small or simple products. In larger cases there needs to be a 'breaking down' stage. The overall product specification needs to be broken down into smaller, more manageable parts. There are several ways of achieving this breakdown. At the top level the simplest is to divide the product into the obvious major constituent sub-assemblies. The following example illustrates this 'sub-assembly partitioning' method.

Worked Example 3.1   The specification for an hi-fi audio amplifier is shown in Table 3.1. From this specification, produce a first level product breakdown in the form of a sub-assembly structure chart.

Table 3.1 Specification for hi-fi audio amplifier

1	Performance		
	1.1	Frequency range	10Hz - 20kHz
	1.2	Input signal	5 mV peak to peak
	1.3	Input impedance	1kΩ
	1.4	Output power	100W peak to peak
	1.5	Output impedance	8Ω
	1.6	Total harmonic distortion	<0.00001%
2	Power supply		
	2.1	Mains powers 100V - 250V AC 50Hz	
3	Controls		
	3.1	On/off switch	
	3.2	Volume control	
	3.3	10 band graphic equaliser	
	3.4	Balance control	
4	Inputs		
	4.1	Tape #1, tape #2, tuner, compact disc, microphone #1, microphone #2, auxiliary	
	4.2	Mains input	
5	Case		
	5.1	Size 40cm x 10cm x 40cm	
	5.2	Weight <1kg	
6	Environmental		
	6.1	Temperature	0 to 50C
	6.2	Vibration	Transportation vibration only. Unit will be housed in transit packaging.
	6.3	Humidity	IP1
7	Production		
	7.1	Target manufacturing cost	£100
	7.2	Target volume	10 000
	7.3	Max. production rate	100/week

One way of dividing the product into major sub-assemblies is: the electronics; case and power supply. Figure 3.1 shows this top level structure.

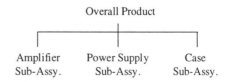

Fig. 3.1 Top level product structure.

The system partitioning assumes a basic understanding of the product and what it entails. The choice of partitions is somewhat arbitrary, its purpose being mainly to start the process of fragmentation. In this case, the breakdown has followed the convention of separating electronics from mechanics. The power supply has been separated because it is to be designed by a team who specialise in the design and development of power supplies.

Top level functional diagram

Each of the top-level sub-assemblies can be sub-divided into smaller assemblies as appropriate. In some cases this level of fragmentation will be purely electronic in nature. In such cases the sub-division takes the form of a 'functional diagram', a collection of boxes representing circuit functions, interconnected by electrical connections. The version of the functional diagram which shows the least detail is called the 'top level' functional diagram. At this level the major functional parts only are shown. The following example illustrates one possible top level functional diagram as well as the next level of detail of product structure breakdown.

Produce a second level breakdown for the hi-fi amplifier and a top level functional diagram for the electronic section.

Worked Example 3.2

The case can be sub-divided into the front panel, the rear panel, body and internal chassis. The power supply can be sub-divided into housing, input filter, transformer and voltage stabiliser. The amplifier can be divided into power amplifier, graphic equaliser and input circuitry and selector. Figure 3.2 shows the second level structure chart which reflects this choice of product breakdown.

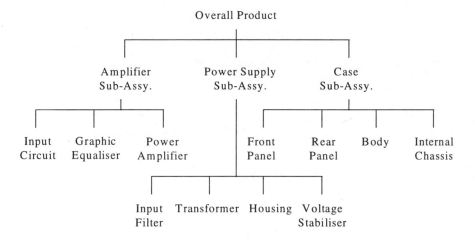

Fig. 3.2 Second level structure chart for hi-fi amplifier.

The structure of the electronic part of the product can also be drawn in such a way as to show the electrical connections between the modules. When drawn in this way the top level functional diagram results. Figure 3.3 shows the top level functional diagram for the structure using the breakdown as shown in Fig. 3.2.

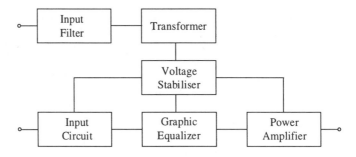

Fig. 3.3 Top-level functional diagram for hi-fi amplifier.

The specification for each sub-assembly must be such that, when all the sub-assemblies are connected together, the whole product meets the overall specification. In some cases aspects of the overall product specification can be assigned to specific sub-assemblies. For example, the 'power amplifier' sub-assembly directly supplies the output power. Since the required output power, from Table 3.1, is 100W p/p, the power amplifier must be capable of generating this amount of power. To be exact, it must be capable of supplying slightly more than this power since there will be a small, but non-zero, loss between the output of the power amplifier circuitry and the connections for the loud-speakers on the rear panel.

The input to the power amplifier is not, however, the specified input level to, say the tape input. This is the input to one of the channels of the input circuitry and section functional block. The input to the power amplifier is what is known as an 'internal specification'. It is part of a sub-assembly, or functional block specification which is not directly seen by the external product specification, only by another sub-assembly. Figure 3.4 illustrates the internal and external interfaces of the hi-fi amplifier example.

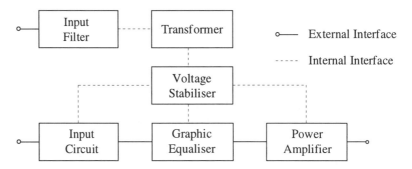

Fig. 3.4 Internal and external interfaces of the hi-fi amplifier example.

The partitioning of a product and the quantification of internal specifications is arbitrary in that it needs to suit only the sub-assemblies or functional blocks that form the interface. The selection can, however, have a pronounced impact on the design and development process and on the quality of the overall product. In assigning internal partitions and specifications attention needs to be paid to all aspects of the specification as developed in chapter 2, to minimise the risk of poor partitioning compromising one aspect of the specification.

In the hi-fi amplifier the main fuse is housed within the input filter which is, in turn, mounted inside the power supply housing. What is the effect of the main fuse failing? How could the design be improved and how would the second level structure and functional diagram charts be changed to reflect the design improvement?

Locating the main fuse with the input filter, which is physically located inside the power supply sub-assembly housing will require quite a complicated procedure to be followed in the event of fuse failure. The case sub-assembly body will need to be removed, the power supply sub-assembly housing removed before access can be gained to the fuse. The reverse procedure will be required to re-assemble the amplifier.

The external specification is clearly fixed by the customer or the organisation's representative of the customers requirements, usually the Marketing department. The internal specifications are decided at the system design stage and provide a few degrees of freedom within design and development. There can be trade-offs at internal interfaces should it be necessary. Use is made of these trade-offs in later chapters on reliability, cost and tolerance.

Given the existence of an overall product specification, the external specification and a preliminary system partitioning, sub-assembly specifications can be produced. A 'specification assignment matrix' is a useful tool at this stage to ensure no aspect of the specification or any sub-assembly is missed. The specification assignment matrix is formed by listing all the specification line items as rows and all sub-assemblies or functional blocks as columns. The particular specification line item or clause reference is inserted in each cell as appropriate. Blank cells indicate that the specification line item is not relevant to the sub-assembly. To add clarity, it is useful to consider the electronic aspects of the specification and assign them to functional modules in one matrix, the 'functional specification assignment matrix'; and the physical aspects of the specification and assign them to the sub-assemblies in a second 'physical specification assignment matrix'. The following example illustrates the formation of these two matrices.

Produce a functional specification assignment matrix and a physical specification assignment matrix for the hi-fi amplifier.

Table 3.2 shows the functional specification assignment matrix which relates the functional blocks of Fig. 3.4 to the electronic aspects of the specification, namely sections 1 and 2, from Table 3.1.

Table 3.3 shows the physical specification assignment matrix which relates the product sub-assemblies of Fig. 3.2 to the physical aspects of the specification, namely sections 3, 4 and 5, from Table 3.1.

It is important to include all aspects of the specification in the assignment matrix, not just the electrical aspects. Some aspects of the specification, such as reliability and cost, are applicable to the whole product but require a little more work before a meaningful specification results. Aspects of the specification such as reliability and cost need to be apportioned across the sub-assemblies. Apportionment is introduced later in this chapter.

Table 3.2 Functional specification assignment matrix for hi-fi amplifier

	Input filter	Trans-former	Voltage stabiliser	Input circuit	Graphic equaliser	Power amplifier
Frequency range				1.1	1.1	1.1
Input signal				1.2		
Input impedance				1.3		
Output power						1.4
Output impedance						1.5
Total harmonic distortion				1.6	1.6	1.6
Mains voltage	2.1	2.1	2.1			

Table 3.3 Physical specification assignment matrix for hi-fi amplifier

	Amplifier sub-assembly	Power supply sub-assembly	Case sub-assembly
On/off switch			3.1
Volume control	3.2		3.2
10 band graphic equaliser	3.3		3.3
Balance control	3.4		3.4
Inputs			4.1, 4.2
Size	5.1	5.1	5.1
Weight	5.2	5.2	5.2
Temperature range	6.1	6.2	6.2
Vibration	6.2	6.2	6.2
Waterproofing			6.3
Target manufacturing cost	7.1	7.1	7.1

The specification assignment matrix ignores the internal interface specifications. It is therefore not a sufficient tool for the generation of complete sub-assembly specifications. The decision as to what additional specification aspects need to be defined depends on where the internal interfaces are placed. To complete the specification, reference needs to be made back to the product structure and/or functional block diagram which provides keys to the missing information.

Worked Example 3.5

For the power amplifier functional block identify the internal interfaces required to enable a complete specification to be formulated.

The internal interfaces are:

- electrical input from the graphic equaliser output;
- DC power from the voltage stabiliser;
- mechanical connection to the case internal chassis and front and rear case panels;
- thermal connection to the case internal chassis or rear case panel for heat sinking of the output power transistors.

Standard lists of parameters can be used to ensure a complete specificat.. ᴏn of an internal interface. Table 3.3 shows a list of the parameters that need to be specified for an electrical connection (AC or DC) between two functional blocks.

Certain product specification requirements apply to the product as a whole, rather than to one particular interface to it. Examples of such requirements are cost and reliability. The target manufacturing cost for the product is frequently specified in such a way that the business plan for the product development and sales is acceptable within the organisations rules or future plans. The product reliability, in terms of time between failures, is an important part of a product specification as it affects the customer's perception of the product and hence the perception customers have of the organisation as a whole. Neither of these requirements however, can be equally applied to all sub-assemblies as can, temperature say. It is obviously incorrect to say that if the target cost of manufacture of the product is £100, then the cost to make each sub-assembly is also £100. All of the sub-assemblies together must cost a maximum of £100. The process by which a total product requirement is divided among the sub-assemblies is called 'apportionment'.

Table 3.3 Standard parameters for an electrical connection

• Voltage level :	Value with tolerance or frequency response
• Phase :	Value with tolerance or frequency response
• Power level :	Value with tolerance or frequency response
• Frequency range :	Minimum and maximum
• Impedance :	Value with tolerance or frequency response

Apportionment

The objective of apportionment is to divide the total product requirement across the constituent sub-assemblies in such a way that each has a reasonable amount. Consider as an example, the hi-fi amplifier. The overall target manufacturing cost is £100. The top level product structure, Fig. 3.1, shows three sub-assemblies, the amplifier, the power supply and the case. The £100 must cover the cost of all three sub-assemblies plus the cost of connecting the three sub-assemblies together, testing the product and packaging it with any manuals and accessories. There are a number of approaches to apportionment:

- past experience;
- catalogues / quotes;
- estimate.

Past experience

The collective wisdom of the organisation can be bought to bear in apportioning sensibly. The organisation may, for example, have produced similar products in the past. In such cases the division of costs on the previous product can be used as a starting point. In the past a different type of product may have required a power supply, or a case similar, or close enough, to the one being considered for the product, to make a reasonable cost estimate.

Catalogues / Quotes

Where no past product experience exists the highest priced items within the product can be priced using latest catalogues or quotes from manufacturers. High priced items would include transformers, special devices, connectors, printed circuit boards, major case parts, and so on. Low priced items include resistors, common transistors, capacitors, nuts, bolts, etc.

If the product system design has been performed carefully and thoroughly a fair idea of how the product is to be built will have emerged and with it an idea of the complexity of the various parts. This complexity can be used to estimate the approximate number of components. The hi-fi amplifier might for example, be considered to be composed of a power amplifier with 20 low power transistors, 50 resistors, 25 capacitors, etc. The cost associated with the manufacture, assembly and test in terms of labour hours can also be estimated. The combined parts and labour estimated costs can be used as a first pass apportionment figure. This approach could lead to the sum of the parts exceeding the available product cost budget. In such a case the apportioned costs need to be reconsidered and reduced to enable a fit to be achieved.

Estimate

If all else fails and there is no past history or an inadequate picture of the product from which to form an educated estimate the figures can always be guessed, at least as a first pass. If the result seems reasonable then it can serve as the initial targets.

The three methods are of decreasing accuracy reflecting the reducing amount of product background knowledge. The results are really targets which can be 'traded' between modules during design and development as is considered necessary. The cost structure of products is explored in more detail in chapter 4 and the apportionment of reliability in chapter 7. The methods also require that there is a basic understanding of how the product can be realised. In the case of the electronic design, this might not always be true. The following example illustrates where the performance required is such that the two conventional solutions to the problems do not work and a novel design is called for.

Worked Example 3.6

Design a digital frequency counter to work over the frequency range 0.001Hz to 1GHz with an resolution of at least six significant figures, that is, 1 part in 10^6.

42

There are two ways of measuring the frequency, by direct counting or using the reciprocal of the period between pulses.

• **Direct counting**: Count the number of input pulses over a fixed time period, as shown in Fig. 3.5. This gives the frequency directly in terms of the width of the measurement time period. That is, the frequency, f is given by:

$$f = \frac{N}{T} \, \text{Hz}$$

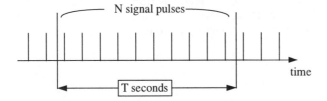

Fig. 3.5 Direct counting method of frequency measurement.

This is simple to implement as it requires only an accurate time period generator, an input signal gate, a counter and a display, as shown in block diagram form in Fig. 3.6.

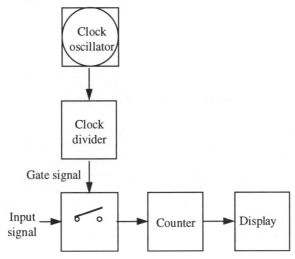

Fig. 3.6 Direct counting method of frequency measurement block diagram.

Note that in general a high resolution requires the use of a high frequency crystal clock followed by binary dividers in order to provide the gate time.

• **Reciprocal period**: Count the number of clock pulses over the signal time period, as shown in Fig. 3.7. and take the reciprocal to get the frequency.

$$f = \frac{1}{M} \, \text{Hz}$$

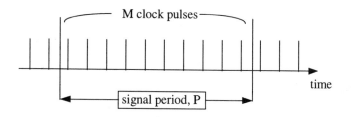

Fig. 3.7 Reciprocal period method of frequency measurement.

This method is similar in implementation as it requires an accurate high frequency clock, an input signal gate, a counter, a reciprocal block and a display, as shown in block diagram form in Fig. 3.8.

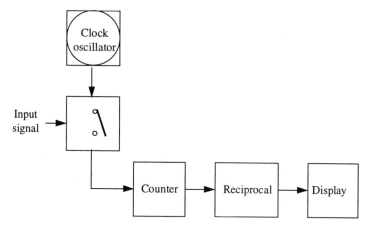

Fig. 3.8 Reciprocal period method of frequency measurement block diagram.

Note that the one of the main implementation differences is that the signal gates the clock signal rather than the other way round in direct implementation. Both methods require similar amounts of hardware although the reciprocal is harder to do in hardware than software. However both methods have very different performances at the different extremes of the frequency range.

The direct counting method has excellent resolution at high frequencies where there are a large number of signal periods within a gate time. The ultimate resolution is determined by the maximum frequency that can be counted accurately within a given gate time. Unfortunately at low frequencies there are fewer pulses within the gate time and so the method has a lower resolution here than the reciprocal period method, unless the gate times are made very long. If the gate time is t_g, the resolution for the direct method, R_{dir} is given by:

$$R_{dir} = \frac{1}{t_g f}$$

The reciprocal period method has excellent resolution at low frequencies where the period can be measured accurately with a high frequency clock. The ultimate resolution is determined by the maximum clock frequency that can be generated and counted accurately. It can also provide a measurement after one period of the input signal and so can provide a measurement more quickly at low frequencies compared to the direct method. Unfortunately at high frequencies there are fewer pulses per period and so the method has a lower resolution than the direct method here. If the clock frequency is f_c, the resolution for the reciprocal method, R_{rec} is given by:

$$R_{rec} = \frac{f}{f_c}$$

The accuracy for both methods as a function of the frequency being measured is shown in Fig. 3.9, assuming a gate time of one second and a clock frequency of 100MHz.

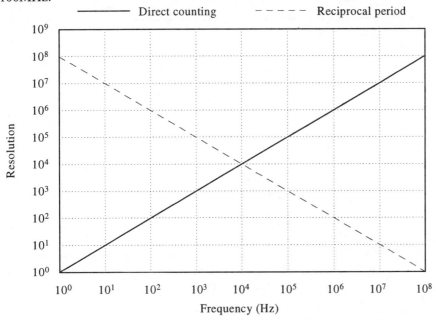

Fig. 3.9 Accuracy of the two measurement methods as a function of frequency.

Clearly neither approach manages to perform well over the whole frequency rang. However, the reciprocal method can be improved by recognising that it does not have to count just the number of clock pulses within one signal period. In fact, any number of signal periods can be used providing that the number of periods fits within the measurement period. This method is shown in Fig. 3.10.

If the number of cycles per gate time is N_{gt}, the equation for the resolution for the modified method is:

$$R_{rec} = \frac{f}{f_c N_{gt}}$$

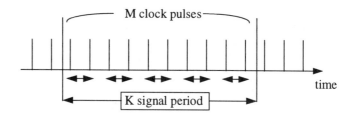

Fig. 3.10 Improved reciprocal period method of frequency measurement.

The accuracy for the improved method as a function of the frequency being measured is shown in Fig. 3.11, assuming a gate time of one second and a clock frequency of 100MHz.

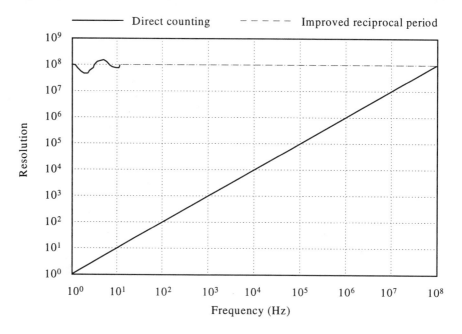

Fig. 3.11 Accuracy of the improved reciprocal period as a function of frequency.

Implementing the improved method requires the addition of an extra counter in order to count the number of periods within a measurement interval. The modified block diagram is shown in Fig. 3.12.

The modified reciprocal period method has a constant accuracy over the measurement frequency range. In order to meet the specification, the minimum clock frequency would have to be 10MHz if a one-second measurement period were required and a 100MHz clock would allow a measurement time of 0.1 second. Note that the counters would have be able to work at 1GHz to meet the specification. Therefore it would be more normal to set the clock at 1GHz and either reduce the measurement time, (although 0.1 second would be an acceptable update rate), or increase the accuracy. From the graph it would be possible to increase it by two digits which would give a potential eight digit display. Note that for frequencies which have only one period per measurement the time is a function of the period of the waveform and the accuracy is potentially higher.

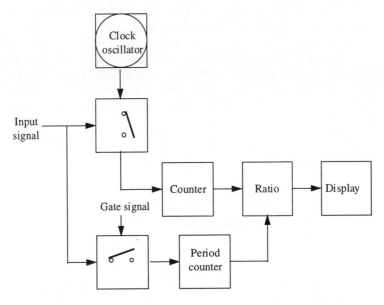

Fig. 3.12 Improved reciprocal period method block diagram.

In principle, successive measurements can be averaged to give a √N improvement in resolution where N is the number of averaged measurements. Precautions must be taken to break up correlation between the instrument and the signal. This is best achieved by phase modulating the clock with random noise. This serves to break up any potential correlation. Phase modulation is used because it avoids any baseline frequency error as might happen with frequency modulation of the clock.

Taking the idea of top down design as a methodology, complex products can be divided into smaller, more manageable modules. The performance requirement of each module can be documented as a formal specification that can be used as the basis for more accurate planning and estimating. The requirement specification can also be used to identify the testing required to ensure the module, once designed and built, will function correctly and minimise problems when the module is integrated into the system.

Bottom-up build

Given a system broken down into modules, each with a formal requirement specification and test specification, the separate modules can be designed, developed and verified. To build the product effectively from these modules requires a carefully planned integration plan.

Figure 3.4 shows the breakdown of the hi-fi amplifer product into a series of functional block modules. Each block has a test specification to enable its performance in isolation from the other modules to be verified.

At one end of the spectrum of integration methods is the strategy of connecting all the functional blocks together and switching the system on. Whilst this approach gets the system together quickly, it is gambling on whether it will work as a system first time. If theory has worked and the initial top-down system analysis and partitioning was good, all the individual modules have been designed and developed successfully and there are no interface problems, this strategy can result in a working system. If the system does not work first time, fault finding might prove to be a complex problem and might well require the system to be broken down into smaller sets of modules. A more structured approach to system integration is to interconnect modules and verify that the combinations work, adding more modules at each stage of integration.

Any electronic product or module can be shown as a block with a set of inputs and a set of outputs, as shown in Fig. 3.13.

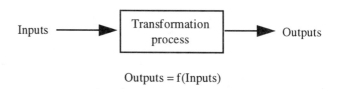

Outputs = f(Inputs)

Fig. 3.13 Simple functional block representation of a product or module.

The functional specification states the transformation processes which act on the inputs to produce the required outputs. The module test specification lists the tests, with a definition of the inputs and expected outputs, to verify each mode of operation of the module.

When two modules are connected together a new set of tests can be formed that test the interaction between the two modules. Figure 3.14 shows two modules connected together and the how a new set of tests can be found.

There is no need to verify the correct operation of the two modules separately in the integrated test, only that the two module transformation processes correctly take the inputs to module 1 and produce the required outputs at module 2. As an example, consider the audio amplifier functional block diagram of Fig. 3.3. The input circuit is a separate module and can be tested as such. Similarly the graphic equaliser can be tested as a separate module. In the case of the input circuit one of the tests would be to verify that it amplifies the input signal to the level decided by the system partitioning process as suitable for the input to the graphic equaliser. One of the tests of the graphic equaliser involves supplying it with an input voltage equal to the agreed level and testing to see that it amplifies the signal to the correct output level. The test of the interconnection of the modules does not need to check that the interconnecting signal is of correct level, but only that the cascade of input circuit and graphic equaliser amplifies an input signal to the required level of the output signal.

Outputs of module 2 = f(Inputs to module 1)

Fig. 3.14 The interconnection of two modules.

Inter-module connectivity creates complexity.

In a similar way the testing of additional modules added onto the above pair can be planned and a set of tests devised to verify the interconnection is good. One of the objectives of inter-module testing is to verify that there are no odd effects occurring which have been introduced by the interconnection itself. If the system partitioning has been well designed and the modules carefully specified why should integration be required in this piecewise fashion? The answer lies in the reality of being able to ensure, through a written specification, that the interconnection will work. It is quite possible for the performance of one module to be affected by the one it is connected to simply because it is connected to it. One module might present a load to the other module different from that used during testing, the result being an interconnection problem. One module might result in harmonics being passed back which causes additional distortion, and so one. Careful integration is the key to avoiding system level problems of this nature.

The special case of software

Software engineers have, for a number of years, been using the top-down design, bottom-up build approach as a means of ensuring product quality. The basic approach adopted is that described above where the overall software package is functionally divided into smaller modules, procedures and subroutines. These modules can be designed, specified and tested just as a hardware module can be. Testing in the case of a software modules involves sending the module data and verifying that the output is as would be expected from the transformation algorithms. Additional software, in the form of 'test stubs' are used to test the modules.

Consider for example a software module that finds the roots of a quadratic equation. The roots are given by the equation:

$$y = ax^2 + bx + c$$

$$x = \frac{-b \pm \sqrt{b^2 - 4ac}}{2a}$$

There are a few common problems with algorithms for an equation of this type. Firstly the solution equation results in a division by zero error if the coefficient a is zero. Secondly there is scope for a square root of a negative number error if $4ac$ is greater than b^2. Both of these errors will result in a run-time error if they are not checked for and appropriate action is taken within the routine. Any test software should test for known, or potential, problems with input data such as the above singularities.

Creativity in system design

The final part of this chapter briefly looks at creativity and how to design a system when the solution is not obvious. Creativity is the term commonly used to the process of generating novel ideas or novel solutions to problems and as such creativity is often the starting point for new products.

A very widely used idea generating creativity tool used in a team situation, is brainstorming.

Brainstorming

Brainstorming is a technique that starts with a problem statement, usually written on a board clearly visible by all those participating in the brainstorming session. The basic steps in a brainstorming session are:

- Write down the problem.
- Each member of the team offers an idea or possible solution to the problem in turn.
- Each idea is written on the board for all to see.
- Ideas are not commented on or criticised.
- Each member offers ideas in turn until no more ideas are given.
- Members can miss a turn if they cannot think of a new idea.

The key rule of brainstorming is that ideas are not criticised or commented on during the idea generation phase. The whole point is to document all the ideas and for team members to be able to see all the ideas so that they act as mental prompts for new ideas.

Once all the ideas have been written down they are considered one by one to ensure everybody understands what is meant by it. This stage is the clarification and understanding stage. The ideas that are really inappropriate or impossible could be eliminated at this stage. Any that could be a solution should be left for further analysis and consideration.

Creating ideas and potential solutions to a problem is only the starting point for solving the problem. There is likely to be a considerable number of potential solutions identified in a creativity session such as a brainstorm. How are the ideas sorted, ranked and whittled down to a more manageable number? A useful tool for this process is the general problem solving model shown in Fig. 3.15.

The creativity process comprises a series of stages that create ideas and then reduce them against a set of selection criteria. Once the problem has been stated and checked to ensure it is the underlying problem and not one of the symptoms, ideas for possible solutions can be generated. To reduce the number of ideas to a manageable number a set of selection criteria must also be defined. The definition of the selection criteria should be made before any ideas are selected. Once the selection criteria and ideas are available the ideas can be ranked according to the selection criteria. One or a few preferred solutions should emerge from this process. The preferred solutions can be carried forward to a more detailed analysis. The detailed analysis should demonstrate whether the solution meets the overall problem objectives and is practical.

It is important to record all results obtained for future reference. The choice of a system design approach will be made founded on the information available at the time, that is with a certain set of underlying assumptions. As time progresses these assumptions might prove to be incorrect or simple circumstances might change them. In such cases a record of the ideas generated and alternatives proposed can form a valuable source of routes to take if the chosen route gets into serious problems.

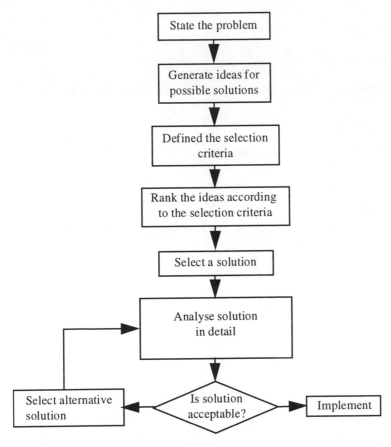

Fig. 3.15 The general problem solving model.

Summary

In this chapter the fundamentals of system design have been examined using a formal top-down design and bottom-up build methodology. The concept of breaking the product down into modules and functional blocks is introduced as a means of dividing what can be large and seemingly unmanageable projects, into smaller parts.

The method of generating specification for modules from the overall product specification, or from the internal partitioning, is explained and demonstrated through an example. The allocation in internal specifications allows a valuable degree of design freedom that can, as will be seen in later chapters, be traded off against other design considerations such as reliability and tolerance design.

Finally an introduction is given to some creativity tools. It will not always be possible to look at a product specification or new product idea and see the solution. In some cases recourse to a more formal creativity approach will be required. A general model for problem solving is offered as the formal structure, with brainstorming as a technique to generate ideas.

As a final note, great care should be exercised at the system design stage. The vast majority of the ultimate cost of the product is decided in the first few stages in the product development process. A poor system design can result in not only a longer and more costly product development but also a higher cost to make each product in production.

Problems

3.1   Produce a structure chart for a domestic central heating thermostatic controller.

3.2   Produce a top level functional block diagram for an electronic radio alarm clock.

3.3   Produce a requirement specification for the graphic equaliser functional block diagram shown in Fig. 3.4.

3.4   Design a test and integration plan for the hi-fi amplifier used as the example in this chapter.

3.5   Select a product you possess that you can disassemble. Produce a detailed structure chart showing its key parts. Form a product structure chart from your findings.

Costs and product development   4

At the end of this chapter you will be able to:

- State the cash-using and cash-generating parts of a product development
- Produce a project development plan for a new product development
- Determine the cost of any activity within a development plan and the cost of the overall project
- Produce a Bill of Materials for a product and use it to determine the unit manufacturing cost
- Quantify the impact production set-up has on the cost of manufacturing a product
- Quantify the impact production yield has on the cost of manufacturing a product
- Assess whether an organisation should, from a financial point of view, develop a product
- Determine the net present value of a future cash stream

The financial success of a product is not simply dependant on the ability to produce it profitably in production. The profit generated through sales must be sufficient to repay the total cost of advancing the product from original idea to sellable form and to add to the financial growth of the company.

This chapter reviews the costs associated with the total cost of product development and of its subsequent manufacture and how these costs affect the overall company profitability. It should become clear that careful attention needs to be paid to costs throughout the product's life cycle if a financially successful project is to result. In particular, consideration of the unit manufacturing cost cannot be left until the production phase; the majority of the cost will be set very early in the product's development. Due attention must, therefore, be paid to product costing from the outset.

To illustrate the concepts introduced in this chapter the development of a personal computer will be used. The PC, is to be made up of a monitor, keyboard, mouse, software and a processor box. The processor box contains the main processor, interface cards, hard and floppy disks, memory and the power supply. Additional detail of the PC will be developed through the chapter. It is assumed that everything except the software will be developed by the company. The software will be bought in for each PC manufactured.

The total cost of advancing any product can be sub-divided into the costs of designing and developing it, the cost of marketing it and the cost of producing the quantity to be sold. Figure 4.1 illustrates these cost categories.

In the case of the PC example, the development costs include all the costs associated with the design and development of the monitor, keyboard, mouse and processor box plus the cost of verifying that the software to be bought in for each PC manufactured will work with the developed hardware. The development cost also includes all the costs associated with proving the product and developing the production process that will be used to manufacture sellable products.

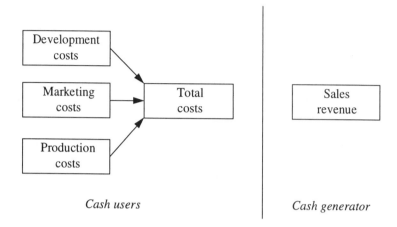

Fig. 4.1 Product life-cycle activity cash flow.

The marketing costs include the costs of any marketing surveys to establish the requirement, the cost of sales brochures, product advertising, marketing samples and any promotional offers. Production costs include the material, component and labour cost required to manufacture each PC.

These cost descriptions are a very simplified version of the total costs associated with each activity but should give a flavour of the type of costs that are incurred and illustrate the way the costs are grouped. A more detailed picture of the costs of each activity will be developed through the chapter.

The activity costs shown in Fig. 4.1 also omits the timing of the money needs of the project. The development costs will be incurred before the product can be manufactured and both will be incurred before product can be sold. The time between starting product development and receiving money from sales can range from months for simple products to many years for large systems.

The pattern of costs through the product life cycle

In considering the pattern of cost through a product's life cycle it is necessary first to consider the phases the product goes through. Assuming initially that the product is to be developed and manufactured by the same organisation there are a range of activities that need to be completed to sell the product successfully: The product must be:

- designed;
- developed and made producible in quantity;
- marketed;

- produced;
- distributed;
- sold.

All but the last in the above list are what are referred to as 'cost items'. They cost time and money to complete with no direct return in terms of cash input. Only the selling of product results in an input of cash. Taking this simplistic approach, minimising the cash-using activities and maximising the cash-injecting activities, would seem to be a sensible business approach. The picture is, however, complicated by time. The cash-using activities occur at one time and the cash-generating activity at a later stage. A simple addition of cash results in a distorted picture of profitability. The time dimension to cash flow for a project is an important consideration in the decision as to the financial merit of a product development. This notion will be developed in detail in this chapter.

The total costs of the business

The costs shown in Fig. 4.1 are those which relate directly to the creation of the product and are hence attributable directly to the product. There are, in addition to these costs, other costs which are associated with maintaining the overall running of the company. The cost of the board of directors, the human resources department, the finance department, building rent and rates, service bills, and so on all support the development of new products and the sale of existing products. In accounting terms such costs are referred to as 'overheads' or 'overhead costs'.

The profit made by an organisation is the sales revenue less all the costs incurred in the normal operation of the company, the directly attributable costs and the overheads. An important part of understanding the finances of a company and the profitability of any particular product is the way in which the overhead costs are dealt with. Consider as an example a company that produces three different types of products, product A, B and C. The annual sales revenue and costs for each product line and the overheads is shown in Table 4.1. Table 4.1 shows that the combined sales revenue of the company is £1 300 000 and the total direct costs £995 000. This amount of business results in a gross profit of £305 000 which allows the overhead costs of £250 000 to be paid and leave a net profit of £55 000.

In this method of showing overheads, the overhead cost has been kept separate from the revenue and direct costs of each product. This approach is good for presenting a summary picture of the financial position of the company and is the accepted way of presenting a profit and loss statement. However, it is of less use for deciding whether a product line is actually profitable.

Consider as an example the allocation of the overheads simply on the basis of the sales revenue each product line generates. The following worked example illustrates the problem in this approach.

Table 4.1 Total costs of a business

		£000
Sales Revenue		
	Product A	350
	Product B	550
	Product C	400
	Total	1300
Direct Costs		
	Product A	245
	Product B	450
	Product C	300
	Total	995
Gross Profit		305
Overheads		250
Net Profit		55

Worked Example 4.1

Allocate the overheads given in Table 4.1 to each product line on the basis of sales revenue. What impact would the result have on the performance of the organisation?

From Table 4.1 the total overheads are £250 000 and the total sales revenue is £1 300 000. Allocating the overheads on the basis of product line sales revenue results in an allocation of overheads as follows:

Product A:
Sales revenue = £350 000
% of total revenue = £350 000 / £1 300 000 x 100 = 27%
27% of the total overheads = £250 000 x 0.27 = £67 308.

Similarly product B generates 42% of total sales revenue. 42% of overheads is £105 769. Product C generates the remaining 31% of sales revenue. 31% of the overheads is £76 923.

Adding the overheads to the direct costs for each product line results in a different picture of the profitability of each product line. Table 4.2 summaries the results.

Table 4.2 shows that product line B is actually loosing the company nearly £6,000 per year, not a good situation. At first sight it might seem a good business decision to stop producing product line B all together. If this strategy is adopted the results will be as shown in Table 4.3.

The result of stopping product line B removes the sales revenue and the direct costs associated with the product but has not removed the overheads. In practice such a move is likely to result in a drop in the overheads but not an elimination of them. The overheads that do remain are spread over the remaining two product lines, again in proportion to their sales revenue. The result is that neither product line is now profitable, both should be closed down resulting in an unprofitable company! This process has taken us from a business that is making £55 000 to one that is losing £45 000 annually.

Table 4.2. Profitability of product lines after allocation of overheads

Product	A	B	C	Total
Sales revenue	£350 000	£550 000	£400 000	£1 300 000
Direct costs	£245 000	£450 000	£300 000	£ 995 000
Overheads	£ 67 308	£105 769	£ 76 923	£ 250 000
Total cost	£312 308	£555 769	£376 923	£1 245 000
Net profit	£ 37 692	£ -5 769	£ 23 077	£ 55 000

Table 4.3. Profitability of product lines with line B removed

Product	A	B	C	Total
Sales revenue	£350 000		£400 000	£750 000
Direct costs	£245 000		£300 000	£545 000
Overheads	£116 667		£133 333	£250 000
Total cost	£361 667		£433 333	£795 000
Net profit	£-11 667		£-33 333	£-45 000

The above example illustrates that, whilst overheads need to be dealt with, a simple allocation on the basis of the sales revenue generated by each product line can result in a very interesting result! How then should the overheads be dealt with? The treatment of overheads is, in many organisations, a very contentious issue and one which absorbs many hours of management time. A common approach is to levy on every hour spent on work that is directly attributable to the generation of sales revenue, an overhead charge; and onto every purchase made, a purchasing levy. The purchasing levy could be of the order of 15% of the total purchase value, whilst the labour overhead levy could be of the order of 40% of the prime labour cost. The method of determining the overhead charge is outside the scope of this book, since it requires consideration of accounting practice for which there is insufficient space. The remainder of this chapter will make reference to the overhead charge so that realistic answers result from worked examples and illustrations.

As a lead in to the formation of the overall picture of the cost structure of a project it is useful to look at the income and expenditure of each phase of the product life cycle. In considering each phase, the impact of cost should emerge as will the important design considerations and constraints.

Design and development costs

Cost is incurred in any activity that is required as part of the design and development of the product. Costs result from the use of labour, the purchase of materials or parts for prototypes or for concept proving models, for the hire of services and from the use of, or hire of equipment.

As a fundamental step in the management of a project a project development plan or schedule is usually produced. This can range from a simple bar chart to a multi-level PERT (Programmed Evaluation and Review Technique) chart

PERT - Programmed Evaluation and Review Technique

based on a carefully planned Work Breakdown Structure (WBS). In either case, sufficient detail should be used to indicate the resources required and the timing of them, to ensure they can be planned for and provisioned to enable the project activities to be completed as and when scheduled.

WBS - Work Breakdown Structure

The PERT chart or bar chart is used as a means of identifying the resources required to complete the design and development. Once identified in terms of timing and amount, these resources can be costed. The cost of materials and parts or the hire of services is relatively straight forward. The cost will be the actual cost of the item to be acquired plus any mark-up imposed by management to cover purchasing overheads. It is not uncommon for a fixed percentage to be added to all purchases to cover the cost of purchasing, goods inwards and, albeit temporary, storage. Percentages as high as 15% can be imposed.

Total hourly labour rate = prime labour rate + overhead labour rate.

In a similar way there may be a fixed charge against every hour of labour required by a project. The actual cost of labour is usually referred to as the 'prime' labour rate. This rate will be fixed annually for each grade of employee and will be derived from the average salary plus contributions to National Insurance and pension funds appropriate to the grade of employee. In addition to the 'prime' rate there could well also be a contribution to the running costs of the organisation charged on an hourly rate to every activity within the organisation. This charge is commonly referred to as the 'overhead' charge. The actual rate for each hour of time required by each type of resource will therefore be the appropriate prime rate plus the overhead rate.

Absorption costing.

This method of accounting for the costs of running the company is called 'absorption costing'. The term describes the way in which the costs of running the company, that is the rent, rates, heating, lighting, management, secretarial, etc. costs are spread across all the activities within the organisation. Absorption accounting is not without its problems but is common within electronics companies, especially the larger, well established organisations.

The project development plan for the PC example will contain a very large number of individual activities carefully sequenced to ensure all activities are completed at the appropriate time for other activities and for the completion of the overall design and development phase. It is common for the development plans for projects of this complexity to be organised in a hierarchical manner with each 'level' showing more detail of an activity at the next level up.

Developing a basic activity plan

There are no rigid rules governing the structure of a development plan. Each is unique. The top level activity plan for the PC development could look like that shown in Fig. 4.2. The format shown is a simple bar chart.

The next level of detail for the processor box may contain activities such as those shown in Fig. 4.3. Each of the activities shown could be further divided into more detailed and specific activities such as is shown in Fig. 4.4 which shows the next level of detail for the motherboard design and development.

The process described above is a common one adopted to plan large projects. The overall project is broken down into smaller activities. Each smaller activity is then broken down into more detailed sub-activities, and so on. Progressively more levels each with increased detail until, at the lowest level, the time required and costs associated with the completion of the task can be reasonably accurately estimated.

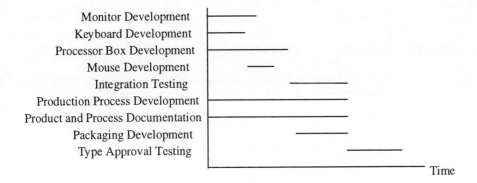

Fig. 4.2 Top level development plan for the PC project (design and development phase).

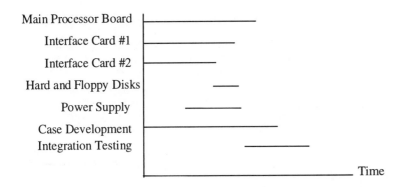

Fig. 4.3 Processor box development plan (design and development phase).

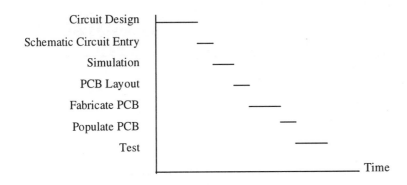

Fig. 4.4 Motherboard development plan (design and development phase).

As an example the design of the motherboard may be sufficiently detailed to allow an estimate to be made. The estimate might be that it will take two weeks of a skilled digital designer working full time plus three full time days of a technician to enter the circuit diagram into a computer-aided-design software package ready for simulation. The cost of this activity can be found by multiplying the cost per hour for each type of resource, in this case skilled digital designer and technician, by the number of hours of each that are required. Assuming the company operates an absorption costing approach, the hourly rates for the resources are as shown in Table 4.4.

Table 4.4 Total hourly rate for digital designer and technician resources

Resource type	Prime rate (£/hr)	Overhead rate (£/hr)	Total rate (£/hr)
Skilled digital designer	12.50	24.25	36.75
Technician	7.00	24.25	31.25

Note that it is not uncommon for the overhead rate to exceed the prime labour rate.

Worked Example 4.2

Assuming that the company operates an eight hour working day, what is the total cost of the 'motherboard design' task?

By extracting the required resources from the project plan and the total hourly rate for each resource required, from Table 4.4, the total cost of the activity can be calculated. Table 4.5 shows how the total cost is found to be £3 690.

Table 4.5. Total cost of the 'motherboard design' task

Resource type	Hours	Total rate (£/hr)	Total cost (£)
Skilled digital designer	80	36.75	2940
Technician	24	31.25	750
Total			3690

Mathematically the cost of the activity is given by:

$$C_1 = \sum_{R_i=1}^{n} (L_{pi} + L_{oi}) h_r$$

where:

C_1 = total activity labour cost
R_i = resource type
n = total number of different resources required by the activity
L_{pi} = prime labour rate for resource type i
L_{oi} = labour overhead rate for resource type i
h_r = number of hours required of each resource, i

This equation says that the total labour cost of an activity is the sum of the total hourly rate for each resource (prime labour rate plus overhead labour rate) multiplied by the number of hours of that resource required in the activity, summed across all the resource types required to complete the activity.

A subsequent activity would include the purchase of components to produce a prototype. The cost of the components would be added to the activity labour cost by taking their actual purchase price and adding in any purchasing overhead.

Worked Example 4.3

The cost of a set of parts for the PC motherboard is £176. If the purchasing overhead is 15%, what is the actual cost to the project of the set of parts?

Cost of parts	£176.00
Purchasing overhead	15%
Cost of parts charged to project	£202.40

This cost would be added to the labour cost for the activity to give the overall activity cost.

Mathematically this total activity cost is given by:

$$C_t = \sum_{R_i=1}^{n} \left\{ h_r (L_{pi} + L_{oi}) + C_p (1 + P_o) \right\}$$

where:

C_p = purchase cost
P_o = purchasing overhead

This method is used to calculate the cost of every activity in the Product Development Plan. The overall design and development activity cost can then be found by adding together all of the individual sub-activity costs.

If an accurate estimate of the total design and development cost is to be achieved, considerable care must be exercised in the creation of the costed plan. The plan must be:

- of sufficient scope to ensure all activities are included;
- of sufficient detail to ensure no sub-activity is missed;
- broken down to a level that permits accurate estimation;
- checked to ensure no double counting of activities has occurred.

A poor or inadequate project plan can lead only to a poor and inaccurate estimate of the design and development cost. An inaccurate estimate of the cost will result in an incorrect picture of the financial profitability of the project to the company.

Poor plans result in poor cost estimates.

The costing of all the activities within the Product Development Plan gives not only the overall cost of design and development but also the timing of the expenditure. The development plan for the design of the case for the PC 'processor box' above might look like that shown in Fig. 4.5.

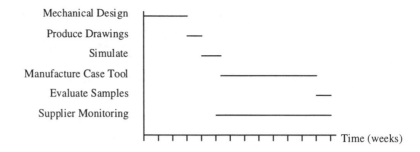

Fig. 4.5 Simplified processor case development plan (design and development phase).

Just as for the motherboard design, each of the activities can be costed according to the resources required. The activity and total cost of the plan is shown in Table 4.6. The costs within the activity can also be plotted against time. Figure 4.6 shows the accumulation of cost in weekly increments assuming the tooling cost is spent as soon as the order for it is raised. At the time the order is raised and sent to the tool supplier the amount of the order is said to be 'committed'. It becomes spent when the work is complete, the supplier has sent the invoice for the work done and the invoice is paid. In this case payment will be at least 16 weeks after the order is raised, in reality probably in excess of 30 weeks. This timing difference is one of the reasons why, in the management of a company's finance, it is essential to monitor both committed costs and cash flow. Once funds are committed there is a liability and the risk of an impact on the company profit and loss. Between commitment and receipt of-invoice there is, of course, a time when the order can be cancelled, albeit usually with some consequential financial penalty.

Worked Example 4.4

If the hours to complete the tasks shown in Fig. 4.5 are as given in Table 4.6 produce a plot showing the accumulation of cost. Assume all activity is spread evenly over the allotted time periods.

Table 4.6 Time and hourly rates required to complete activities

Activity	Resource	Hours	Prime Rate (£ / hr)	Overhead Rate (£ / hr)	Purchase Cost (£)	Purchase Overhead (%)	Total Cost (£)
Mechanical Design	Mech. Designer	80	12.50	24.25			2 940.00
Produce Drawings	Drawing Office	40	9.50	21.65			1 246.00
Simulate	Mech. Designer	20	12.50	24.25			735.00
Manufacture Tool					5 000	15.0	5 750.00
Evaluate	Mech.	40	12.50	24.25			1 470.00
Samples	Designer Technician	80	7.00	24.25			2 500.00
Supplier Monitoring	Mech. Designer	50	12.50	24.25			1 837.50
TOTAL							**16 478.50**

The detail of the content of activities within the above part of the project plan is not the subject of this book. They are included to indicate that a range of different tasks and resources can be required to complete even a small part of a project. In brief, the overall activity starts with a mechanical design task in which a mechanical designer has a budget of 80 hours to design the processor case. The design is turned into a set of drawings by the drawing office who have a budget of 40 hours to complete the task. The mechanical designer simulates the design using a computer-aided design package to verify that the design will meet the stated requirements. A tool to manufacture the cases is then produced from the drawings by a sub-contract organisation. Samples of the case are produced from the tool and are evaluated jointly by the mechanical designer and a technician. Throughout the entire time the sub-contractor is making the tool they are supervised by the mechanical designer.

Table 4.7 shows a spreadsheet of the allocation of costs on a weekly basis. The cumulative cost is plotted in Fig. 4.6.

Table 4.7(a) Allocation of activity costs by week (weeks 1 to 8)

Week	1	2	3	4	5	6	7	8
Mech. Design	980	980	980					
Produce Drawing				1246				
Simulate					490	245		
Manuf. case tool							5750	
Evaluate samples								
Supplier monitoring						230	230	230
Total	980	980	980	1246	490	475	5980	230
Cumulative	980	1960	2940	4186	4676	5151	11130	11360

Table 4.7(b) Allocation of activity costs by week (weeks 9 to 13)

Week	9	10	11	12	13
Mech. Design					
Produce Drawing					
Simulate					
Manuf. case tool					
Evaluate samples					3970
Supplier monitoring	230	230	230	230	230
Total	230	230	230	230	4200
Cumulative	11590	11819	12049	12279	16479

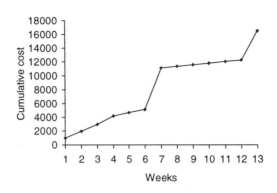

Fig. 4.6 Accumulation of cost in weekly increments.

The worked example demonstrates the ability to plot, spend or forecast spend, against time for an activity within the overall project plan. In exactly the same manner the total Project Development Plan costs can be plotted against time to show the design and development cost finance requirements. Remember this money is spent before any product can be sold and hence profit made. The company must therefore, finance these costs as they occur either out of its internal reserves or from external sources such as a loan. We will return to this later in the chapter when all the costs associated with the project, both 'cash-out' and 'cash-in', are known.

In reality the actual cost of designing and developing a product will differ from the planned cost. Part of the responsibility of the project management function is to track the actual cost of design and development for use in the assessment of the actual profitability of the project.

Marketing costs

In addition to the cost of designing and developing the product, there will be costs associated with informing customers and potential customers of the existence of the product. Brochures and sales leaflets will need to be designed and produced; advertising campaigns, perhaps involving television or magazine advertising; education of sales persons; the establishment of a sales network or distribution network to ensure the products can be conveyed from manufacturer to the customer swiftly and safely. Just as for design and development a marketing plan is produced which includes all activities and their timing and hence allows the total costs associated with the marketing activity to be quantified.

These activities, as with design and development costs, are incurred before product is sold and hence before revenue is generated. The sums involved are not insignificant in some cases and must be taken into account in the up-front planning of the product if an accurate overall product costs is to be obtained.

Production costs

The third and final set of cash users associated with a product as shown in Fig. 4.1 are the production costs. Production costs include all the costs associated with the purchase of raw materials and/or components, adding value to them through the production process and supplying them to the location or customer who will be paying for them. Depending on the product in question and the method of working within the company this may include the transportation of finished products directly to end user customers or to an intermediary such as a distributor. In the case of personal computers a manufacturer may sell direct, possibly through mail order, or through a chain of shops which act as the distributor.

To understand fully the costs in the production category, consider first the production of a single product. A single PC is our example.

The company needs to purchase all the constituent parts, the components that go to make up the motherboard, the monitor, the case and so on. It needs to take these parts and put them through value adding production stages such as printed circuit board population, module assembly, inspection and test. The most common method of defining the product and the processes through which it will pass is by producing a Bill of Materials.

The operation of placing individual components in their correct place in a printed circuit board is called board 'population'.

Bill of Materials

The BOM is a document that defines, for a specific product, the structure of the product in terms of its modules, sub-assemblies, individual components and raw materials and the processes through which it needs to pass. The BOM, therefore, represents a statement of the build standard of the product and must be changed whenever the design of the product changes or when any process through which any part passes is changed. It is essential to maintain very careful issue control of the BOM to ensure that products produced to it are actually required.

The BOM is normally a hierarchical list of the composition of a product with the top level being the product as a whole. The top level BOM for our PC would be as shown in Fig. 4.7.

Personal Computer PC001 Issue 1

```
├──── Monitor (Boxed)............ MON01...... 1 ..... Issue 3
├──── Processor Box (Boxed).. PROC01..... 1 ..... Issue 2
├──── Keyboard (Boxed)......... KEYB01.... 1 ..... Issue 1
├──── Mouse (Boxed)............. MS01......... 1 ..... Issue 1
└──── Software...................... SW06......... 1 ..... Issue 2
```

Fig. 4.7 Top level BOM for pc.

The top level of the BOM, in this case, is effectively the instruction to the despatch department as to which boxes need to be included in the shipment of a single finished product. Note that the BOM includes the company part number for each part and, if appropriate, the issue number of it. This permits the unique identification of the correct part for this particular build standard. In the case of the processor box the despatch of an issue 1 version of part PROC01 would be incorrect for PC build standard issue 1.

The next level down of the BOM takes each part and breaks it down to its next level appropriate for the production process being used to produce it. To illustrate consider the processor box (boxed), part number PROC1.2 from Fig. 4.7. To get to a boxed stage various parts come together in a packaging stage. The BOM for this process stage would be similar to that shown in Fig. 4.8.

This level of the product shows that parts and an assembly process are required to produce a 'processor box (boxed)' item. The assembly process refers to a procedure document or production instruction which defines what needs to be done and how. In this case it says that the tested processor box is put inside the plastic bag then, with one 'from support left' and one 'from support right' in a 'carton' together with a manual and a warranty card. The box is then sealed.

At this level there is an assembled part, the 'processor box (tested)' and several parts obtained from suppliers. The parts obtained from suppliers have an associated cost which, adjusted for the purchasing overhead, become costs against items and the BOM. The assembly process will have been designed as part of the product design and development activity and will have a labour time for a particular resource type allocated to it. This item can be translated to a cost. The result is that every line item of the BOM so far, except the 'processor box (tested)' has a cost attributable to it, as shown in Fig. 4.9.

Processor Box (Boxed).. PROC01.. Issue 2

```
├── Processor Box (Tested)....... PBT01........... 1 ..... Issue 2
├── Manual............................... 0001.136........ 1 ..... Issue 2
├── Warranty Card................... 0001.184........ 1 ..... Issue 1
├── Carton............................... CT06.............. 1 ..... Issue 1
├── Plastic Bag......................... 0004.013....... 1 ..... Issue 2
├── Foam Support, Left............. 0010.016....... 1 ..... Issue 3
├── Foam Support, Right.......... 0010.017....... 1 ..... Issue 3
├── Assembly........................... 6000.189........     Issue 1
└── Packaging Procedure.......... 6050.145........     Issue 1
```

Fig. 4.8 PC processor box (boxed) level BOM.

Processor Box (Boxed).. PROC01.. Issue 2

Cost (£)
```
├── Processor Box (Tested)....... PBT01........... 1 ..... Issue 2 .....
├── Manual............................... 0001.136........ 1 ..... Issue 2 ..... 1.20
├── Warranty Card................... 0001.184........ 1 ..... Issue 1 ..... 0.05
├── Carton............................... CT06.............. 1 ..... Issue 1 ..... 0.12
├── Plastic Bag......................... 0004.013....... 1 ..... Issue 2 ..... 0.02
├── Foam Support, Left............. 0010.016....... 1 ..... Issue 3 ..... 2.45
├── Foam Support, Right.......... 0010.017....... 1 ..... Issue 3 ..... 3.56
├── Assembly........................... 6000.189........     Issue 1 ..... 2.45
└── Packaging Procedure.......... 6050.145........     Issue 1
```

Fig. 4.9 PC processor box (boxed) level BOM with costs.

To see the cost of the 'processor box (tested)' reference needs to be made to the next and lower levels of the BOM. The BOM level immediately below 'processor box (tested) would be 'processor box (untested)' as shown in Fig. 4.10.

Processor Box (Tested).. PBT01.. Issue 2

Cost (£)

```
├── Processor Box (Untested).........  PBUT01.....   1.....     Issue 2 .....
├── Floppy Disk Drive Transit Card...  0003.006....  1.....     Issue 2 ..... 0.01
└── Test ......................................  2000.056..............        Issue 1 ..... 5.80
```

Fig. 4.10 Processor box (tested) BOM with costs.

Here again test is a designed process and hence has a time for a particular resource and hence cost associated with it. The floppy disk drive transit card is a purchased item that gets inserted into the drive compartment to prevent damage during transit. As a purchased part it has a cost price.

Finally, for the purposes of this illustration, the processor box (untested) BOM is that shown in Fig. 4.11.

Processor Box (Untested).. PBUT01.. Issue 2

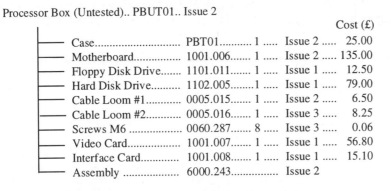

Cost (£)

```
├── Case.............................  PBT01...........  1 .....  Issue 2 .....   25.00
├── Motherboard................  1001.006.......  1 .....  Issue 2 ..... 135.00
├── Floppy Disk Drive.......  1101.011.......  1 .....  Issue 1 .....   12.50
├── Hard Disk Drive..........  1102.005........1 .....  Issue 1 .....   79.00
├── Cable Loom #1............  0005.015.......  1 .....  Issue 2 .....    6.50
├── Cable Loom #2............  0005.016.......  1 .....  Issue 3 .....    8.25
├── Screws M6 ..................  0060.287.......  8 .....  Issue 3 .....    0.06
├── Video Card..................  1001.007.......  1 .....  Issue 1 .....   56.80
├── Interface Card............  1001.008.......  1 .....  Issue 1 .....   15.10
└── Assembly ..................  6000.243................  Issue 2
```

Fig. 4.11 Processor box (untested) BOM with costs.

Most of the items at this level are assemblies but by now it should be clear that the cost of an assembly at any level within the BOM can be found from the sum of all the cost items that go to make it up, together with parts and labour for the appropriate process. All assemblies at their lowest level will comprise purchase parts and a process associated with them, all of which have associated costs.

By starting at the lowest level of the BOM and working upwards, the cost of all intermediate assemblies can be found up to a total product cost. That is the cost to manufacture a single product.

Set-up costs

In one respect the above description is a simplification. It has assumed that a single product is manufactured. In reality there are usually two types of costs associated with the manufacture of products. The first is the actual cost as given by the BOM. The second arises from the cost of setting up the production line to produce the product in question. If the company continuously manufactures the same product, as is the case for a sweet product such as a chocolate bar or photographic film, the mode of manufacture is referred to as 'flow' production and there are only occasional 'down-times' for maintenance and corrective action. In all other types of manufacture, especially 'batch' production where a batch of one type of product is manufactured followed by a batch of another different product, set-ups are required between production of each batch.

Since it takes time to change from one set-up to another there is an associated cost. This cost must be added into the cost of making each unit of the product and must be recorded somewhere.

If the cost of making one product is C_p and the cost of setting up the production line is C_s then some part of C_s must be attributed to each product. The usual way of dealing with the set-up cost is to divide it by the number of products that will be made within the batch and add the cost to the product cost.

Worked Example 4.5

If the product cost C_p is £450 and the set-up cost is £62.50 (two hours of a technician type resource according to previously used total labour rates) and it is proposed to produce the PCs in batches of 10 the total cost of each PC, what is the set-up cost and what is the total cost per PC?

The total set-up cost is £62.50 and they will be produced in batches of 10. The set-up cost per PC is therefore £6.25. The product cost is £450.00 excluding set-up, including set-up the cost of each PC becomes £456.25.

Mathematically, set-up time is dealt with using the following equation:

$$C_u = C_p + \frac{C_s}{n}$$

It should be clear from this that the product's cost to manufacture is now no longer simply a function of the design (the parts used and the processes used to assembly it); the costs have now become a function of the manufacturing strategy. The more diverse the products that are produced on the same 'production line' the greater the set-up time and hence cost, is likely to be. The lower the batch size again the greater the proportion of set-up cost is attributed to each unit produced.

Each process within the product manufacture will have its own set-up cost. These set-up costs can be incorporated into the BOM at the appropriate level such that a more accurate cost can be found directly from the BOM and the number to be produced (the batch size). In this way the BOM becomes even more representative of the true cost of producing products.

The above is also simplistic in its treatment of production in that it makes the bold assumption that every product made is available for sale, that is a 100% yield throughout the production process. To improve the accuracy of the unit manufacturing cost the impact of production yield at each stage must be added in.

The impact of production yield on manufacturing cost

Production yield: the percentage of products that emerge from a production process that are of good quality compared to the total number made.

An activity with less than 100% yield results in the loss of the total value up to and including the cost of identifying the failure (assuming the fault cannot be corrected). Take for example the cost of identifying a failed and unrepairable monitor. The cost of scrapping a monitor is the total cost, or £110.00. If the manufacturing process that leads to finished monitors has a yield of $\eta\%$ for every 100 monitors manufactured 100η will pass and $100(1-\eta)$ will fail.

The cost of each scrapped unit must be included in the total costs. If the scrap cost is spread across the good products made, the cost of each good unit will be increased. The effective cost of each good unit is given by :

$$C_{u(eff)} = \frac{C_u}{\eta}$$

where: C_u = the actual unit cost
         $C_{u(eff)}$ = the effective unit cost

If the process yield is high this cost magnification effect will be small, however as the yield falls costs can escalate. In general the cost magnification factor is the reciprocal of the yield and results in a simple multiplying factor. Fig. 4.12 shows the magnification effect of yield on the actual unit cost. Note that in Fig. 4.12 the magnification factor is unity at 100% yield. This means that the cost of making one product is exactly what is stated in the BOM. For any production yield less than 100% the cost rises above this base level.

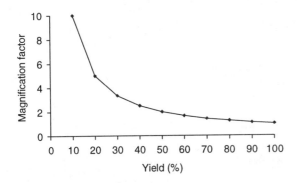

Fig. 4.12 General cost magnification factor versus production yield.

The BOM and product development

The BOM has been described in some detail as it appears at the production stage. The BOM however has an important role to play during the design and development of the product and can be used as a means of establishing targets and monitoring progress towards the target production costs.

Development of BOM and unit production cost targets

Let us assume that, at the beginning of the project, there is a target works cost price for the product to be designed and developed. The target works cost, or as sometimes called the unit production cost, UPC, is the cost of manufacturing one off of the fully developed product using the prescribed production process. In the case of the PC let it be assumed that the target UPC is £350. This amount is arrived at through market research and from accepted product margins within the company. On day one of the project the ultimate UPC is known, or at least the target is, £350. The top level of the ultimate BOM can also be described because the composition of the final product is known with some degree of certainty. If this were not known a preliminary systems study would identify major components. In the case of the PC it is known that there needs to be a processor box, a monitor, a keyboard and some software. Given this initial breakdown and the overall UPC, target UPC's for the constituent components can be planned. The available £350 can be apportioned or spread across the components to form targets for their designated development. It might be decided that the targets shown in Table 4.8 are sensible.

The design of the processor box, then, has a target of £216, the monitor a target of £110.00, etc. During design and development, components will be selected to perform certain parts of the design. A PCB will be required, as will a case and power supply, and so on. As the detail is developed the list of components can be constructed to resemble a BOM in so much as it can be hierarchical and can have line items allocated for the various processes it will need to be subjected to during manufacture. Costs for the components can be obtained from suppliers appropriate for the planned volumes and added to the draft BOM. If a watchful eye is kept on the total of the BOM as it is tracked in parallel with the actual product development, the ultimate production cost can be tracked. As the development progresses the accuracy of the BOM will also develop, as will the accuracy of the final product UPC.

Table 4.8 Apportioned target UPCs for PC example

System component	Target UPC
Processor box	216.00
Monitor	110.00
Keyboard	5.50
Software	15.00
Mouse	3.50
Total	350.00

With the ability to monitor costs as the product is developed early warnings will be received if the product starts to go over UPC budget. An early warning of such an occurrence gives more time for corrective action to be taken to rectify the situation.

Pulling the costs together

So far the design and development costs, the marketing costs and the cost of manufacturing a single unit have been considered. The next stage is to pull all these costs together to see how they affect the overall financial viability of the project. The design and development plan and the marketing plan provide both the costs of these activities and the timing of the expenditures required. Both sets of costs are also required before any product can be manufactured and sold. When the product has been developed and is ready to be produced the sale plan comes into play.

The sales plan is the forecast of sales for the product, quantity versus time. If all goes to plan, the company produces what the sales forecast requires and the manufactured units are all sold. In this event an income will start to result. Each unit will be manufactured for the BOM cost, the UPC, and will be sold at the selling price. The difference between the selling price and the manufacturing cost is called the 'gross profit per unit' or the 'margin'. The higher the margin the more money is made on each unit manufactured and sold.

The development cost of the PC is £25 000 in the first quarter of year 1 (the year within which the product was developed), £85 000 in quarter 2, £65 000 in quarter 3 and £25 000 in quarter 4. Sales commence in the first quarter of year 2 at a selling price of £550 which is maintained constant throughout the five years of sales. The unit production cost is also maintained at a constant £350. If quarterly sales are as shown in Table 4.9 what is the overall project profit and what is the shape of the cash flow curve?

Table 4.9 Quarterly PC sales figures (units sold)

	Q1	Q2	Q3	Q4
Year 2	25	50	75	100
Year 3	150	200	250	250
Year 4	250	250	250	250
Year 5	200	200	200	200
Year 6	150	100	50	25

Using the information provided above a table can be drawn up showing the quarterly cash flow. During the development stage cash will flow out of the organisation. During the sales period cash will flow into the organisation. Using normal conventions cash flowing into the organisation will be shown as a positive number while cash flowing out of the organisation will be shown as negative. Table 4.10 shows the quarterly cash flow for the size year project duration.

Cash flow is the name given to the amount of actual money that is spent or committed through the raising of a purchase order, or money that is received for products or services sold. If each cash input or output is summed over time the result is called the culmulative cash flow. Both must be carefully monitored to ensure the financial security of the organisation.

Table 4.10(a) Quarterly cash flow for years 1 and 2

	Q1	Q2	Q3	Q4	Q5	Q6	Q7	Q8
Sales revenue					13.75	27.50	41.25	55.00
Cost of sales					8.75	17.50	26.25	35.00
Gross profit					5.00	10.00	15.00	20.00
Development cost	25.0	85.0	65.0	25.0				
Cash flow	-25.0	-85.0	-65.0	-25.0	5.00	10.00	15.00	20.00
Cumulative cash	-25.0	-110	-175	-200	-195	-185	-170	-150

71

Table 4.10(b) Quarterly cash flow for years 3 and 4

	Q9	Q10	Q11	Q12	Q13	Q14	Q14	Q15
Sales revenue	82.50	110.0	137.5	137.5	137.5	137.5	137.5	137.5
Cost of sales	52.50	70.0	87.5	87.5	87.5	87.5	87.5	87.5
Gross profit	30.00	40.0	50.0	50.0	50.0	50.0	50.0	50.0
Development cost								
Cash flow	30.00	40.0	50.0	50.0	50.0	50.0	50.0	50.0
Cumulative cash	-120	-80.0	-30.0	20.0	70.0	120.0	170.0	220.0

Table 4.10(c) Quarterly cash flow for years 5 and 6

	Q16	Q17	Q18	Q19	Q20	Q21	Q22	Q23
Sales revenue	110.0	110.0	110.0	110.0	82.5	55.0	27.5	13.75
Cost of sales	70.0	70.0	70.0	70.0	52.5	35.0	17.5	8.75
Gross profit	40.0	40.0	40.0	40.0	30.0	20.0	10.0	5.00
Development cost								
Cash flow	40.0	40.0	40.0	40.0	30.0	20.0	10.0	5.00
Cumulative cash	260.0	300.0	340.0	380.0	410.0	430.0	440.0	450.0

Fig. 4.13 shows the cumulative cash flow against time for the whole project duration.

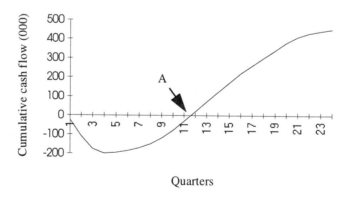

Fig. 4.13 Plot of cumulative project cash flow for the PC product example.

In the above example it has been assumed that profit is immediately turned into cash. In general this will not be true. Firstly, components and parts will not be purchased for cash but will be purchased on account. The account will be paid at some date in the future depending on the purchase terms. Similarly, sales will not be for cash but will be on credit. How quickly margin is turned into cash therefore depends on how quickly debts are paid and credit is collected.

The shape of the cumulative cash flow curve shown in Fig. 4.13 resembles an 'S' on its side and is frequently referred to as the project 'S-curve of costs'. It is a useful way of showing cash flows during the project and clearly shows where the cumulative cash flow becomes positive. In accounting terms this point, shown as point A on Fig. 4.13 is called the 'accounting break-even point'. After the accounting break-even point all costs incurred in creating the project having been paid off and all margin is profit as far as the overall project is concerned.

The project S-curve
Margin is the difference between the product selling price and the total cost of producing it.

The ABP is a simplistic view of cash flow because it ignores the time value of money. If you have £100 today and you invest it, in a year's time it will be worth the original £100 plus the interest earned on it, say £7 if the interest rate is 7%. Similarly if you left the £100 in for two years you would have £114.49 in two years time. Which would you prefer to have, £100 today, £107 in a years time or £114.49 in two years time? Assuming you were looking at the money on purely financial grounds, the answer is that you should have no preference because they are all the same, provided the interest rate remains constant at 7%. Table 4.11 summarises this growth concept.

ABP - accounting break-even point.

Table 4.11 Growth of money with time (7% interest rate)

Year	1	2	3	4	5
Balance at start of year	100.00	107.00	114.49	122.50	131.08
Interest	7.00	7.49	8.01	8.58	9.18
Balance at year end	107.00	114.49	122.50	131.08	140.26

Mathematically the balance at the end of any year is given by :

$$C = P(1+r)^n$$

where C is the balance at the end of the appropriate year
P is the principal amount invested
r is the interest rate
n is the number of years

The equation shows that the greater 'n' or the greater 'r' the more the resultant cash balance will be. This is not an unsurprising result since it is the equation used to calculate the growth of money when we make investments in interest-bearing accounts.

Given that the value of money changes with time, the usual way of dealing with a future predicted cash stream is to refer all cash in-flows and out-flows to one common point in time and discounting forwards or backwards to that point.

If we were to receive £200 today, £250 in one years time and £325.00 in two years time how much is that incoming cash stream worth to us at today's money value? Assumed that the interest rate is 7%. Table 4.12 summarises the question.

Worked Example 4.7

Table 4.12 Valuing a future cash stream

Year time	Now	1	2
Cash in-flow stream	200.00	250.00	325.00
Value of cash now	200.00	?	?

We receive £200 today, so the value of this cash in-flow in today's money must be £200. The £250 we receive next year is, however, worth less to us today because we could invest less than £250 in the bank at the 7% interest rate, to make £250 in a year's time. The amount needed to be invested can be determined by solving the following equation:

$$\text{amount invested} \times (1 + \text{interest rate}) = £250$$

The amount invested needs to be £233.64.

Similarly the £325 received in two years time is worth less to us today because we could invest a smaller sum for two years at 7% seeing it grow to £325. The amount needed can again be found by solving the following equation:

$$\text{amount invested} \times (1 + \text{interest rate})^2 = £325$$

the amount invested needs to be £283.87.

If the three present values of the three cash in-flows are added together the result is the net present value or NPV. Table 4.13 shows the present value of the cash stream and the NPV.

Table 4.13 The value of the cash stream

Year time	Now	1	2
Cash inflow stream	200.00	250.00	325.00
Value of cash now	200.00	233.64	283.87
Net present value	717.51		

The growth equation above can be rearranged to show P in terms of C. P is the amount that would need to be invested and interest rate r for n years to achieve a value C. In this case C is £250, r is 0.07 (7%), n is 1 (invested for 1 year). Rearranging the equation gives a new equation:

$$C = \frac{P}{(1+r)^n}$$

The discount factor is: $\dfrac{1}{(1+r)^n}$ which is always less than one.

The equation shows that the cash value C can be multiplied by a factor to produce its present value. The multiplying factor is called the discount factor. The discount factor will always be less than unity.

This discounting can be applied to all the annual cash flows, positive or negative. If the result is summed, the net present value or NPV results. This figure is the overall value of the project taking into account the time value of money. Simplistically, if the result is a positive number the project is worth doing, if negative it is not. Whilst the NPV is one of the methods by which the decision on whether to progress with a project or not can be based, there is still the issue of whether the company can afford the total project costs.

Financing the total project costs

The negative part of the product life cycle cost curve must be financed. Salaries must be paid and materials and services paid for. The funds to cover these costs can come from existing company funds or from borrowing. In either case there will be a cost associated with using the money.

Borrowing money to develop the product

If money is to be borrowed, interest will be due on the amount borrowed. Taking the simple method of borrowing, that of a bank overdraft facility, interest will be calculated periodically on the balance of the account over the period. Interest due will then be added to the amount due. Clearly as the cumulative costs rise, so too will the interest due, increasing the depth of the negative part of the life cycle cost curve. In this case the interest rate would be the rate that is used in the NPV calculation above to test whether the project is financially worthwhile.

Using company funds to develop the product

It might be tempting to think that using internal money to develop a product incurs no interest charges and is hence 'free'. This is an incorrect assumption. Investors put money into companies with the expectation of a return on their investment. It is the responsibility of the management of the company, as custodians of the shareholders' funds, to realise the investors expected return. The result of this is that management is expected to make all cash within the organisation work to generate more money.

Investors have a choice. They can invest their money in the bank to obtain a very low risk return on the sum invested or alternatively they can invest in shares of a company. In reality there are other investment opportunities but they are not relevant here. Investment in a company is more risky than investing in a bank. Investors expect a higher return for carrying this additional risk. It is this expected return that influences the return the company managers must try to achieve from their available internal funds.

The cost of using internal money is therefore not free, but is related to the investors expected return in the company, a figure that is invariably greater than the bank borrowing rate. In this case it is this internal rate which is used as the interest rate in the NPV calculation described above.

Summary

In this chapter the effect finance has on the product development process has been considered. Both the cost of development and the cost to manufacture each product in volume are crucial factors in determining the overall profitability of the organisation. In the chapter the pattern of cashflow has been considered through the product's life cycle. During design and development cash flows out of the organisation in the form of salaries and the purchase of parts, tools and services required to develop the product. During production cash flows out of the organisation to pay production wages and for parts required to make each product. Also during the production phase, cash flows into the organisation from sales of manufactured products.

To assist in the formation of an accurate estimate of the cost of developing the product, the concept of project planning and the PERT and activity plan is introduced and used to predict the pattern of costs that will arise during the development stage. The BOM is introduced to allow the cost of manufacture of a single product to be predicted during development and determined during production.

Production rarely yields all good products. The less than perfect yield has a cost impact on the product. A model is developed that shows the impact on cost of yield with and without reworking the failed products. The impact of setting up the production line, or part of it, to enable a batch of products to be made is also allowed for.

The costs come together to show the accounting break-even point and whether the whole project, via a net present value calculation, is worth pursuing from the organisation's point of view.

Finance and accounting is a large subject in its own right. Many books have been written on the subject and a good text is well worth pursuing if you become regularly involved in the 'numbers game'. This chapter should, though, have laid the essential foundations.

Problems

4.1   Produce a top level development plan, in the form of a bar chart, showing the development of an electronic domestic central heating thermostatic controller.

4.2   Develop a mathematical equation for the effective cost of a batch of manufactured products with less than 100% yield assuming that failed products are repaired and made sellable.

4.3   If the actual cost of manufacturing and testing a product is £250 and the yield is 85%, what is the effective cost of the product?

4.4   If you are to receive £750 in five years time and the current bank interest rate is 4%, what is the sum worth to you now?

4.5   In the above question what is the sum worth to you now if the interest rate is 4% next year but then rises to 5% for the following years?

4.6   It will cost £500k to develop a new widget, a cost incurred in year 1 (this year). If sales are expected to generate a net profit of £125k per year for years 2 to 6 inclusive, over which time the interest rate will remain constant at 6%, should the company spend the money to develop the product?

Tolerance design

5

At the end of this chapter you will be able to:

- Explain the terminology of tolerance analysis and design
- Analyse circuits for the effects of tolerances using a number of different methods
- Quantify the expected production yield associated with a particular circuit and its component tolerances
- Quantify the cost associated with tolerances
- Design circuits in the presence of tolerances

Every parameter of a manufactured component or circuit has a tolerance associated with it. This fact, and it is an important fact to remember in the design of any circuit, requires careful thought and attention during the design and development stage of any product. The resistance of every resistor, the capacitance of every capacitor, the gain of every transistor, all vary across a sample of devices. If, as an example, a thousand resistors specified as $1k\Omega$ $\pm5\%$ are tested and their resistance values noted they will not all be 1000.00Ω. The measured values should lie somewhere between 950Ω and 1050Ω with some distribution within these limits.

If an electronic circuit requires a very precisely controlled performance such as a precise output voltage, resistance or stage gain, a very precise resistance value may be required. For a one-off circuit such as a prototype a batch of resistors can be measured until the exact value is found. This value can then be used in the circuit. This approach is acceptable for a one-off critical design. It is not acceptable if the design is to be manufactured in any volume, at least not without some precautions being taken in the design and development stages of the project. If this practice were to occur in design and was passed through to production the result would be a very poor production yield.

Tolerance design and production yield

A circuit will normally be designed using 'nominal' component values. The simple potential divider shown in Fig. 5.1 shows a 'nominal' design.

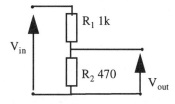

Fig. 5.1. Potential divider circuit showing 'nominal' component values.

If V_{in} is nominally 24V, V_{out} will be nominally 7.67V. In reality the actual resistors used will not be exactly on nominal and it is likely that V_{in} will not be exactly 24V. The result is that V_{out} will not be exactly 7.67V but will vary either

$$V_{out} = \left(\frac{470}{(1000+470)}\right) * 24$$

side of the nominal value as the values of V_{in}, R_1 and R_2 vary. Given a required range for the output voltage of say 7.5V to 7.75V, the distribution of actual values of V_{out} may lie wholly or partially within the specification range. Figure 5.2(a) shows a distribution in which the whole range is within the specification range. In this case a production yield of 100% results and there is a margin of safety in the design. Figure 5.2(b), on the other hand shows a distribution which is wider than the specification range. The result is less than 100% production yield and scrap or, at best the need for rework. The wider the variation in V_{out} the lower the production yield and the higher the scrap or rework.

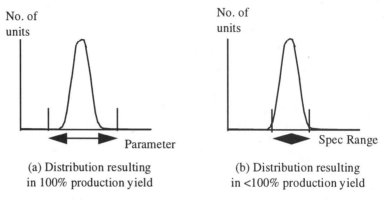

(a) Distribution resulting
in 100% production yield

(b) Distribution resulting
in <100% production yield

Fig. 5.2 Parameter distribution and production yield.

The illustration of yield for a single value parameter such as that shown above is easy to illustrate and understand. In practice it is frequently necessary to measure an output performance such as the frequency response of a circuit. In filters or amplifiers the performance is often specified graphically. Figure 5.3 shows two examples, (a) a filter and (b) an amplifier.

The shaded areas represent regions of failure.

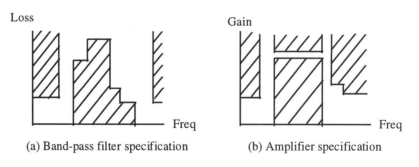

(a) Band-pass filter specification

(b) Amplifier specification

Fig. 5.3 Filter and amplifier frequency response specifications.

The Figures show the region of performance that pass the specification and those that do not. In Fig. 5.3(a) for example, if the response of a filter overlapped a shaded area it would have an unacceptable performance.

Products can be tested to these specifications either by viewing the whole frequency specification or by selecting a series of discrete frequencies and measuring the response at each, comparing it with the appropriate specification range. In this latter case, as illustrated in Fig. 5.4, the production performance and distribution of results degenerates to a series of single parameter distributions each of which is similar to that shown in Fig. 5.2.

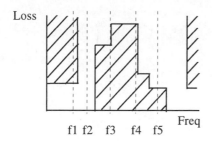

Fig. 5.4 Discrete frequency assessment of a frequency response.

If, however, a full view of the frequency response is required, a series of graphs will result. Figure 5.5 shows two examples for the filter specification shown in Fig. 5.3(a). Figure 5.5(a) shows a clear failure; the filter is out of specification in two ranges. Figure 5.5(b) shows a filter response which is just within specification; a marginal pass. Attempting to produce a quantity of filters for which the marginal frequency response of Fig. 5.5(b) were obtained in design and development is very likely to result in a less than 100% production yield. Figure 6 shows the spread in frequency responses that might result from a batch of filters of this type.

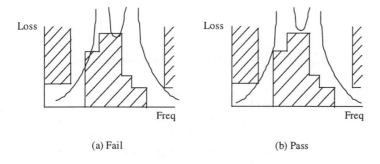

Fig. 5.5 Filter frequency response, fail and marginal pass.

How can this spread in performance be predicted and what can be done about it? These are the two fundamental questions underlying tolerance design. The quantification of circuit performance in the presence of component parameters that have a tolerance associated with them is called 'tolerance analysis'. The derivation of circuits whose performance is acceptable with any component parameter within the allowed component variation range is called 'tolerance design'.

Tolerance analysis

Tolerance analysis is the quantification of circuit performance in the presence of component parameters that have a tolerance associated with them. In any circuit, each component parameter that has a tolerance associated with it represents a degree of freedom of the circuit and as such can be represented as an axis against which one or more overall circuit performance measures can be

79

plotted. For example, in the simple potential divider circuit shown in Fig. 5.1, V_{out} can be plotted against R_2 with all other parameters held constant, as shown in Fig. 5.7.

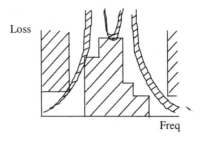

Fig. 5.6 Production spread of filter responses.

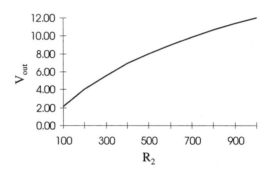

Fig. 5.7 V_{out} against R_2 for a simple potential divider.

In the same way a plot of V_{out} against R_1 could be produced. An alternative to a series of individual plots of one output parameter against one input parameter would be to plot V as the Z-axis of a three dimensional plot as shown in Fig. 5.8.

Viewing Fig. 5.8 along the Z-axis shows a series of circuit designs, each circuit design being represented by a specific combination of R_1 and R_2. This two-dimensional representation is shown in Fig. 5.9.

Each point represents a potential divider circuit, for example, the nominal value circuit shown in Fig. 5.1 is represented by point 'A'. Figure 5.9 is called the 'component space'. If the tolerances for each resistor are now considered, each component has a range added either side of the nominal value representing the component value tolerance. This results in the formation of a rectangle in the component space, as shown in Fig. 5.10. For any real potential divider circuit the value of a nominal 1kΩ ±5% resistor will be 1kΩ ± 50Ω, and the 470Ω will be ± 23.5Ω. These value limits define the boundaries of the rectangular region in the component space within which a random circuit will lie. This region is called the 'tolerance region'.

The potential divider is a simple, two-dimensional problem and can be visualised without too much difficulty. In circuits where there are more than two components or component parameters which have tolerances associated with them, visualisation is not as easy and computer techniques are usually required to enable a solution to be found.

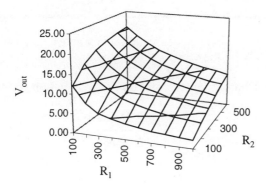

Fig 5.8 Three-dimensional picture of V_{out} against variations in R_1 and R_2.

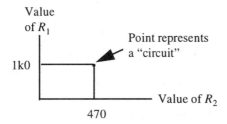

Fig. 5.9 Two-dimensional representation of the potential divider circuit.

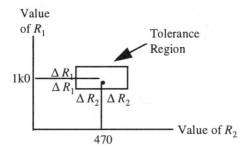

Fig. 5.10 Tolerance region for the potential divider circuit.

As is shown in Fig. 5.8 the third axis shows the value of an output parameter, in this case the value of V_{out}. Given a specification for this value a second set of boundaries can be shown on the R_1, R_2 component space, one boundary for each limit of the specification(s). Take for example the specification for a potential divider:

- Output voltage: $7.5V < V_{out} < 7.75V$
- Input resistance: $1500\Omega \pm 50\Omega$ (with output load of 100kΩ)

These specifications each impose constraints on the values of R_1 and R_2 which will lead to a potential divider circuit that meets the specification.

Worked Example 5.1
For the potential divider circuit specification given above, determine the region of acceptability by solving the specification equations.

Consider the limit of output voltage of 7.5V. The equation for output voltage is:

$$V_{out} = V_{in}\frac{R_2}{\left(R_1 + R_2\right)}$$

which, when rearranged gives:

$$R_2 = R_1\frac{V_{out}}{\left(V_{in} - V_{out}\right)}$$

Given an input voltage of 24V and an output voltage of 7.5V the above equation becomes:

$$R_2 = 0.455R_1$$

This equation is that of a straight line in R_1, R_2 space passing through the origin with gradient 0.455. Similarly the other output voltage limit of 7.75V results in a straight line through the origin of gradient 0.477. These two lines are shown in Fig. 5.11.

The other specification is that of input resistance:

$$R_{in} = R_1 + R_2 \quad \text{or} \quad R_1 = R_{in} - R_2$$

This equation represents a straight line of gradient -1 and intercept with the R_1 axis at a value of R_{in}. With the specification limits of R_{in} of 1450Ω and 1550Ω two lines result, as shown in Fig. 5.12.

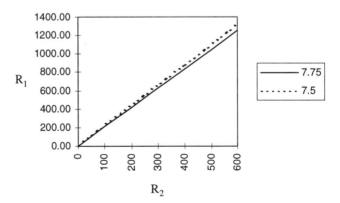

Fig. 5.11 The boundaries resulting from the output voltage specification.

The boundaries shown in fig.'s 5.11 and 5.12 can be combined to a second single region called the 'region of acceptability', as shown in Fig. 5.13.

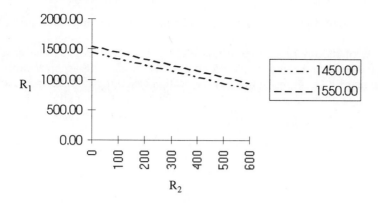

Fig. 5.12 The boundaries resulting from the input resistance specification.

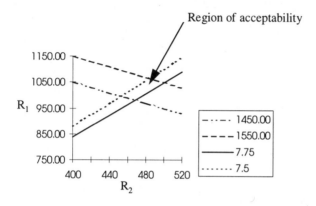

Fig. 5.13 Region of acceptability for the potential divider circuit.

Any circuit, that is any combination of R_1 and R_2, that lies within the region of acceptability will produce a circuit performance that passes all aspects of the specification and will hence be an acceptable circuit.

Since the 'tolerance region' and the 'region of acceptability' are areas on the same set of axes they can be shown simultaneously, as in Fig. 5.14. The commonality between the two regions provides information about the likely production yield. If the tolerance region lies wholly within the region of acceptability, 100% yield will result. If any part of the tolerance region lies outside the region of acceptability less than 100% yield will result.

If the distribution of components is even across the range, that is, if there is an equal chance of a 5% 1kΩ resistor being any value between 950Ω and 1050Ω calculate the resulting production yield.

Worked Example 5.2

The production yield can be calculated by considering areas. The ratio of the area of the tolerance region within the region of acceptability, area A in Fig.

5.14, divided by the area of the tolerance region, area B, will give the production yield.

The area of the tolerance region is 100Ω by 47Ω or $4700\Omega^2$. The area of the overlap between the tolerance region and the region of acceptability can be determined by counting squares or by, in this case, approximating the shape to that of a parallelogram and solving the problem geometrically. The resulting area is $1325\Omega^2$. The resulting approximate production yield is 1325 / 4700 or 28%.

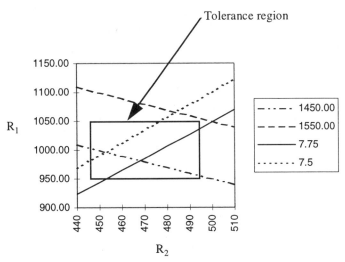

Fig. 5.14 Simultaneous view of 'tolerance region' and 'region of acceptability'.

Tolerance analysis methods

There are a number of different ways of analysing the effects of tolerances. The available methods can be divided into groups according to the approach taken. The overall range of methods can be divided into those that focus on the worst case tolerance combinations and those that do not. Of those that do not focus on worst case tolerance sets there are sampling methods and analytic methods. Table 5.1 summarises the available methods.

Table 5.1 Tolerance analysis methods

Analysis type	Method
Worst-Case Analysis	Vertex Analysis
- Non-Worst-Case Analysis	
- Sampling Methods	
+ Statistical Sampling	Monte Carlo
+ Deterministic Sampling	Regionalisation
	Simplical Approximation
- Non-Sampling Methods	Method of Moments

Vertex analysis

In vertex analysis the extreme values of each component are determined and circuits formed from the combination of these extremes. The circuit is then analysed for each worst case combination. Figure 5.15 illustrates the method for a circuit with three variables P_1, P_2 and P_3.

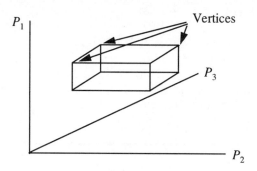

Fig. 5.15 Vertex analysis.

The main advantage of vertex analysis is that the circuits that need to be tested can be created with relative simplicity. Each of these circuits is analysed and a pass or fail obtained. The advantage of the method is that if all of the vertices result in a pass, a level of confidence in the circuit can be gained using a very straightforward and simple-to-implement method. The assumption made is that the extremes of the component tolerance values will coincide with extremes of the circuit performance. This may not be the case and out-of-specification points or areas may be missed using this technique.

For the potential divider example determine the vertices and whether the circuit represented by these vertices will pass or fail.

There are two variables, R_1 and R_2, each with two extreme values. R_1 has extremes of 950Ω and 1050Ω while R_2 has extremes of 446.5Ω and 493.5Ω. There are therefore four extreme value circuits or four vertex points each of which represents a circuit:

R_1	R_2	V_{out}	R_{in}	**Pass/Fail**
950	446.5	7.673	1396.5	Fail
950	493.5	8.205	1443.5	Fail
1050	446.5	7.161	1496.5	Fail
1050	493.5	7.673	1543.5	Pass

The analysis shows that at three of the four extremes of tolerance combinations the design will fail to meet the specification. This result tells us that the circuit is very likely to fail if the components are on the limits of their tolerance range. Beyond this information the method provides no information about production yield.

Worked Example 5.3

V_{out} is given by:

$$V_{out} = \left(\frac{R_2}{(R_1 + R_2)} \right) * 24$$

R_{in} is given by: $R_{in} = R_1 + R_2$

A further serious drawback of this technique lies in the number of circuit combinations that need to be tested in examples more complex than the one illustrated here. If there are k component parameters that are variables then there will be 2^k circuits that need to be analysed. If k is 20 (and this would not represent a particularly complicated circuit), the number of circuit combinations rises to 1 048 576. A computationally intensive task.

Monte Carlo analysis

The Monte Carlo method is a probabilistic approximation to the solution of a problem by using statistical sampling techniques. Applied to the analysis of tolerances the method is to select, at random, a circuit using values that lie within their tolerance range and analyse the performance of the circuit. This is repeated over a number of random circuits until a picture of the spread of circuit performance is obtained.

Worked Example 5.4

For the potential divider circuit perform a Monte Carlo analysis and from it estimate the likely production yield. Assume a flat distribution of component values within their tolerance range.

Table 5.2 below shows an example of a Monte Carlo analysis of the potential divider example. Ten random circuits have been tested and, as can be seen from the pass/fail column only a 50% pass rate has been achieved.

Table 5.2 Monte Carlo analysis of the potential divider circuit

The values in the table were selected using the pseudo-random number generator built into the Microsoft 'Excel' spreadsheet package.

Spreadsheets are an excellent tool for the Monte Carlo analysis of simple circuits.

R_1	R_2	V_{out}	R_{in}	Pass/Fail
1032.225	467.3349	7.479553	1499.56	fail
972.8208	464.9632	7.76133	1437.784	fail
999.1007	475.5695	7.73981	1474.67	pass
1027.235	471.6609	7.552135	1498.896	pass
968.5155	484.0865	7.998113	1452.602	fail
1005.031	466.8407	7.612197	1471.872	pass
967.139	487.5991	8.04432	1454.738	fail
974.8617	482.8999	7.95027	1457.762	fail
998.9926	470.1856	7.680793	1469.178	pass
1020.749	484.4048	7.723937	1505.154	pass
1004.4	449.3491	7.418323	1453.749	fail

If the number of random circuits is increased to 1000 the pass rate is approximately 27.5%, approximately because it is a result based on a random sample of 1000 circuits. No two random samples will give exactly the same results. The larger the sample the more accurate the approximation to the yield that will actually result.

The Monte Carlo method is a very easy to implement method and is frequently included in circuit analysis computer packages. SPICE, for example, has a Monte Carlo option. Provided the required tolerances are included with the component definitions in the circuit model, SPICE will compute the circuit performance using random combinations of component values within each tolerance range a specifiable number of times. Whilst this does increase the computational time it is controllable through the selection of the number of circuit trials.

Regionalisation

In Fig. 5.10 the tolerance region is shown as a single large region in the component space. This single large region can be divided into a number of smaller regions and a circuit within each sub-region tested. This is the basis of the regionalisation method. The tolerance region is divided into regions or is regionalised. The circuit that is selected within each sub-region could be the centre or one of the corners of the sub-region. Figure 5.16 shows a two-dimensional tolerance region divided into 100 sub-regions, 10 sub-regions per tolerance with the centre of each sub-region being the circuit which will be tested. As each circuit combination is tested a pass or fail will result. The passes map out the shape of the region of acceptability within the tolerance region. The smaller the division of each tolerance the larger the number of circuits that need to be evaluated but the more accurate the picture of the region of acceptability becomes.

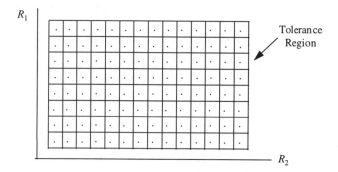

Fig. 5.16 Regionalisation of the tolerance region.

For the potential divider circuit determine the circuit component combinations if the tolerance region is to be divided in 100 sub-regions. Evaluate the circuit at each of the 100 resulting circuits and plot the tolerance region showing the pass sub-regions. **Worked Example 5.5**

In the divider example, R_1 lies between 950Ω and 1050Ω. Dividing this range into 10 gives steps of 10Ω and using the mid-value as the test value results in the following values of R_1 being used in the test circuits:

955Ω	965Ω	975Ω	985Ω	995Ω
1005Ω	1015Ω	1025Ω	1035Ω	1045Ω

Similarly equally spaced values of R_2 are selected with the following values:

448.85Ω   453.55Ω   458.25Ω   462.95Ω   467.65Ω
472.35Ω   477.05Ω   481.75Ω   486.45Ω   491.15Ω

	453.6	458.3	463.0	467.7	472.4	477.1	481.8	486.5	491.2
955									
965									
975									
985			*						
995		*	*	*	*				
1005		*	*	*	*	*			
1015			*	*	*	*	*		
1025				*	*	*	*	*	
1035					*	*	*	*	*
1045						*	*	*	*

Fig. 5.17 Regionalisation analysis of the potential divider circuit.

The 100 combinations of these component values then form circuits which can be pass/fail tested. If the fail regions are marked, a picture of the pass shape starts to emerge. This pass shape is the region of acceptability. Figure 5.17 shows the results of this analysis, the failed regions are shaded.

Simplical approximation

Simplical approximation is another deterministic approximation method. The objective of the method is, like regionalisation, to map the boundary of the region of acceptability. In regionalisation, all sub-regions within the region of acceptability are analysed. In simplical approximation this does not happen, rather an iterative approach is taken to finding points on the boundary. The following procedure describes the method as applied to the potential divider example.

Step	Description
1	Evaluate the nominal circuit to find a pass circuit
2	Increment one parameter until a fail occurs and find the pass/fail boundary
3	Increment same parameter in opposite direction and find the second pass/fail boundary
4	Increment second parameter until a fail occurs and find the pass/fail boundary
5	Increment same parameter in opposite direction and find the second pass/fail boundary
6	Determine the longest distance between boundary crossovers, find the mid-point of this arm
7	Repeat steps 2, 3, 4 and 5
8	Repeat steps 6 and 7 until sufficient resolution of the region of acceptability has been obtained

The key advantage of simplical approximation is its iterative nature which makes it well suited to computerisation. However the complexity does increase with the number of component variables making the region of acceptability difficult to visualise and describe.

For the potential divider circuit plot out the region of acceptability using the simplical approximation method.

Step 1. Start at the nominal circuit design.

R_1	R_2	V_{out}	R_{in}	Pass/Fail
1000	470	7.673	1470	Pass

Step 2. Increment one parameter by a small increment until a fail occurs. If R_2 is chosen to be incremented in steps of 5Ω the following results:

R_1	R_2	V_{out}	R_{in}	Pass/Fail
1000	470	7.673	1470	Pass
1000	475	7.729	1475	Pass
1000	480	7.784	1480	Fail

From these results it can be seen that the pass/fail boundary lies between 475Ω and 480Ω. The actual boundary lies at 476.9Ω. A closer approximation to the boundary could be obtained by reducing the step size, or by numerical interpolation. Pictorially the route to the boundary is shown in Fig. 5.18.

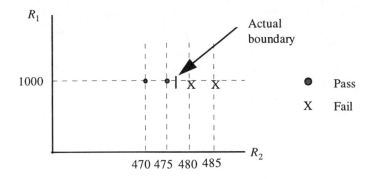

Fig. 5.18 Simplical Approximation - Locating a point on the boundary.

Step 3. Locate the boundary in the opposite direction. In this case R_2 would be decreased until a fail occurs. The boundary is then found by interpolation or reduced step size. The following results

R_1	R_2	V_{out}	R_{in}	Pass/Fail
1000	470	7.673	1470	Pass
1000	465	7.618	1465	Pass
1000	460	7.562	1460	Pass
1000	455	7.505	1455	Pass
1000	450	7.448	1450	Fail

By interpolation the value of R_2 at the boundary is 454.5Ω. Figure 5.19 shows the two located points on the boundary.

Step 4 and 5. Increment another component value in either direction to find another two points on the boundary. To do this the first component value is returned to its starting value. In the potential divider case this means returning R_2 to 470Ω and varying R_1 either side of the nominal 1000Ω until fails occur. The following results

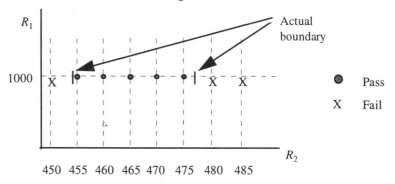

Fig. 5.19 Locating a second point on the boundary.

R_1	R_2	V_{out}	R_{in}	Pass/Fail
1000	470	7.673	1470	Pass
1005	470	7.647	1475	Pass
1010	470	7.621	1480	Pass
1015	470	7.596	1485	Pass
1020	470	7.570	1490	Pass
1025	470	7.545	1495	Pass
1030	470	7.52	1550	Pass
1035	470	7.495	1555	Fail
995	470	7.700	1465	Pass
990	470	7.726	1460	Pass
985	470	7.753	1455	Fail

By interpolation the boundaries lie at 1034Ω and 985.5Ω. Figure 5.20 shows this step with the two new boundary locations.

Step 6. Figure 5.20 shows that a cross has been used to find four boundary locations. If the lengths of the vertical and horizontal arms of the cross are found the longer can be identified. In the example the vertical arm is 48.5Ω long and the horizontal arm 22.4Ω long. Step 6 involves finding the mid-point of the longest arm and using that as the starting point to find two further boundary crossings.

Steps 7, 8. Mid-point of the vertical arm in the example is 1009.75Ω. Varying R_2 in steps either side of 470Ω will produce the two additional boundary crossing locations as shown in Fig. 5.21. Note the change of meaning of the small circles.

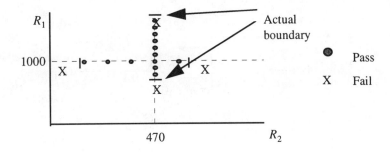

Fig. 5.20 Location of two further boundary points.

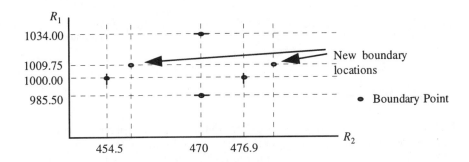

Fig. 5.21 Two additional boundary crossings.

As can be seen in Fig. 5.21 the shape of the region of acceptability is starting to emerge. To complete the method step 5 is repeated as many times as is required to trace out the whole picture of the region of acceptability. As can be seen, the shape of the region of acceptability revealed in Fig. 5.21 is the same as that which emerged using the regionalisation analysis as shown in Fig. 5.17.

Method of moments

The method of moments approach relies on detailed knowledge of the distribution of the input variables, that is, the component value variations, and the how the circuit transforms these component value inputs into outputs. Pictorially the approach is shown in Fig. 5.22.

The Probability Density Function is a mathematical formula relating the value of a characteristic to the probability of its occurence.

A Gaussian distribution is the distribution commonly obtained if the number of occurences of particular values of a large sample of components is plotted.

The equation describing Gaussian distribution is:

$$y = \frac{1}{\sigma\sqrt{2\pi}} e^{\frac{-(x-\mu)^2}{2\sigma^2}}.$$

Where μ is the mean of the sample and σ the standard deviation.

The mean of any sample of values can be found using:

$$\mu = \frac{1}{n}\sum_{i=1}^{n} y_i$$

The standard deviation of any sample can be found using:

$$\sigma = \sqrt{\sum \frac{(y_i - \mu)^2}{n-1}}$$

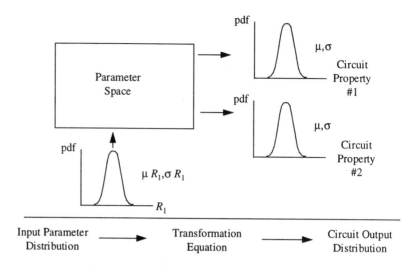

Fig. 5.22 Pictorial representation of the method of moments.

Tolerance design methods

Tolerance design is the derivation of circuits whose performance is acceptable with any component parameter within the allowed component variation range. To be able to design a circuit for the applicable tolerances it is first necessary to be able to analyse the tolerances and their impact on circuit performance. This was the subject of the previous section. With this understanding a number of ways of dealing with component variations emerge.

- reduce component variations;
- change component nominal values;
- negotiate the specification;
- design improvements;
- component screening.

Reduce component variations

All the tolerance analyses considered up to this point in the chapter have used as an example a potential divider made up of two 5% tolerance resistors. Using the Monte Carlo analysis method the resulting production yield is approximately 27.5%. Clearly, this would in practice be a low yield and one which would result in considerable production problems.

A potential solution to the yield problem is to reduce the tolerance of the resistors. Given that the tolerance of an output parameter, V_{out} in this case, must be a function of the tolerances of the input variables, R_1 and R_2 in this case, it is reasonable that reducing the input tolerances will result in a reduction in the output tolerance.

Using the Monte Carlo method over a sample of 5000 circuits, the production yield has been determined assuming both resistors have the same tolerance. Figure 5.23 shows the results.

Figure 5.23 clearly shows that by reducing the component tolerances an improvement in production yield can be achieved. In practice there are limits to this approach. Firstly the assumption is made that tighter tolerance components can be purchased. In some cases this will be true, in others it will not. Very close tolerance capacitors are not readily obtainable, nor are transistors with close tolerance gains. If close tolerance devices are available they are likely to carry a cost premium. Component cost can, therefore, be a reason why this approach to tolerance design is a limited one.

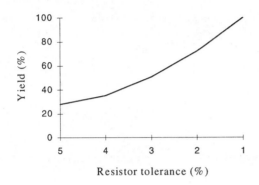

Fig. 5.23 Production yield versus resistor tolerance.

Design centring

An alternative approach to reducing the tolerance of circuit components is to alter their nominal values. Consider the situation depicted in Fig. 5.24. The component distribution is not central within the tolerance range with a consequential poor production yield. The width of the distribution would lie within the tolerance range if the nominal value were to be lowered to be central to the tolerance range.

In the potential divider example Fig. 5.14 shows that the centre of the tolerance region is not coincident with the centre of the region of acceptability. This is a direct indication of a poorly centred design.

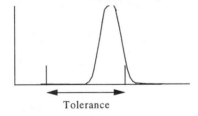

Fig. 5.24 Poorly centred design.

The objective of design centring is to position the tolerance region such that the maximum tolerance region can be completely contained within the region of acceptability thereby achieving 100% production yield with maximum achievable tolerances. Figure 5.25 shows the largest square area that can be placed completely within the region of acceptability for the potential divider example. A square area implies the tolerance of both resistors is the same. An alternative would be to consider rectangular areas in which case the tolerance on the resistor values would be different.

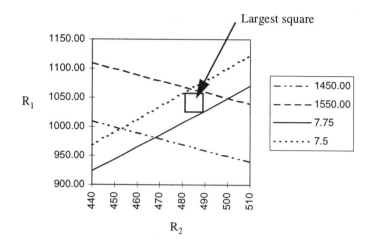

Fig. 5.25 The largest accomodatable centred tolerance range.

Component screening

In some cases reducing the tolerance of components might be the only solution but cannot be achieved through purchasing closer tolerance components. The same effect can be achieved by component selection or 'screening'. In screening a batch of components are measured and those with parameter values within the required range accepted and those outside the range rejected. Figure 5.26 shows how screening produces closer tolerance components.

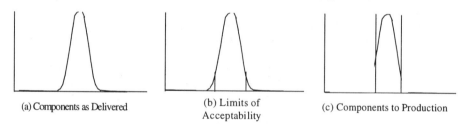

Fig. 5.26 Component screening.

Component screening is not a solution to be adopted without careful thought, it has drawbacks. There are two disadvantages namely the associated cost and the waste, or scrap.

There is a cost associated with testing each component. There is the cost of mounting it on the test machine, testing it and making the pass/fail decision. There is also the cost of keeping a record of the results. Since fewer than 100% of the components are likely to pass the screening test there will some components which are rejected. The cost of these components may be considered as scrap that is of no other use to the business.

Take as an example the selection of resistors to 1% tolerance from a batch purchased to a 2% tolerance. It would not be reasonable to expect a 100% yield. The cost of testing must be allowed for as must the cost of all those components that have failed the test. Note that the failed components have also been tested and have thus had value added to them before being declared failures. The total added value is the cost of scrap, not simply the purchase cost. If a batch of 100 resistors are purchased at a unit cost of C_p and each is subjected to a screening test which costs C_t the total value of each resistor after screening is $C_p + C_t$. If the screening process yields n% good devices the effective cost of each good device is given by:

$$C_{eff} = \frac{\left(C_p + C_t\right)}{n}$$

Worked Example 5.7

If the purchase price of a resistor is 2p and each requires a screening test time of one minute performed by a tester whos time is charged at £15.00 per hour (direct labour cost plus overheads), what is the effective cost of the resistor assuming a 75% screening test yield?

One minute at a labour rate of £15.00/hour is 25p. The screening test adds 25p to each resistor making the value of the tested resistor 27p.

If the yield is only 75%, that is, 25% of the resistors tested have to be scrapped, then the effective cost of each resistor is no longer 27p, but it has risen to:

$$C_{eff} = \frac{(2+25)}{.75} = 36p$$

Whilst this is a very significant rise it may be justified. If the cost of an alternative way of achieving a high overall product yield exceed this, it might prove to be the most cost effective solution.

The second issue is scrap. The components that are purchased, tested and failed, are effectively scrap as far as the particular application in question is concerned. If this is the only product the organisation makes that uses the particular component, then the components are indeed scrap. However, if the organisation uses the same component in other products these other products may be less sensitive to component tolerance variations and may be able to accommodate the rejects. In such a case the components are not scrapped and some of the previous scrap cost can be recovered. If the components can be used in other products the cost of testing is still required and must be allowed for in the overall costing.

Negotiate the specification

It may seem a cheat to suggest that, if a circuit cannot be designed to meet a specific specification 100% of the time, the specification should be changed. This is, however not such a absurd idea. In chapter 3 the concept of specification apportioning was introduced. If the circuit specification is an internally derived specification there may well be scope for change. Consider the example depicted in Fig. 5.27.

Sub-system #1 produces an output voltage V_{out} which serves as the input to sub-system #2. During the system design phase the specification for the output voltage was defined as $7.5 < V_{out} < 7.75$. The design of sub-system #1 has resulted in an acceptable nominal design but is one in which it would be excessively expensive to produce because component selection would be required to achieve 100% production yield. On reconsideration it is found that the design of sub-system #2 is such that it can accommodate a wider variation in V_{out}. The specification can therefore be 'traded' between the two modules' specifications without impacting upon the overall product specification and the performance customers will observe.

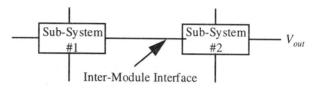

Fig. 5.27 Inter-module interface.

In the limit, negotiation of an overall product specification with the customer is not a forbidden thing to do. In some cases a relaxation may be granted, especially if the customer is not seriously affected by the change or where the customer sees an overall value in the proposed change.

Design improvements

There are frequently many different ways of achieving the same electronic performance. The different ways will have different tolerance sensitivities. An alternative approach to a tolerance problem is therefore to redesign the circuit to be less sensitive to tolerance effects.

Overall

There is no single correct way of designing for tolerances, nor a single solution to a tolerance problem. Component screening has been shown to be expensive in so far as it magnifies the purchase and screening test cost. However, if the total cost of screening is compared to the cost of a redesign to reduce the circuits overall sensitivity to tolerances it may prove to be a cost effective approach. The optimal solution to any problem of this nature should be made with all facts available and due consideration taken of all influencing factors.

Summary

This chapter has focused on another fact of 'reality'; that of imperfect components. Purchased components are not all the same and a design that works for the prototype components only is a design that will cause many problems in production. The chapter has introduced the two sides of dealing with component tolerances, the analysis of circuit performance in the presence of tolerances and designing to cater for the effects of tolerances. Both parts of design for tolerance are required skills for a good designer. The goal of circuit design is to produce a design that can be manufactured. A key to the success of this goal is to be able to design good circuits in the presence of tolerances.

There are a number of techniques for tolerance analysis ranging from the purely analytic to the purely statistical. No single method fits all situations, although the Monte Carlo method is the most widely available and most commonly used. Equally, there is no single best method for designing circuits to cater for the effects of tolerances. The designer needs to be aware of all available techniques so that the most appropriate can be used in any given situation.

Problems

5.1   A single order low pass filter of cut-off frequency 1kHz is required. The load impedance can be assumed to be high enough to have no loading effect on the filter. The filter is realised using a 10% tolerance resistance and a 20% tolerance capacitor. Using vertex analysis determine the four extremes of the cut-off frequency. What can you conclude from the results?

5.2   In the above filter the specification for the cut-off frequency is 1kHz $\pm$ 1%. Assuming a flat distribution of component values within the tolerance range, what production yield would result?

5.3   Is there an RC combination with the defined tolerances that would give optimum production yield? If so what are the values and what is the production yield?

5.4   Using the regionalisation method determine the shape of the region of acceptability within the tolerance range given.

Design for the physical environment

6

Objectives

At the end of this chapter you will be able to:

- State the meaning of the various categories of failure
- Explain how the physical environment affects product design
- Produce a formal specification of the physical environment
- Define the terminology used in the formal environmental approval testing of products

Designing a product that will function in a laboratory environment requires skills in top-down system analysis, specific skills in the design of the detail of the product and a structured approach to verification. To say such design is simple would be underestimating what is involved. However, when compared to designing a product for practical use in a harsh physical environment, the issues become buried in the greater problem of making the product conform to the entirety of the specification.

In this chapter, the physical environment of the product will be explored and the impact it has on the design process considered. The physical environment includes environmental factors such as heat, vibration, humidity, the presence of contaminants and so on, as well as the effects of operational use, storage and carriage and normal user abuse. The actual physical environment will vary from product to product, customer group to customer group and according to whether the product is destined for inside use or for use where it will be exposed to the elements. The geographic destination of the product is important from a temperature and humidity point of view as is the proposed method of transportation. The design process must consider the very wide range of environmental factors involved and build them in from the start of the product design.

To illustrate the concepts introduced in this chapter the development of a personal safety beacon will be used. A personal safety beacon, alternatively called a Personal Locator Beacon (PLB) or Emergency Locator Transmitter (ELT) is a radio transmitter that emits a modulated radio frequency signal on an internationally recognised distress frequency when the bearer is in a life threatening situation. Such beacons are licensed pieces of equipment and restricted to carriage by aviation and maritime vessels. As a direct consequence of their purpose, ELTs must be capable of surviving a very harsh environment including the crashing of the host aircraft. The specification for the aviation version ELT is the Civil Aviation Authority (CAA) Cap 208 section 10 in Europe. The same basic product is recognised world wide although each country has its own name and specification. For example, the name for such a product in the USA is the PLB. Reference to the name ELT and the CAA specification will be made throughout this chapter. The kind permission of the CAA for permission to reproduce parts of their specification is acknowledged.

PLB - Personal Locator Beacon.

ELT - Emergency Locator Transmitter.

The physical environment

The physical environment is the environment within which the piece of equipment or system that is being designed and developed is expected to operate or can reasonably be expected to be operated. A common example of a physical environment is the temperature range over which the equipment is required to function to specification. The environment, in reality, embraces many other factors such as humidity, vibration, waterproofing, shock, fungal growth, chemical attack, damage due to abuse and many others. Many of these factors will put constraints on the mechanical and electronic design which will not always pull in the same direction. The final design is therefore likely to be a compromise that produces a design that is adequate for the purpose.

In understanding the physical environment and how it has an impact upon product design it is necessary to understand the meaning of 'failure'. Is, for example, slight cosmetic damage a failure? If, as a consumer, the front panel of a video recorder or hi-fi system is scratched when the product is first taken out of the box it would not be unreasonable to send the item back requesting a replacement. In other words this would constitute a failure. Conversely if, after a years use, the front face was accidentally scratched in cleaning, continued operation would be expected and the problem would not be classed as a failure, at least not on the part of the equipment. If, however the equipment had failed after cleaning, most would consider it unreasonable and would complain to the manufacturer. The above introduces the difficulty in defining a 'failure'. To be of practical use a more formal understanding is required.

What constitutes failure?

The formal definition of the term failure relates to non-performance. Non-performance is a very wide term encompassing total non-operation to degradation of capability to a point where the product ceases to meet its formally agreed or declared specification. In the strict sense a failure occurs when the product does not meet its declared specification. This definition is acceptable for the defined characteristics and especially those that can easily be quantified. However, it becomes less satisfactory in areas where the specification is vague, incomplete or relates to customer expectations.

Consider as a brief example, a laptop personal computer. The product is designed to be portable and be capable of withstanding a rough environment, but how rough? Operated on board a small boat in rough seas or during a particularly bumpy landing of an aircraft would it still survive? Would it be reasonable to expect it to survive? The owner would be quite irate if, for example, the hard disk drive was damaged and all her information was lost. The owner might consider this a reasonable environment while the designers might consider it a hostile environment. Subjectivity and perception enter the definition.

Categories of failure

Failure ranges from rendering the product unsafe to operate through to insignificant and unnoticeable. The following list shows a range of possible failure modes.

Product unsafe

The product fails to a state that makes it unsafe to operate. An example of this would be a television that failed such that any metal parts on the front panel become short circuited to either mains or the anode voltage of the cathode ray picture tube. This would result in the potential for a lethal electric shock.

Product produces misleading information that could endanger life

The product gives all the outward symptoms of working but gives the wrong indications. An example of this would be a marine RADAR system that gave an incorrect distance reading. In conditions of poor visibility this could cause the pilot to make the wrong navigational decisions thereby endangering life and property.

Total failure

The product totally and obviously fails. An example of this is the television set that does nothing when switched on, no picture, no sound, no on-light. This failure case can be less severe than the previous two categories because the user knows the product is not working and can therefore make other arrangements. There are situations however where total product failure is life threatening as in the case of the emergency locator beacon.

Total loss of some functionality

Some functions of the product completely fail. An example of this would be the picture of a television working correctly but a total loss of sound.

Partial loss of some functionality

Some function of the product partially fails. An example of this would be the loss of sound volume of a television. Sound can still be heard but not of sufficient volume for normal use.

Out of specification

Some function of the product works but does not meet its specification. An example of this would be the audio power output of the television falling from the specified 8 Watts down to 6 Watts. The customer may or may not realise however, strictly speaking, that the product is failing to meet specification and is thereby faulty.

These broad categories of 'failure' vary in severity, as seen by the user, from catastrophe to possibly insignificance. They do, however, form the basis of a structure against which the level of acceptability of failure can be formally agreed. The specific wording used in CAP 208 is that at the completion of this test, ensure that all mechanical devices operate satisfactorily. The statement requires that, where switches are used, they should be operable, antennas should be intact and so on. It does not state that the paint finish should be as new or that the product should physically look the same as it did when it was taken out of its box for the first time. A level of physical change to the product is therefore allowed providing the operational purpose of the product can be met after all the tests have been performed on it. The extent of these changes will be described through this chapter.

Physical environment considerations

The physical environment is considered, for the purposes of this chapter, as being made up of a number of categories of factors:

- physical user attributes
- environmental considerations
- transportation
- user abuse.

Each of these categories of factors and the specific contents of each is considered in turn.

Physical user attributes

The physical user attributes deal with the characteristics that directly interface with the person who will actually use the product and it includes the aesthetic design, the cosmetic finish, labelling and the weight and portability of the product. All these aspects must be designed with the physical environment in mind if the product is to meet the expectations of the customer.

It might be argued that the positioning of control is as important as their functionality. Provided the functionality is provided, it is argued here, that functionality is subordinate to the aesthetic design.

Consider, as an example, the ELT. One version of the ELT, the personal carry device is carried by the pilot of a light aircraft and, in the event of an emergency situation, is manually activated. The emergency situation could be in very cold conditions where the pilot would be wearing gloves. A small intricate, and possibly recessed, switch would not be easy to operate with gloved hands. Such a design, whilst meeting the overtly stated specification, may fall foul of the expectations of the user. The documentation of a requirement of this nature is not a simple task. Even the simple statement operable by a gloved hand is complex without a definition of the type of glove and size of hand for example. The dexterity ability of a hand in a fingered glove is very different from that of a hand in a mitten. In many cases acceptability defaults to reasonable interpretation of the specification. CAP 208 requires of its ELT(S) that the equipment shall be designed so that it may be bought into operation using one hand only.

Aesthetic design

The aesthetic design of a product includes the positioning of switches, knobs, buttons, displays, screen(s), handles, all the parts of the product that the user needs to come into contact with as part of the normal operation. The positioning and size of the user interfaces affects the usability of the product, especially in extreme environmental conditions. For example, in the ELT example above, the transmitter might need to be activated when the outside temperature is -40C. At these temperatures the skin will stick to metal and frostbite will result. If a transmitter were designed such that the switch was small and, perhaps, shrouded to prevent damage in the event the transmitter is dropped, operation might only be possible by an ungloved hand. Clearly the product would fail to meet the expectation of the user, namely the ability to activate it and not get frostbite!

In the case of more common products such as a portable personal stereo player designed to be operated by a single hand, the layout of the controls will suit either a left- or right-handed person. Should a left-handed and right-handed version be designed? There are many aesthetic considerations and dilemmas.

Cosmetic finish

The cosmetic finish of the product is there to make the product attractive or for durability. In either case consideration of all aspects of the environment and cost is crucial if the finish is to meet customer expectations. Figure 6.1 shows these major influencing factors.

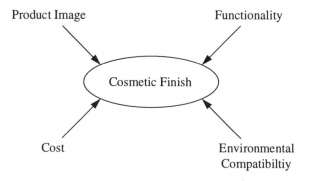

Fig. 6.1 Major factors which influence cosmetic finish.

There is a wide range of finishes available, some dependant on the underlying material. Examples of finishes are:

- Paint loaded plastic
- Painted plastic
- Varnish
- Painted metal
- Passivated metal
- Elasticised metal
- Stainless steel
- Wood.

Every finish has a set of material properties that react with the environment in different ways and the particular response of the material to the environmental factor affects customer satisfaction. The more important properties of the cosmetic finish are:

- Strength
- Durability with time
- Thermal properties
- Electrical conductivity

- Degree of waterproofing

- Resistance to physical shock
- Resistance to flame and burning
- Solar radiation absorption characteristics
- Resistance to liquids and chemicals
- Resistance to fungal and other living organism growth
- Resistance to wear, rubbing, scratches, etc.
- Potential damage to users, sharp corners, edges, etc.

103

In the design process, a matrix of potential cosmetic finishes and required environmental characteristics can be constructed.

Environmental	Paint loaded plastic	Painted plastic	Varnished metal	Painted metal	Passivated metal	Plasticized metal	Stainless steel	Wood
Thermal conductivity	Low	Low	Med	Med	High	Med	High	Low
Strength	Low	Low	High	High	High	High	High	Med
Resistance to physical shock	Low	Low	High	High	High	High	High	Low
Solar radiation absorption characteristics								
Electrical conductivity								
Resistance to liquids and chemicals								
Resistance to fungal and other living organism growth								
Resistance to flame and burning								
Degree of waterproofing								
Resistance to wear, scratches, etc.								
Durability with time								
Cost								
Potential damage to users, sharp corners, edges, etc.								

Fig. 6.2 Partially completed influence matrix.

When completed, the matrix should provide a picture of the trade-offs open for the product and allow an informed decision as to which cosmetic finish is the most appropriate. For completeness, the matrix should also include other factors introduced in this book such as cost, compatibility with current or proposed manufacturing capability or availability of the process through sub-contract. Figure 6.2 shows a partially completed matrix for a small number of generalised finishes and a sample of environmental characteristics.

In addition to the impact the physical environment has on cosmetic finishes there is also the potential for certain cosmetic finishes to give off poisonous vapours when they burn, a hazard that is now prohibited in certain environments, in particular inside aircraft.

Other generic environments which impose specific sets of problems include desert, maritime, polar and rain forest environments.

Labelling

Product labelling and identification serve a number of purposes including:

- Knob, button, switch, etc. labels and legends
- Product identification, make, model, serial number, etc.
- Inspection labels
- Safety warning labels
- Calibration labels.

Any label or marking on the outside of a product forms part of the cosmetic finish of it and as such everything said in the previous section applies to labelling. The durability of the labelling, resistance to wear, temperature, chemical attack, water, and so on. All need to be considered.

There is one additional aspect to labels in particular, that needs to be considered. Labels are attached to the product, so the attachment method also needs to be reviewed, options considered and pros and cons of each, for each environmental factor considered.

In the case of stuck-on labels the glue used needs to be considered. Will the adhesion be affected by temperature, water, solvents used in any recommended cleaning procedures for the product, or solvents commonly used by the target customer group?

One way to avoid the use of adhesives is to rivet or bolt the labels on. However, this has the potential disadvantage of differential thermal expansion causing buckling of the label, or electrochemical action resulting from the contact of dissimilar metals (case to label, case to rivet, rivet to label).

Whilst labels might seem on the surface, a rather mundane aspect of design, they are one of the keys to customer product perception. A poorly labelled product is likely to be one that is more difficult to operate than one which is clearly labelled. Product labelling requires careful attention to space required for appropriate labels and to the actual method of labelling.

Weight and portability

The weight of the product should be specified in the product specification. Is an overall specification for the weight of the product sufficient for a good quality design? Consider the example of a piece of rack mounted test equipment, shown schematically in Fig. 6.3.

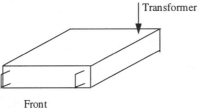

Fig. 6.3 Schematic of a piece of rack-mounted test equipment (front handles).

For electromagnetic compatibility reasons the mains transformer is mounted at the rear of the equipment, the handles at the front. Consider the implications of this type of weight distribution as the user withdraws the equipment from the rack. If the equipment is particularly heavy there could be a safety hazard resulting from the weight distribution. A commonly adopted way of overcoming this problem is to place handles on the sides, as shown schematically in Fig. 6.4, often in addition to ones on the front.

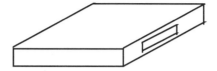

Fig. 6.4 Schematic of a piece of rack-mounted test equipment (side handles).

The above example is a very simple illustration of one problem associated with weight and its distribution. Other considerations that need to be borne in mind during the design process include ensuring the carrying handles and their attachment to the equipment are strong enough for the weight of the equipment.

The internal design of the product must also take weight into account, the weight of parts and their attachment method. Consider, for example, a printed circuit board mounted to an internal chassis. Relatively heavy components attached to the central area of the printed circuit board are likely to result in significant flexing of the board under shock, bump or vibration. Flexing of a printed circuit board can damage surface mount components and can result in microcracks within the fabric of the PCB resulting in a degraded reliability and, sometimes intermittent board functionality.

Environmental considerations

The major groups of characteristics of the physical environment are summarised in Table 6.1.

Table 6.1 Major environmental characteristics

• Thermal	• Vibration
• Humidity	• Contaminants
• Electrical	• Survival

This is not an exhaustive list. It does however, cover the most frequently encountered environmental conditions and survival which are used to illustrate some of the more extreme conditions that may be met.

Each characteristic needs to be considered for the situations the product will need to endure. The three main situations are normal operation, storage and transportation. For some products there will be a range of specifications for different types of operation or different modes of transportation. For example, if a product is to be carried both by lorry and by air there will be two different transportation specifications. In such cases an itemised list of specification items should be drawn up and the worst specification against each line item used.

A matrix of factors and situations can be constructed and used as a check to ensure all aspects of the product specification are being considered and whether the specification is complete. An example of the matrix is shown in Table 6.2.

Table 6.2 Environmental characteristic matrix

	Operation	Storage	Transportation
Thermal			
Vibration			
Humidity			
Contaminants			
Electrical			
Survival			

Each cell of the matrix is filled with the relevant clauses of the specification(s) or the details of the requirements. Any blank cells at the end of the exercise should be specifically considered to see whether it has been omitted from the specification or really is an irrelevant factor. The left-hand side can be a list generated from the specification(s) or can be a generic list produced for a particular organisation, or for a particular product line.

Products destined for a regulated market, such as the ELT(S), will have an environmental requirement clearly defined. The ELT(S), being destined for the aviation market comes under the authority of the Civil Aviation Authority. Examples of other regulating bodies are British Telecom (for equipment connected to the telephone network), the Department of Trade and Industry (for all maritime products), British Standards and European legislation (for imported and exported goods). Whilst this is not a comprehensive list, it does illustrate the wide range of sources for existing specifications that can be used as reference documents or as a starting point for the creation of a new specification.

Where additional specifications are referenced in the main product specification, the inclusion of these specifications is required when formulating an overall product requirement. For example CAP 208 refers the reader to additional documents EUROCAE ED-63 and the COSPAS-SARSAT specification C/S T.001. All sections of these specifications become part of the ELT(S) specification by virtue of their being referenced in the main specification. It would not be unacceptable to commence design of an ELT(S) without taking account of the contents of these specifications.

COSPAS-SARSAT is an international system for the detection of transmissions from ELTs and other distress radio beacons operating on the internationally recognised distress frequencies and having the correct modulation.

COSPAS - Cosmicheskaya Sistyema Poiska Avariynych Sudov (space system for the search for distress vessels).

SARSAT - Search and Rescue Satellite-Tracking.

Thermal

Operating temperature range. The most common form of thermal specification is the operating temperature range. It is normally specified as a range of temperature such as:

$$0 \text{ to } 50C$$
$$\text{or} \quad -50C \text{ to } +125C$$

In the case of the ELT(S) the operating temperature range is specified using the second technique with a lower temperature limit of -40C and an upper temperature of +55C. The storage temperature range is similarly specified as being -55C to +85C. These actual values can be used to update the environmental characteristic matrix as shown in Table 6.3.

Table 6.3 Environmental characteristic matrix

	Operation	*Storage*	*Transportation*
Thermal			
• Lower temperature limit	-40C	-55C	
• Upper temperature limit	+55C	+85C	
Vibration			
Humidity			
Contaminants			
Electrical			
Survival			

The specification is simple to write but slightly more complicated to verify. The design of any test should specify in detail all characteristics of the test. Consider the example of a product that is to be tested for operation to the upper operating temperature limit of +55C. Temperature testing of products is usually performed by placing the product inside a 'temperature chamber', a thermally insulated cabinet, the internal temperature of which can be raised or lowered as required. Figure 6.5 shows the temperature profile within the temperature chamber when raising the temperature from room temperature to the test temperature of +55C. It is important to realise that an instantaneous temperature change does not occur, neither is the product evenly at the internal chamber temperature as soon as the chamber reaches the target temperature. There is always a thermal lag, the product can take some time to thoroughly heat through.

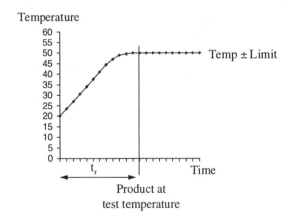

Fig. 6.5 The temperature behaviour inside the temperature chamber.

The temperature within the chamber rises from room, or 'ambient' temperature to the test temperature at a rate which can, on modern temperature chambers, be set to any desired rate up to the limit of the capability of the chamber. The rate of rise (or fall) of temperature should be specified when defining a temperature test. The units of temperature change being in degrees per minute.

As the internal temperature of the chamber rises, the temperature of the outside of the product also rises. The product will have a thermal inertia which means that it will not evenly heat throughout its volume instantly. It will take time to warm through thoroughly. The time taken between starting a test and the time at which the product is considered to be at an even enough temperature to make the test valid is called the stabilisation time and is denoted in Fig. 6.5 as t_s. The stabilisation time also must be stated in the definition of a temperature test. CAP 208 specifies a stabilisation time of three hours. In the absence of any specific information about the thermal inertia of the product a common rule of thumb is to allow a minimum of 20 minutes stabilisation time for small products, longer for larger, at the test temperature to allow the product to heat through evenly.

The final parameter that needs to be taken into account and specified is the stability of the test temperature. The test temperature in the example is +55C. It is unrealistic to require the temperature to be maintained at exactly +55C, instead an allowable tolerance should be specified such as ± 2C.

Worked Example 6.1

A temperature test of an ELT(S) is required to be specified. Acceptable performance must be assessed for operation and storage at the upper and lower temperature limits. Using the data provided in the text, design a temperature test cycle. Assume that the time required to perform a set of electrical tests to verify that the product is working to specification is 15 minutes. (i) How long will the overall test cycle take? (ii) What practical problems might arise from the test cycle?

The test sequence required is summarised in Table 6.4. A total of 14 test stages are required, the operation for which is shown in the second column. The temperature at which the operation is performed or the change of temperature required in the test stage is shown in the third column and the overall time required is shown in the last column, in minutes. Note that the third column includes the tolerance within which steady temperatures must be maintained and the maximum rate of change that can be used when temperature is being changed. The table thereby forms a specification for the test as well as a statement of the overall cycle.

(i) The total test time is just under 17 hours.

Ambient temperature is normally taken to be 20C.

(ii) The most important practical implication of this, is that assuming it is required to be performed without a break, 17 hours of attention is required. A possible solution to this would be to automate the entire cycle including the electrical testing. If this is possible then the cycle can be started and left unattended. If however the electrical testing requires manual intervention such as activation using manual switches, somebody is required to be present during the electrical test stages. The test stages start at 0 mins, 6 hours 33 mins, 13 hours 19 mins and 16 hours 41 mins from the start of the test. This means that if the test starts at 8.00 am the final test will need to take place at around midnight! Some of the problems associated with testing at that time include authorising of overtime, access to the building and supervision for safety reasons.

Table 6.4 ELT(S) temperature test cycle

Test Stage	Operation	Temperature	Time required (mins)
1	Electrical test	Ambient	15
2	Decrease temperature	Ambient to -55C Max. rate 5C/min	15
3	Stabilise	-55C ± 2C	180
4	Increase temperature	-55C to -40C Max. rate 5C/min	3
5	Stabilise	-40C ± 2C	180
6	Electrical test	-40C ± 2C	15
7	Increase temperature	-40C to +85C Max. rate 5C/min	25
8	Stabilise	+85C ± 2C	180
9	Decrease temperature	+85C to +55C Max. rate 5C/min	6
10	Stabilise	+55C ± 2C	180
11	Electrical test	+55C ± 2C	15
12	Decrease temperature	+55C to Ambient Max. rate 5C/min	7
13	Stabilise	Ambient	180
14	Electrical test	Ambient	15
	Total test time		1016 16.93 hours

Thermal shock

Another type of thermal test common in electronic products is the thermal shock. A thermal shock is a very rapid change of temperature, as close to instantaneous as can be achieved. Consider the example of an ELT(S) in a pilot's pocket in the cockpit of a heated aircraft, the ambient temperature would be around +20C. If the aircraft crashed into the sea in the arctic where the water is around 4C the ELT(S) would be exposed to a 16C drop in temperature the instant it came into contact with the water. Clearly the beacon would be expected to operate after this thermal shock. CAP 208 requires that the ELT(S) should survive a 30C thermal shock.

The specification of a thermal shock is very similar to the specification of a normal temperature test. The starting temperature must be achieved and the device allowed to stabilise for an acceptable period. The temperature must be specified with tolerance limits. The rate of change should be specified, or the method of achieving the thermal shock should be stated, as should the new temperature with limits and stabilisation time.

Achieving very high rates of temperature change is difficult in a single chamber. A more common approach is to have two chambers adjacent to each other. One chamber being set and stabilised at the start temperature and the second at the finish temperature. The product is then manually transferred between chambers at the appropriate time.

Thermal cycling

Whenever two different materials are connected to each other the differing thermal expansions of the materials causes mechanical stresses to be introduced as the temperature changes. With repeated temperature cycling of the product in its normal usage these stresses can result in connection failures. For example, the rigid connection of a printed circuit board to a metal case will result in the physical distortion of the PCB as the temperature changes. As the temperature is lowered, the metal will shrink more than the PCB material this will result in a compression force between the mounting points. As the temperature rises the metal will expand faster than the PCB material resulting in an expansion force between the mounting points. Temperature cycling will repeatedly subject the mountings to expansion and compression which can, in severe cases, result in failure of one or more of the mounting points or the working loose of the PCB relative to its mountings. As soon as the PCB works loose it will start to rattle and more damage will result.

Temperature cycling of products is therefore a test which can uncover longer term reliability problems, especially if used in conjunction with a simultaneous vibration test.

Designing a product to work over the specified temperature range requires two things:

- All the components must individually function over the full temperature range. Any semiconductors or integrated circuits must have guaranteed performance over the full temperature range. Batteries must be safe and able to deliver the required power at the temperature extremes, and
- The overall circuit performance must be maintained over the full temperature range.

These two aspects are different. It is possible for example to take a sample of a plastic encapsulated integrated circuit (which would normally be guaranteed over a temperature range 0C + 50C) and test it over a range - 40C to +85C. The sample may well work and, being plastic would be significantly less expensive than its ceramic counterpart (guaranteed over the -40C + 85C temperature range). From this test is it valid to say that plastic encapsulated devices are suitable for use over the range -40C to +85C? If the answer to this was yes, why would manufacturers also produce a ceramic packaged device? The answer lies in the fact that generally, plastic encapsulated ICs should be used only in the zero to + 50C temperature range.

Vibration

Vibration testing is the common way of verifying that a product will withstand the rigours of being physically moved around during its life. Most products need to be transported from the place of manufacture to their place(s) of usage. Many products are designed to be carried around and physically handled on a daily basis. The risk of being dropped onto a table or the floor, placed in the boot of a car or in the hold of an aircraft unprotected by its transit packaging is very real. Damage resulting from drops or bumps can seriously impact the user's perception of the product and the manufacturer as a whole. The objective of a vibration test programme is to attempt to simulate the vibration environment that the product could experience during its operating life.

As with temperature, there could well be different vibration environments for normal operation, storage, transportation and for survival.

To assess the survivability of products a number of different vibration related tests are available, examples of common ones are shown in Table 6.5.

Table 6.5 Common types of vibration related tests

- Sinusoidal
- Resonance Search
- Bump

- Random
- Shock
- Drop test

Sinusoidal vibration testing

Sinusoidal is the simplest method of vibration testing. It simulates the steady vibration encountered when an object is being carried or operated under steady conditions. If you were to balance a cup of water on the dashboard of a car whilst it is moving at a steady speed there would be some speeds where you would be able to see a steady pattern of ripples on the surface of the water. This pattern, also called the 'standing wave' pattern, is created by a predominantly sinusoidal oscillation within the car that is affecting the water in the cup. The same standing wave pattern could be created by placing the cup of water on a vibrating platform and exciting the platform with the correct frequency oscillation.

A vibrating platform is, in effect, a very powerful low frequency electromagnet with a moving core. The same principle as a loud speaker but without the sound amplifying cone. Figure 6.6 shows a sketch of the principle of a vibrating platform.

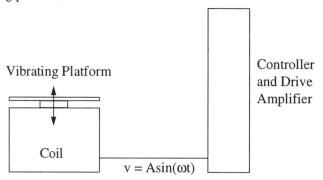

Fig. 6.6 Sketch of vibrating platform and controller.

The controller produces a lower power signal at the desired vibration frequency, ω which is amplified by the drive amplifier to produce a voltage input to the vibrator. This input signal, $A\sin\omega t$ causes the vibrator to oscillate up and down at frequency ω and with the amplitude a. The maximum acceleration of the platform is then $\omega^2 a$, usually expressed in units of g, where 1g is the earth's gravitational acceleration, 9.81ms^{-2}.

The controller will normally allow the frequency of vibration to be varied in a programmable way. The most common way of sinusoidal vibrating a product is

112

to sweep the frequency across a test range with a defined amplitude profile. Figure 6.7 shows an example of a sinusoidal vibration profile.

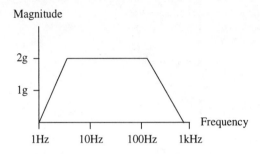

Fig. 6.7 Typical sinusoidal vibration profile.

Sinusoidal vibration is the simplest type of vibration to visualise, it is however the least representative of reality. In practice there is likely to be a complex spectrum of vibration frequencies present at any time, each of different amplitude. With modern computer controlled arbitrary waveform generators, almost any shape of frequency distribution of drive signal can be created and fed to the vibration platform. This type of testing is so called because the vibration frequency and amplitude may be varied over a wide range of different combinations.

Resonance search

A variant of the sinusoidal test is the resonance search test. In resonance search the equipment is vibrated whilst monitoring the vibration on its surface or on one of its internal components. The monitoring is achieved using an accelerometer which produces an output voltage proportional to the vibration level applied to it. Figure 6.8 shows a sketch of a typical arrangement and Fig. 6.9 the resulting frequency response.

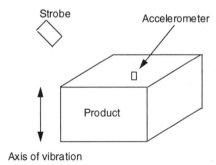

Every mechanical structure has a natural frequency at which its response is very large and may result in failure.

Fig. 6.8 Sketch of typical resonance search test.

A resonance search test will identify the frequency or frequencies at which the product absorbs the vibration energy. Such frequencies are bad for the product because the absorbed energy is internally dissipated in the form of vibration of parts relative to each other. Such relative movement can cause fractures and wear leading to longer term failures. A good illustration of the effect of resonance is that of a mounted printed circuit board as illustrated in Fig. 6.10.

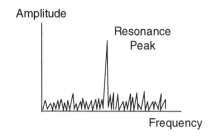

Fig. 6.9 Typical resonance search frequency response.

The surface mount integrated circuit shown in the centre of the board in Fig. 6.10 will be subject to significant forces as the board vibrates. At resonance the vibration will result in the largest deviation of the board and could, in extreme cases, cause cracking of the integrated circuit.

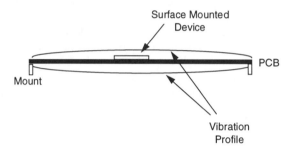

Fig. 6.10 Resonant vibration of a mounted printed circuit board.

If, as is shown in Fig. 6.8, a stroboscope, synchronised to the vibration frequency, is used to illuminate the product as it is being vibrated, the bending of visible parts of it will be clear to see. This technique is particularly valuable in identifying where the vibration is occurring and what damage is likely to be caused.

Random

The alternative approach to sinusoidal vibration where each individual frequency within a given range is excited separately is random vibration. In random vibration the signal fed to the drive amplifier of the vibration platform is a shaped noise signal. As such it contains every component of frequency within a given range, each with constant peak amplitude. Shaping can be achieved using filters where necessary, to achieve a particular frequency spectral shape.

Practicalities of vibration testing

Products in real use are rarely held exactly in one attitude such as upright, at all times. To test a product in just one attitude is not sufficient. Most specifications require the product to be vibration tested in each of the three axes of the product. Figure 6.11 shows these axes for a regular shaped product.

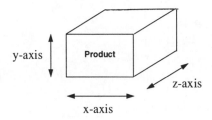

Fig. 6.11 The three vibration axes.

The final practical aspect of vibration testing a product is that of mounting the product to the vibration platform. It is necessary to attach the product securely to the platform and to be able to do so such that it can be vibrated in any of the three vibration axes. This can require a fairly complicated attachment jig which will need to be specifically made for the task. Time will need to be allowed for the design, fabrication and testing of the jig. The cost of design, fabrication and testing will also need to be allowed for in the overall project cost plan.

Shock and drop

Products in normal use are regularly subjected to physical shock. A shock is experienced whenever something is knocked over or drops onto the floor. The g force experienced under such conditions can be very high and can cause parts to break off or internal parts to break loose. A common test is to drop the product onto a hard surface from a height of one metre. For example the specification for a commercial bar-code reader was that it should survive being dropped from a height of one metre three times on each of its six faces (it being roughly rectangular in shape). The physical appearance was allowed to change and certain parts were allowed to break or break-off. The product was required to correctly read and decode bar-codes after all the drops.

When designing or specifying a drop test it is particularly important to define accurately what constitutes a failure before the test is started.

CAP 208 specifies a crash shock test for the ELT(S) with a minimum value of 50g and duration of 11 ms $\pm$ 2 ms. The beacon under test is subjected to six shocks of this magnitude, one in each of the three axes of vibration with one in each direction of each axis. The beacon must be fully functional after being subjected to the shocks.

Bump

Bump testing is another method of simulating the physical environment that is experienced during product transportation. Bump is the name given to the forces experienced by a product as it is bounced on a hard surface. To illustrate bump consider what a box would do if it was placed in the back of a hard floored lorry as it was driven along an unmade road. The box would bounced up and down in sympathy with the lorry movement. Some bumps would be small, corresponding to small holes in the road, whereas others would be large bumps corresponding to larger holes.

A bump is characterised by its amplitude, duration and shape as illustrated in Fig. 6.12.

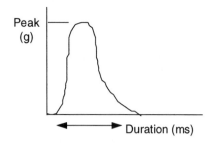

Fig. 6.12 Characterisation of a 'bump'.

The typical range of peak bump amplitude is 40g with common test values of 1, 5, 10, 25 and 40g. A typical duration is of the order of less than 10 ms. A practical bump test might consist of subjecting the product to 4000 bumps of a given amplitude and shape in quick succession. To give some feel for what a bump feels like, a human would not be able to survive many, if any, bumps of 40g magnitude!

Humidity and waterproofing

Products in real life are rarely kept and operated in dry, air conditioned environments. Some products, such as large computer systems, are kept in such conditions usually for good reasons. The norm however, is for products to be exposed, even for short periods, to water from rain or spillage, if not from exposure to high humidity climates or occasional immersion in water. Designing a product for such environments is more than simply totally sealing the product. Such a solution can be extremely expensive as well as being a problem for servicing and maintenance.

A design that is sympathetic to the waterproofing needs of the product and what can be considered reasonable abuse is the optimal design solution. There are a range of specifying waterproofing including:

- ability to withstand 10 days of salt fog;
- exposure to a long period (14 days plus) of 95% relative humidity warm air;
- immersion to 1 metre of water;
- ability to withstand continual dripping water;
- ability to withstand a wave strike.

These requirements range in severity and impact on product design. A useful widely accepted standard for waterproofing is the 'IP rating'. The IP rating is a three digit number which states the degree of protection the product has against ingress of dust, liquids and impacts. The second digit is the protection against ingress of water. It ranges from 0 denoting no protection at all to 8 which means the product can be immersed for long periods of time in water over 1 m in depth. Numbers in between denote levels of protection between these extremes. Table 6.6 shows the IP waterproofing rating scale.

For completeness the first digit refers to the protection offered against solid objects and the third digit the protection against mechanical impacts. Tables 6.7 and 6.8 give the meanings of the numbers for the first and third digits respectively.

Contaminants

The section on humidity and waterproofing addressed the needs and methods of specifying the making of the product immune to water. There are, in addition to water, other organic and inorganic substances which may come into contact with the product, one of the most common being cleaning materials. It is not unreasonable to expect the product to need cleaning, the question is with what? There are a wide range of domestic and industrial cleaning materials ranging from a damp soft cloth to industrial strength solvents. Where along this scale is the product to be placed and how will the 'limitation' be communicated to uses? The usual solution to this problem is to include recommended cleaning practices in the user manual.

Table 6.6 IP Waterproofing rating scale.

IP x0x	No protection
IP x1x	Protection against condensation
IP x2x	Protection against water spray up to 15° from the vertical
IP x3x	Protection against water spray up to 60° from the vertical
IP x4x	Protection against water spray from all direction. Limited water ingress into the product is allowed
IP x5x	Protection against low pressure water jets from all direction. Limited water ingress into the product is allowed
IP x6x	Protection against high pressure water jets from all direction. Limited water ingress into the product is allowed
IP x7x	Protection against immersion in water between 15cm and 1m depth
IP x8x	Protection against immersion at specified depth for long periods of time

Table 6.7 IP Solid object rating scale

IP 0xx	No protection
IP 1xx	Protection against solid objects greater than 50mm. For example accidental human hand touch
IP 2xx	Protection against solid objects greater than 12mm. For example accidental human finger touch
IP 3xx	Protection against solid objects greater than 2.5mm. For example wires and tools
IP 4xx	Protection against solid objects greater than 1.0mm. For example wires and tools
IP 5xx	Protection against dust. Limited ingress permitted
IP 6xx	Totally protected against ingress of dust

Table 6.8 IP Mechanical impact rating scale

IP xx0	No protection
IP xx1	Protection against 150gm impact from 15cm
IP xx2	Protection against 250gm impact from 15cm
IP xx3	Protection against 250gm impact from 20cm
IP xx5	Protection against 500gm impact from 40cm
IP xx7	Protection against 1.5kgm impact from 40cm
IP xx9	Protection against 5kgm impact from 40cm

Cleaning materials are only one of the general sets of contaminants that can come into contact with products. Take the ELT(S) as an example. It is a product aimed at the aviation market. A substance the ELT(S) must be capable of withstanding is aviation fuel, a highly corrosive and volatile substance which will, like petrol and other liquid fuels , dissolve some types of plastic and some paint finishes.

Salt is another very common contaminant. Salt promotes the corrosion of metals especially when in the form of salt vapour. Many products including the ELT(S) must be subjected to a period of up to a month in a salt spray environment, usually at a temperature above ambient. These conditions will promote corrosion and visible signs will be evident if corrosion is taking place.

In addition to the inorganic contaminants there is a range of organic substances to which some products must be inert. The ELT(S) must, for example, be resistant to growth of a range of fungi. Medical products must also be resistant to fungus and should not have surface materials which promote or act as a culture to fungi.

Given that, for any product, there will be a range of contaminants against which resistance must be designed , a check matrix can again be useful. If all the contaminant substances are listed as row titles and all the external and accessible surfaces as column titles a simple, but thorough means of checking material suitability results. At the simplest level each cell in the matrix can be ticked when the particular external or accessible surface has been checked for resistance to the particular contaminant. A more thorough strategy would be to put notes in each cell or a reference to where information is available to support the compatibility claim.

Worked Example 6.2

The parts of the ELT(S) that interface to the physical environment are the case, case seal, switch, lanyard, antenna and label. If the product is to be exposed to salt spray, sand, dust, aviation fuel and fungus growth, create a contamination check matrix.

Table 6.9 shows the constructed matrix with comments added about the compatibility based on previous in-company knowledge. Where question marks remain notes are added to show that additional information needs to be sought.

Table 6.9(a) Example contamination check matrix

Contaminant	Case	Case seal	Switch cover
Salt spray	Tests required	Tests required	Marine rubber. Should be OK
Sand	Known good	Tests required	Marine rubber coating. Should be OK
Dust	Known good	Tests required	Marine rubber coating. Should be OK
Aviation fuel	Tests required	Tests required	Tests required
Fungus	Tests required	Tests required	Tests required

Table 6.9(b) Example contamination check matrix

Contaminant	Lanyard	Antenna	Label	Label adhesive
Salt spray	Marine rope. Should be OK	Marine rubber coating. Should be OK	Marine compatible. Should be OK	Marine compatible. Should be OK
Sand	Marine rope. Should be OK	Marine rubber coating. Should be OK	Marine compatible. Should be OK	Marine compatible. Should be OK
Dust	Marine rope. Should be OK	Marine rubber coating. Should be OK	Marine compatible. Should be OK	Marine compatible. Should be OK
Aviation fuel	Tests required	Tests required	Tests required	Tests required
Fungus	Tests required	Tests required	Tests required	Tests required

How can compatibility be designed in? The most straightforward way is to approach the supplier of the surface finish, that is, the paint, manufacturer for a paint finish, the seal manufacturer or the label manufacturer with a list of the contaminants and ask for evidence of suitability. Often the response will be a partial one. Manufacturers may well have tested their products against some of the specified contaminants and not others; the gaps may be filled by reference to other products which use the same finish and need to be resistant to the particular contaminant. Where no evidence is available a specific test to verify resistance may need to be designed and carried out before the material is finally selected for use on the product.

During the design process a number of different materials will be considered for the case finish, the seal, the label, etc. A compatibility matrix can be used to ensure the choice made takes contaminates into account. Table 6.10 shows an example.

A first pass look at these finishes may result in focusing on the paint finish as being the most fruitful avenue. A similar matrix could then be used to compare the paint finish option.

Table 6.10 Example contamination check matrix for the case finish

Contaminant	Passivated Metal	Painted	Plasticised
Salt spray	Long term corrosion (especially post scratch)	OK - previous project evidence	OK - previous project evidence
Sand	May damage passivation	OK - previous project evidence	OK - previous project evidence
Dust	May damage passivation	OK - previous project evidence	OK - previous project evidence
Aviation fuel	Should be OK	?	Risk of plastic dissolving
Fungus	Unlikely to promote growth	?	?

At all of these stages the generation and completion of a matrix where the contaminants come directly from the product requirement, ensures that no contaminant is omitted and that the end product should withstand the required product approval testing.

Survival

Some products must be capable of withstanding very special sets of environmental conditions. Robots used for inspection inside nuclear installations must, for example, be able to withstand high radiation levels. The ELT(S) must be able to withstand the crashing of the aircraft carrying it.

Each particular special environment will carry with it a set of environmental requirements that are over and above the normal ones, those listed in Table 6.11. In this final section the special, survival requirements of the ELT(S) will be used to illustrate some more unusual environmental characteristics which can appear in product requirement specifications.

Table 6.11 ELT(S) survival tests

- Crash shocks
- Penetration
- Crush
- Flame
- Immersion

CAP 208 part 10 requires the ELT(S) to survive the following

1. *Crash Shock* The ELT(S) must function to a defined set of electrical criteria after it has been subjected to six 50g shock pulses of 11ms ± 2ms duration, in each of the positive and negative x, y and two-axis direction as shown in Fig. 6.13.

2. *Penetration test* The ELT(S) must function to a defined set of electrical criteria after it has been subjected to a penetration test on each of its main surfaces. The penetrator is a shaped piece of aluminium of Rockwell C40

hardness as shown in Fig. 6.14. The penetrator is loaded with weight such that its total mass is 25 kg.

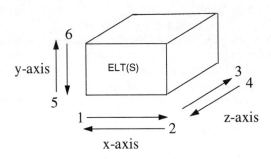

Fig. 6.13 ELT(S) crash shock orientations.

With the ELT(S) placed on an unyielding surface each penetration test consists of dropping the penetrator from a minimum height of 15 cm above the surface of the product such that at least half of the penetration impacts within a 2.5 cm radius of the most vulnerable area of the surface of the ELT(S).

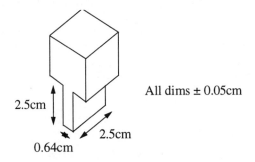

Fig. 6.14 ELT(S) test penetrator.

To give some feel for the severity of this test, the penetrator will punch a hole straight through a diecast box.

3. *Crush test* The ELT(S) must function to a defined set of electrical criteria after it has been subjected to a crushing pressure of 690 kPa for a period of five minutes, successively to each of the main diagonal axes.

4. *Flame test* The ELT(S) must function to a defined set of electrical criteria after it has been placed at a height of 1m above a tray containing 10 litres of burning Avgas.
    The heat given off from burning Avgas is unbearable to naked skin at a horizontal distance of several metres. At a height of 1m above the centre of the burning liquid most plastics and paint finishes melt or burn. Chord lanyards burn and paper labels burn and disappear.

5. *Immersion* After all of these tests, which must be performed in the stated sequence the ELT(S) must survive being immersed to a depth of 1m in salt solution at a temperature of +35C for a minimum period of 1 hour. At the end

of the immersion period the ELT(S) must function to a defined set of electrical criteria.

Whilst these tests are clearly excessive for the majority of commercial products they are very appropriate for the ELT(S) and serve to illustrate the severity of the physical environment for some products. To produce a product that meets this specification requires very careful attention to the requirement from the outset and sympathetic design throughout, very careful attention to the selection of materials, both mechanical and electronic is required as are design proving tests during development to build confidence in the design. The cost of testing a product to the requirement is expensive and time consuming.

Summary

This chapter has introduced the physical environment as an important aspect of product design. Appropriate terminology has been introduced and defined along with an explanation of how some environmental characteristics can be specified and tested for. Rarely is a product required to operate in a totally benign environment. The reality is that it will be physically abused, exposed to the elements and still be expected to work. To understand how to design products to meet these challenges requires the designer to understand the way the environment interacts with products, how to specify the environment and how to test for survivability.

Designing products to survive harsh environments is expensive in time and money. Care and attention in the design and development phase is essential if all environmental characteristics are to be addressed whilst not over-designing the product. An optimum design is one which meets its requirements at minimum product cost.

Problems

6.1   Produce a list of environmental factors appropriate for the design of products for polar applications.

6.2   Produce a list of environmental factors appropriate for the design of products for rain forest applications.

6.3   Investigate the vibration environment a product will encounter during transatlantic air transportation.

6.4   Study a personal music player or similar product you have access to. Note the materials and surface finishes visible from the outside of the product. Comment on how suitable the product is for the environmenmt it is used in. Make notes on how you would make it more environmentally protected. Note especially any labels and comment on their durability.

6.5   Design a complete type approval test plan for the tests, where defined in this chapter, for the ELT(S).

Design for reliability

At the end of this chapter you will able to:

- Explain the terms MTTF, failure rate, reliability and reliability growth
- Estimate the reliability for series, parallel and fault tolerant systems
- Calculate the effect of environmental stress on reliability
- Design an electronic product for a specific end of life reliability
- Measure reliability, failure rates, reliability growth and product compliance

In this chapter the effect of reliability on the product will be considered. In particular we will consider how we might measure and predict the reliability of a given product or system and how this affects its design. This is important for two reasons. Firstly, we might need to be confident that a product will not fail because the consequences of failure are severe. For example, if an aircraft landing system fails the result is likely to be the deaths of several hundred people. Secondly we want customers to be confident about purchasing and using the product. That is, we want a reputation of reliability. In both of these cases it is useful to be able to predict reliability and to inform the design process so that design approaches which achieve a desired reliability specification can be used.

What is reliability?

The dictionary definition of reliability is 'the ability to be relied on; having of sound and consistent character or quality' This can be rephrased in engineering terms to say:

> Reliability is a measure of the ability of a component, product or system to perform its required function, in an adequate manner, for a given period.

Clearly, this is an important aspect of any product. Of particular note is that reliability is a time-dependent quantity and therefore the expected product life is an important factor to consider.

Unfortunately we can know only the reliability of a component or system once it has failed, at which point it is no longer reliable! In addition, generally the time at which any component or system fails is unknown and random. Therefore reliability measures are statistically-based predictions on the likelihood of failure in a given period of time. This is an important concept to grasp because it is statistically possible for either a highly reliable component to fail within seconds of being turned on or a highly unreliable component to last for years. Note that this natural statistical behaviour is often used to justify patterns of pleasurable human activity which have an associated health risk, for example, 'My grandfather smoked 40 fags a day, drank like fish and lived until he was hit by a bus aged 96! I say a little bit of what you fancy does yer good!' Thus reliability is inherently a measure of average behaviour of a group of components or systems and not the individual ones in that group.

So we can add to the above definition the additional caveat:

Reliability is a statistical measure of the likelihood that a component or system will perform its required function, in an adequate manner, for a given period.

This does imply that it will be impossible to achieve 100% reliability

The importance of reliability

As already mentioned, reliability is an essential part of the design and specification of a product. The reasons are as follows.

- Failure may cost lives or damage property. In particular, apart from considerations of morality, if the damage or injury is shown to be a consequence of the failure of your product then you may well face litigation from the aggrieved parties. The court costs, damages and stress involved has serious consequences for both the company and the individuals.

- The cost of repairing or replacing faulty products once they have been distributed to the customer is far greater than the cost of repairing or rejecting the product at the factory. Typically there is a factor of ten difference between the cost of repairing a product at the factory gate compared with that of repairing it at the customer's premises.

- The confidence of your customers is reduced if your product fails too often. This has a twofold effect. Firstly you get a reputation for producing poor quality equipment. Secondly, because customers no longer trust the product they look for faults. This results in a higher level of returns and complaints whenever the product fails to do what the customer expects. Note that the product may well be working perfectly but, because the customers are sensitive to faults they overreact to deviations from normal behaviour. In extreme cases this may result in the unwarranted destruction of the product. As an example, there have apparently been several cases in which pilots flying fly-by-wire military aircraft have ejected because they didn't feel right and therefore felt that the system had failed. Subsequent analysis of the wreckage found no faults but because the pilot had lost confidence in the system, usually due to a pattern of earlier crashes, any slight deviation from the norm, even if it was within specification, was seen as threatening.

- Faulty products also cost the customers money, or inconvenience them, because while the product isn't working they are deprived of its use. This aspect is recognised by washing machine manufacturers who often use the combination of high reliability in conjunction with a rapid response service organisation as a selling point for their products.

Clearly then, reliability matters. But what level of reliability is appropriate for a given product? The answer is that it depends on the consequences of failure, the operating context of the product, and the market.

For example, an electronic system which is part of a safety critical product, such as an aeroplane or medical equipment, must have a very high degree of reliability, whereas a domestic electronic product would have a less stringent requirement. However, even equipment which does not need an exceptional amount of reliability may still have parts which must be more reliable because the failure of that part affects many other systems. A classic example would be a telephone system where the reliability of common components such as the system power supply must be more reliable than the individual telephones because the failure of a common component affects many users.

In practice one of the key decisions at the specification stage is the level of reliability required of the product. In a few cases this will be set by external legal requirements but in most cases it will be an internal decision based on customer requirements, cost, and market image. In either case one must have some way of estimating and measuring the likely level of reliability of a product.

The nature of failure

Failure of a product may be defined as anything from a slight degradation of its performance to a condition of total failure. It is relatively easy to define failure when the criterion concerned is quantifiable, but the definition is less satisfactory where the specification is vague or incomplete. It might be said that a product has failed because it simply did not do what the customer expected.

However, if we are going to calculate or measure reliability we must have some idea of the type and nature of the likely failures in order to know the applicability of our calculations and the most appropriate design directions.

Failure ranges from that which renders the product unsafe to operate through to the insignificant and unnoticeable. Examples are:

- **Fail to danger**: The product fails to a state that makes it unsafe to operate. An example of this would be a television that failed such that metal parts on the front panel become short circuited to either mains or the anode voltage of the cathode ray picture tube.

- **Fail to safety**: In this case the failure does not create a hazard but instead results in the product behaving safely, although possibly inconveniently. An example of a fail to safety system would be a train braking system in which the brakes are held off by the braking system so that if the system fails the brakes fail to the braking condition.

- **Hard failures**: The failures in the device, sub-system or product are permanent and must repaired or replaced.

- **Soft failures**: The failures in the device, sub-system or product are temporary or intermittent so that the product can function after the failure. However, the operation of the product during the failure is compromised. As an example, computer memories suffer from soft failures and if one occurs during the running of a program it might result in a program crashing.

- **Partial failure**: The product may not fail totally but will continue to work although out of specification. For example, an amplifier may continue to work even if a component value has changed due to a failure. However, it may distort more easily.

- **Malicious**: The failure may be due to the user and not the equipment. For example, a computer system kept failing frequently during night shifts and the investigation of the fault revealed (on a hidden camera) that one of the operators was applying a battery to random bits of the backplane! The reason was that he got paid for the whole shift even if the computer failed and so this was a way of getting some extra paid sleep. In a another case part of a undersea telephone cable was stolen for its scrap copper value. The coastguard apprehended the felons while they were reeling it in because the fault detection system was able to locate the precise position of the break.

- **Ignorance**: The failure might due to misuse of the equipment through ignorance. For example, most telecommunication firms talk about the 'JCB factor' in system reliability where someone digging up the road cuts a cable, because they did not realise it was there.

Clearly the nature of the failure affects the strategy adopted for coping with it. It also affects the way one measures the reliability. For example, the approach to coping with malicious failures will be different to that for soft failures.

Another aspect of reliability concerns the repair options available to the designer. In safety critical systems such as aircraft or medical equipment, there must be redundancy built in which will keep the system functional in the event of a component failure; in contrast, a domestic appliance can wait for a component to be replaced. The design of the system will reflect these criteria, with consequent effects on its complexity (and hence cost).

Definitions

There are several terms which are used in discussion about reliability:

- **Reliability**: This is a term which represents the probability of no failures of any sort. We shall see later that it is a time-dependent value. The reliability reduces as time increases. It is a statistical quantity so the number represents only a likelihood which will have statistical variability.

- **Probability of failure**: This is the complement of the reliability and can be derived from the reliability as follows:

  Probability of failure $= 1 -$ Reliability

- **Failure rate** is the average number of failures per unit time of a device, product or system. This is the most common way of expressing the reliability of a component because it can be easily used in reliability calculations. However, it assumes that the failure rate is constant, which in many cases is incorrect. The failure rate is typically expressed in four forms.

  1. Failures per hour. This measure results in very small numbers, typically $10^{-6} \sim 10^{-8}$ failures per hour.

  2. Failures per 10^6 hours. This measure scales up the results to small decimal numbers, typically $1 \sim 0.01$ failures per 10^6 hours.

  3. Percentage failures per thousand hours. This effectively scales up the failure rate per hour by a factor of 10^5 and so allows one to express a failure rate as a small decimal number. For example, the previous rates would become $0.1 \sim 0.001\%$ failures per thousand hours. This is a very common unit for expressing failure rates.

  4. FITS. One FIT represents one failure per billion hours and this measure is often used in the semiconductor industry. This measure usually gives small integers for the failure rate as it scales up the failures per hour by

10^9 and the percentage failure per thousand hours by 10^4. Thus our example failure rates become $1000 \sim 10\text{FITS}$.

Note that the very term failure rate implies an underlying statistical failure process, the Poisson, and although this assumption is often used in reliability calculations there are cases where other distributions are used and in these cases the concept of a constant failure rate is inapplicable.

- **Mean time to failure** (**MTTF**): This is a crucial measure of the likelihood of failure of a device or system. It is applicable to many different sorts of failure patterns and can be defined as the average time until the device or system fails.

Only for systems which have a constant failure rate can one use the equation:

$$MTTF = \frac{1}{\text{Failure rate}}$$

The MTTF is usually expressed in hours, although sometimes years are used. It is important to realise that the MTTF is **not** a direct measure of reliability; as we shall see later, a system which is close to its MTTF is very unreliable. Interpreting the MTTF as a measure of reliability is also misleading in systems which have some fault tolerance, as the MTTF often increases only by a small amount, whereas the reliability can increase by a much larger amount.

- **Mean time to repair** (**MTTR**): The mean time to repair is the time it takes to repair a system after it fails. It is a useful concept when analysing system availability.

- **Mean time between failures** (**MTBF**): The mean time between failures is the sum of the MTTF and the MTTR that is: MBTF=MTTF+MTTR.

Calculating reliability

Because reliability is a statistical concept we have to take a statistical approach to its calculation. We need to have some way of relating the observed patterns of failure to the reliability, that is the probability of zero failures. In principle we could measure the probability of failure $f(t)$ within some small time interval Δt around a particular time by observing a batch of the product and counting how many fail in a given time interval. The probability of failure within a particular time interval is a probability density function and would tell us what percentage of the working components are likely to fail at a given instant. However, we are really interested in the probability that zero failures occur up to a particular time. This can be obtained by adding up the probability of failure at a given time from zero to the time required. This will give us the total probability of failure of the product up to a given time. The sum of the probability density function of failure is known as the cumulative probability density function of failure. Reliability is the probability of zero failures so we can obtain the reliability by simply subtracting the probability of failure up to a given time from 1. That is the reliability to a given time can be obtained from the probability of failure by:

Mathematically we can say that the probability of failure at a given time,

$f = f(t) \Delta t$

where $f(t)$ is the probability density function of failure an Δt is a small time interval around t.

The probability of failure up to a given time is given by:

$$F(t) = \int_0^t f(t) dt$$

$$R(t) = 1 - F(t)$$

where $R(t)$ = the reliability at t (7.1)

and $F(t)$ = the probability of failure to up to t

Working with the probability density function of failure, however, is not very useful as it depends on both the rate of failure and the number of devices available for failure. As the number of devices available for failure reduces with time, because more and more fail, this will result in a probability of failure which varies with time, even if the failure rate is constant. In many cases working with the rate of component failure is more useful as it can be used to predict the reliability at a given time. How can the reliability of a device be related to the failure rate? The change in reliability in a small time interval Δt with respect to time is given by the probability of failure at a given time instant. That is:

$$f(t) \Delta t = \Delta R(t) \Delta t$$ (7.2)

We can also say that the probability of failure at a given time instant is the product of the failure rate at that time and the proportion of devices available to fail. The proportion of devices available for failure is also given by the reliability. Thus the probability of failure at a given time

$$f(t) \Delta t = \lambda(t) R(t) \Delta t$$

where $\lambda(t)$ = the failure rate   (7.3)

We can combine equations (7.2) and (7.3) to get an expression for the failure rate purely in terms of the reliability as:

$$\lambda(t) = -\frac{\Delta R(t)}{R(t) \Delta t}$$ (7.4)

The solutions are

$$R(t) = e^{-\int_0^t \lambda(t) dt}$$

$$f(t) = \lambda(t) e^{-\int_0^t \lambda(t) dt}$$

Because the integral of $\lambda(t) = \lambda$ up to a given time t is:

$$\int_0^t \lambda(t) dt = \lambda t$$

Equation (7.4) allows us to estimate the failure rate based on measured values for the reliability. However, we also want to be able to calculate the reliability from a knowledge of the failure rate. This can be done by solving the differential equation implied by equation (7.4) to give expressions for the reliability, and probability of failure at a given instant.

In the case of a constant failure rate system $\lambda(t) = \lambda$ and the reliability is given by:

$$R(t) = e^{-\lambda t}$$ (7.5)

This equation is identical to the equation for the decay of a simple RC time constant but in this case it is $\frac{1}{\lambda}$ which is analogous to the RC time constant τ. This time constant is equivalent to the MTTF of the component or system. The probability of failure at a given time, given a constant failure rate, is given by:

$$f(t) = \lambda e^{-\lambda t}$$

The reliability, probability of failure and failure rate are plotted in Fig. 7.1. We can see that although the failure rate is constant, the probability of failure and the reliability are both decaying exponentially. This is due to the reduction in the number of devices available for failure as the time increases, as mentioned earlier, and because of its shape this failure distribution is called the exponential failure distribution. This is the most used distribution in reliability calculations due to its ease of application. However, it does assume a constant failure rate which is not always appropriate.

128

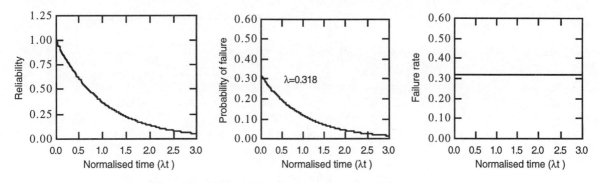

Fig. 7.1 Exponential failure distributions (constant failure rate).

An alternative way of analysing a constant failure rate system is to recognise that it can be modelled by the Poisson distribution which relates the probability of an event occurring in a given period to the average rate of occurrence of the event. We can consider the probability of the events to be the probability of failures and the average rate of occurrence of the event to be the average failure rate. Using the distribution in this way allows us to calculate the reliability of a given system. The equation for the Poisson distribution in this context is as follows:

$$P_n(t) = \frac{(\lambda t)^n e^{-\lambda t}}{n!}$$

Where $P_n(t)$ is the probability that exactly n failures happen in the time period t and λ is the average number of failures per unit time. Note that the units of time for the failure rate must be the same as those measuring the time period.

The Poisson distribution for various numbers of failures is shown in Fig. 7.2. As expected the probability that a given number of failures will occur rises then falls. The time at which the peak probability of exactly that number of failures occurs gets later as number of errors increases. The function decays after the peak because one has an increasing likelihood of more than the required number of failures as the time increases. Thus in the case of zero failures this is most probable at zero time and gets progressively less.

An advantage of the Poisson formulation is that it allows the calculation of the probability of any number of failures, which is useful in fault correction. Since we are particularly interested in zero failures, we simply set n to 0 in the above equation. So, the probability of zero failures in a given period is:

$$P_0(t) = \frac{(\lambda t)^0 e^{-\lambda t}}{0!}$$

which reduces to:

$$P_0(t) = e^{-\lambda t}$$

Note that $0!=1$ and $(\lambda t)^0=1$ also.

P_0 is defined as the reliability of the component or system $R(t)$ and is therefore defined as $R(t) = e^{-\lambda t}$

The above equation relates the reliability of a component or system to two parameters: the failure rate and the length of time that the system has been in operation. As expected, the longer the time of operation the greater the likelihood of failure. Note that this is identical to equation (7.5) which was derived earlier.

129

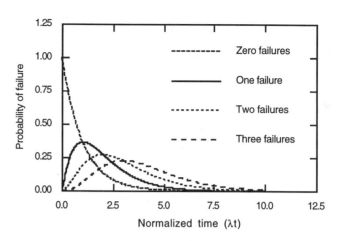

Fig. 7.2 Poisson probability functions for different numbers of failures.

The other parameter, λ, the failure rate, was defined earlier in terms of the mean time to failure, as follows:

$$\text{MTTF} = \frac{1}{\lambda}$$

Thus we can consider the MTTF to be a reliability time constant which sets the reliability of the component or system. However, this is true only for constant failure rate systems.

We might assume from the above equations that we need to ensure only that the product operates for less than its MTTF to assure reliability. This is not true as we often want to be sure that the level of failure is much less because of its consequences. Let us consider some examples.

For other systems the MTTF is the average time to failure, which can be obtained from either the probability of failure at a given time as:

$$MTTF = \int_0^\infty tf(t)dt$$

or from the reliability by:

$$MTTF = \int_0^\infty R(t)dt$$

Worked Example 7.1

Calculate the reliability when the time of operation equals the mean time to failure, MTTF.

The equation for reliability is: $R(t) = e^{-\lambda t}$

The MTTF is given by: $\text{MTTF} = \frac{1}{\lambda}$

In this example $t = \text{MTTF}$ and so $t = \frac{1}{\lambda}$. If we substitute this into the equation for reliability we get:

$$R(t) = e^{-\lambda\left(\frac{1}{\lambda}\right)} = e^{-1} = 0.368 = 36.8\%$$

So when the time of operation equals the mean time to failure we have about only a one in three chance of failure. Or to put it another way we have a two out of three chance of having the product fail. This is clearly not a very good result; to improve it we must operate over periods which are much less than the MTTF.

Worked Example 7.2

Calculate the reliability when the time of operation equals 0.1 of MTTF.

$$R(t) = e^{-\lambda\left(\frac{1}{10\lambda}\right)} = e^{-\left(\frac{1}{10}\right)} = 0.905 = 90.5\%$$

The reliability is greatly improved.

Calculate the reliability when the time of operation equals 0.01 of MTTF.

Worked Example 7.3

$$R(t) = e^{-\lambda\left(\frac{1}{100\lambda}\right)} = e^{-\left(\frac{1}{100}\right)} = 0.990 = 99.0\%$$

There is further improvement.

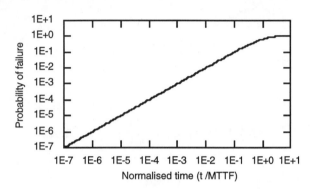

Fig. 7.3 Plot of probability of failure versus time relative to the MTTF.

The curve for the probability of no failures as a function of time, relative to the MTTF ($\lambda t = 1$), in Fig. 7.2, shows the shape of the reliability curve for the above cases. Clearly then we must operate well below the MTTF in order to achieve high levels of reliability. A more useful way of looking at the same information is shown in Fig. 7.3 which shows a plot of the probability of failure as a function of time normalised with respect to the MTTF.

Figure 7.3 shows that for highly reliable systems we must operate well below the MTTF.

So far we have considered only the effect of time on the probability of failure. Clearly, the mean failure rate also has an effect which is of similar proportion in that a tenfold increase in the failure rate will result in a tenfold increase in the probability of failure at a given time.

The probability of failure is given simply as 1-R(t).

As a rule of thumb for a given probability of failure we can operate only for a similar fraction of the MTTF. For example, for a probability of failure of one in a million the equipment can operate for only for one millionth of its MTTF.

Failure pattern during life

We have assumed that the failure rate is a constant quantity for all time. Unfortunately this is not true. Let us consider another example.

Calculate the reliability of a human being at 18 and 100 years of age.

Worked Example 7.4
Psalm 90:10.

The allotted span of man is three score years and ten. This implies a MTTF of 70 years or $70 \times 365.25 \times 24 = 613620$ hours.

$$\lambda = \frac{1}{70} = 1.428571429 \times 10^{-3} \text{ failures per year}$$

the reliability after 18 years of life is given by:

$$R(t) = e^{-\lambda t} = e^{-1.43 \times 10^{-2} \times 18} = 0.773 = 77.3\%$$

which is comforting, if a little low! Interestingly, the reliability at 100 years is:

$$R(t) = e^{-\lambda t} = e^{-1.43 \times 10^{-2} \times 100} = 0.239 = 23.9\%$$

Neither of the above examples corresponds to our experience as we would expect a better reliability at 18 than predicted and yet the reliability at 100 years is in excess of the norm. The reasons for this discrepancy is that the failure rate is not constant. In fact it varies significantly with time. Figure 7.4 shows the typical variation of λ as a function of time for any component or system.

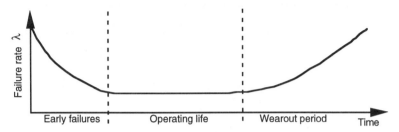

Fig. 7.4 Plot of failure rate λ versus time.

This curve, which is applicable to most components or systems, is called the bathtub curve. It has three regions. Initially failure rate is relatively high, due to manufacturing weaknesses. This is in spite of testing, since some components will just pass the tests but will fail early in their lives. This region is sometimes called the infant mortality region. On the flat part of the curve, the failure rate is at its minimum and remains so for a period until components start to wear out and the failure rate rises again. Guarantee periods for products are carefully geared to the curve. Note also that the two end regions will not necessarily be smooth curves if several failure processes are involved although the general shape will be similar in all cases.

This behaviour explains the discrepancies in our earlier example because at 18 we are in the normal operating region and thus have a lower failure rate than that implied by 70 years. Conversely by the time we has reached 70 the failure rate is higher due to wearout, thus explaining why most people do not make 100! The MTTF of 70 years is the result of averaging the effect of all three regions and thus does not accurately represent any of them.

Although the bathtub curve is often quoted as the archetypal curve for the variation of failure rate as a function of time it must be used with caution as there are significant variations in it which are dependent on the nature of the component which is failing. A modern electronic product is usually a mixture of hardware, software and mechanical components. Each of these has a different variation of failure rate with time.

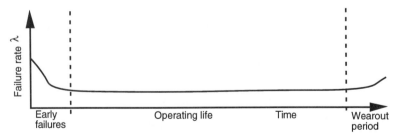

Fig. 7.5 Plot of failure rate λ versus time for many electronic components.

- **Electronic components**: Figure 7.5 shows the typical bathtub curve for electronic components, excluding valves. The important thing to note is that there is a small wearin period, and in some devices this phase is minimal. Then there is a very long constant failure rate period which is probably well in excess of the product, or user's lifetime. In fact for components operated well within their specification, the main wearout mechanism would be mainly due to diffusion, and possibly corrosion, processes in solids at room temperature both of which are likely to take a long time.

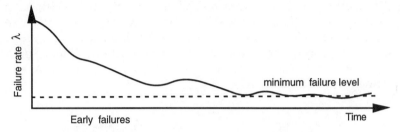

Fig. 7.6 Plot of failure rate λ versus time for software.

- **Software components**: Figure 7.6 shows the typical curve for software components. Software does not 'wear out' and the failure rate will (or should) come down to a low constant level once the initial 'bugs' which have escaped the writer's notice have been fixed. In theory the failure rate should approach zero but, in the case of complex software, fixing one bug may create new ones.

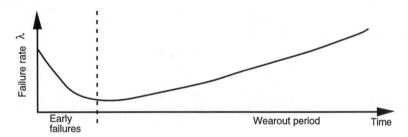

Fig. 7.7 Failure rate λ versus time for components with significant wearout.

- **Mechanical and thermionic components**: Figure 7.7 shows the typical curve for mechanical and thermionic components, which have significant wearout mechanisms, due to mechanical, or cumulative physical/chemical, processes. In this case the failure rate may never be constant. Instead there is an initial early failure period followed by a long wearout period in which the failure rate rises. The rate of rise is often significantly affected by the operating conditions and the operating life is defined between acceptable levels of failure rate, rather than over a constant failure period. These components usually need some form of maintenance, or replacement, schedule in order to assure reliable operation of the product and some of the effort in calculating the reliability will be aimed at determining a safe and cost-effective one. Note that, although they are not mechanical, electronic components with high vacuums, hot cathodes, or ionised gasses will tend to have significant wearout mechanisms. These would include cathode ray tubes, travelling wave tubes, valves (tubes) and so on.

We conclude that generally $\lambda(t)$ is a time varying quantity. In many cases the assumption that $\lambda(t)$ is constant is reasonable. However, we shall see later that sometimes the variation has important implications in design for reliability.

Calculating system reliability

So far we have considered only the reliability of a single component or system given its mean time to failure or its failure rate. However, in most cases we wish to predict the reliability of a complete product using the failure rates of the individual components. Therefore we need a means of combining individual reliabilities in order to have a reliability estimate for the whole system. There are two possibilities to consider.

Fig. 7.8 Series connection of reliabilities.

- The failure of any component or sub-system causes the failure of the system as a whole. This is the most common situation and is equivalent to a series connection of reliabilities; this situation is shown in Fig. 7.8.

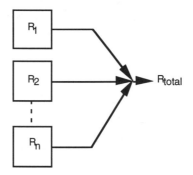

Fig. 7.9 Parallel connection of reliabilities.

- The failure of any component or sub-system does not cause the failure of the system as a whole. Instead two or more components or sub-systems must fail in order for the system to fail as a whole. In this situation there is an element of redundancy in the system and this is equivalent to a parallel connection of reliabilities as shown in Fig. 7.9. Note that the parallel branches might have series connections within them.

Series reliability connection

In this case the overall system is reliable only if all the individual components or sub-system are reliable. In other words we must find the joint probability of reliability of the individual components. This can be calculated by multiplying the individual reliabilities together. That is, the total system reliability is given by:

$$R_{total}(t) = R_1(t) \times R_2(t) \times R_3(t) \times \cdots \times R_n(t)$$

If we substitute in the equation for reliability we get:

$$R_{total}(t) = e^{-\lambda_1 t} \times e^{-\lambda_2 t} \times e^{-\lambda_3 t} \times \cdots \times e^{-\lambda_n t}$$

By using the rules for multiplying exponentials we can simplify the above expression to:

$$R_{total}(t) = e^{-(\lambda_1 + \lambda_2 + \lambda_3 + \cdots + \lambda_n)t}$$

This can be further simplified to:

$$R_{total}(t) = e^{-\lambda_{total} t}$$

Where: $\lambda_{total} = \lambda_1 + \lambda_2 + \lambda_3 + \cdots + \lambda_n$ (7.6)

Calculate the reliability, after 40 hours, of a computer memory system consisting **Worked Example 7.5** of 2048 mega bytes of memory which has been constructed using 1Mbit memory chips with a failure rate of 10^{-6} failures per hour. Ignore the effect of any of the support circuitry.

Total number of chips, $n = 2048 \times 8 = 16384$

$$\lambda_{chip} = 10^{-6} \text{ failures per hour}$$

$$MTTF_{chip} = \frac{1}{\lambda_{chip}} = \frac{1}{1 \times 10^{-6}} = 1 \text{ million hours}$$

$$\lambda_{total} = \lambda_1 + \lambda_2 + \lambda_3 + \cdots + \lambda_n$$
$$\lambda_{total} = n\lambda_{chip} = 16384 \times 10^{-6} \text{ failures per hour}$$
$$\lambda_{total} = 1.6384 \times 10^{-2} \text{ failures per hour}$$
$$MTTF_{total} = \frac{1}{\lambda_{total}} = \frac{1}{1.6384 \times 10^{-2}} = 61 \text{ hours}$$
$$R_{total}(t) = e^{-\lambda_{total} t}$$
$$R_{total}(40 \text{hours}) = e^{-1.6384 \times 10^{-2} \times 40} = 0.519 = 51.9\%$$

Thus one has only about a 50/50 chance of the memory working for a normal working week!

This is not an extreme example. Many computers have a large number of components in their memory systems and these tend to dominate the overall reliability. The early Cray 1 super computers had a MTTF of four hours! This was traced to large number of 1k memory chips that had to be used in its main memory. Note that these were good quality components but there were so many of them that the overall reliability was low.

So far we have considered just failure rates for a collection of components with the same failure rate. Let us look at a example with components of widely different failure rates.

Worked Example 7.6

Calculate the reliability of a switchable attenuator consisting of 13 resistors, 2 connectors, and a rotary switch. The values of λ for the components are:

$$\lambda_{resistor} = 10^{-8} \text{ failures per hour } (MTTF_{resistor} = 10^8 \text{ hours})$$

$$\lambda_{switch} = 1.4 \times 10^{-6} \text{ failures per hour } (MTTF_{switch} = 7.14 \times 10^5 \text{ hours})$$

$$\lambda_{connector} = 5 \times 10^{-7} \text{ failures per hour } (MTTF_{connector} = 2 \times 10^6 \text{ hours})$$

$$\lambda_{total} = n_{resistor}\lambda_{resistor} + n_{switch}\lambda_{switch} + n_{connector}\lambda_{connector}$$

$$\lambda_{total} = 13 \times 10^{-8} + 1 \times 1.4 \times 10^{-6} + 2 \times 5 \times 10^{-7}$$

$$\lambda_{total} = 2.53 \times 10^{-6} \text{ failures per hour}$$

$$MTTF_{total} = \frac{1}{\lambda_{total}} = \frac{1}{2.53 \times 10^{-6}} = 3.95 \times 10^5 \text{ hours}$$

$$R_{total}(t) = e^{-\lambda_{total}t}$$

$$R_{total}(10000 \text{hours}) = e^{-2.53 \times 10^{-6} \times 1000} = 0.975 = 97.5\%$$

From this example we can see that the MTTF and the therefore the reliability is dominated by the most unreliable components if their failure rate is significantly higher than the rest of the components. In the above example the switch is the most unreliable component followed by the connectors and these two components just by themselves give an MTTF of:

$$\lambda_{switch+connector} = n_{switch}\lambda_{switch} + n_{connector}\lambda_{connector}$$

$$\lambda_{switch+connector} = 1.4 \times 10^{-6} + 2 \times 5 \times 10^{-7}$$

$$\lambda_{switch+connector} = 2.4 \times 10^{-6} \text{ failures per hour}$$

$$MTTF_{switch+connector} = \frac{1}{\lambda_{switch+connector}} = \frac{1}{2.4 \times 10^{-6}} = 4.17 \times 10^5 \text{ hours}$$

The resistors however contribute only a small amount to the overall failure rate. From the previous two examples we can observe that a large number of individually reliable components can still result in an unreliable system and the reliability of a system can be dominated by one unreliable component.

As a final example, consider an audio amplifier. Table 7.1 shows the calculations using the failure rates of a number of components. (Note that the reliability of the solder connections has been included.) We observe that the components with the lowest MTTF have the greatest influence on the overall result, which nonetheless indicates a high level of reliability. We also observe that typically electronic components have very long MTTFs. This can cause problems in measuring them, a subject discussed later in this chapter.

Parallel reliability calculations

This technique was known in biblical times. Ecclesiastes 4:12 'A threefold cord is not easily broken.'

Although series connection of reliability is quite common for many electronic systems there are some which can be described as a parallel connection of reliabilities. In this situation there is some redundancy built into the system so that there are alternative ways of performing the function. A trivial example would be the parallel connection of switches so that more than one contact has to fail to stop the switch from connecting. Other areas where this situation applies would be communication systems with parallel links, multiple suspension cables on a suspension bridge, or the fixing of components onto a surface using multiple fixings. All these scenarios assume each individual component or system is capable of performing the required function alone.

Table 7.1 Reliability calculation for an audio amplifier

Component	Quantity	Failure rate (per 10^6 hrs)	MTTF (million hours)	Total failure rate (per 10^6 hrs)	Total MTTF (million hours)
Small signal transistor	8	0.0008	1250.0	0.006	156.3
Power transistor	2	0.0400	25.0	0.080	12.5
Resistor	23	0.0010	1000.0	0.023	43.0
Capacitor	2	0.0010	1000.0	0.002	500.0
Electrolytic capacitor	5	0.0250	40.0	0.125	8.0
Potentiometer	1	0.0400	25.0	0.040	25.0
Connectors	2	0.0200	50.0	0.040	25.0
Soldered connections	97	0.0026	384.6	0.252	3.
Complete amp:				0.57	200 years

In these circumstances the system will not fail unless all the parallel paths fail. This means that in order to calculate the reliability of the system we must first work out the probability of all the parallel paths failing. The probability of failure of a component or system can be derived from its reliability:

$$F(t) = 1 - R(t) = 1 - e^{-\lambda t}$$

In order to work out the probability of all the parallel paths failing we must multiply the probabilities of failure of all the individual paths together. That is:

$$F_{overall}(t) = F_1(t) \times F_2(t) \times F_3(t) \times \cdots \times F_n(t)$$

This is equivalent to:

$$F_{overall}(t) = (1 - R_1(t)) \times (1 - R_2(t)) \times (1 - R_3(t)) \times \cdots \times (1 - R_n(t))$$

or:

$$F_{overall}(t) = (1 - e^{-\lambda_1 t}) \times (1 - e^{-\lambda_2 t}) \times (1 - e^{-\lambda_3 t}) \times \cdots \times (1 - e^{-\lambda_n t})$$

For the case of only two parallel paths the above equation becomes:

$$F_{overall}(t) = (1 - e^{-\lambda_1 t}) \times (1 - e^{-\lambda_2 t})$$

Which can be simplified to:

$$F_{overall}(t) = 1 - e^{-\lambda_1 t} - e^{-\lambda_2 t} + e^{-\lambda_1 t}e^{-\lambda_2 t} = 1 - e^{-\lambda_1 t} - e^{-\lambda_2 t} + e^{-(\lambda_1 + \lambda_2)t}$$

This gives the equation for the reliability of a two path parallel reliability system:

The reliability is related to the probability of failure by

$R(t) = 1 - F(t)$.

137

$$R_{overall}(t) = e^{-\lambda_1 t} + e^{-\lambda_2 t} - e^{-(\lambda_1 + \lambda_2)t}$$

Which can be expressed in terms of the individual reliabilities as:

$$R_{overall}(t) = R_1(t) + R_2(t) - R_1(t)R_2(t)$$

The MTTF of a dual path reliability system can be expressed in terms of the individual paths as:

Because the MTTF is related to the reliability by

$$MTTF = \frac{1}{\lambda} = \int_0^\infty R(t)dt$$

$$MTTF_{overall} = \frac{1}{\lambda_1} + \frac{1}{\lambda_2} - \frac{1}{\lambda_1 + \lambda_2}$$

The above equation shows that the mean time to failure of a dual path system is the sum of the individual MTTFs of the individual paths less a term which is the MTTF of either path. Note that this equation assumes that the paths are independent and that therefore there is no source of failure common to both paths. It also assumes that both paths are active all the time from the beginning of the systems operation. Such systems are known as active parallel systems. Systems in which the parallel path is enabled when a fault occurs, that is standby systems, cannot use the above equations because the failures in the two paths are no longer independent.

Let us consider a simple example of a parallel reliability system, an audio patchbay system such as might be found in a recording studio or a radio station. These enable an engineer to insert additional items of equipment into the signal path by simply plugging them into the patch bay. The sockets on the patch bay have contacts which open to break the signal path. Clearly it is vital that when the patchbay is not being used the normal audio signal path is maintained. As there are two sockets in the patch bay there are two sets of contacts available to maintain this path, although one set only is required to achieve the required function. Thus there are two options for implementation.

- **Single normalled contacts**: Only the set of contacts in the signal input socket is used and the signal path is broken if a plug is inserted into it.

- **Double normalled contacts**: Both sets of contacts are used and the signal path is broken only if plugs are inserted into both sockets.

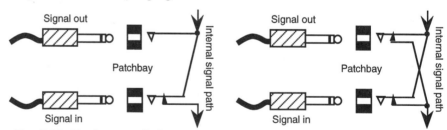

Fig. 7.10 Single normalled contact.   Fig. 7.11 Double normalled contacts.

The connections for the two different types are shown in Fig. 7.10 and Fig. 7.11.

| Worked Example 7.7 | Calculate the reliability of single versus double normalled contacts in an audio patchbay. |

Single normalled contacts:

Number of contacts, $n = 3$, Balanced connections require three contacts .

$$\lambda_{contact} = 10^{-6} \text{ failures per hour (0.1\% per 1000 hours)}$$

138

$$\text{MTTF}_{contact} = \frac{1}{\lambda_{contact}} = \frac{1}{1 \times 10^{-6}} = 1 \text{ million hours}$$

$$\lambda_{total} = n\lambda_{contact} = 3 \times 10^{-6} \text{ failures per hour}$$

$$\text{MTTF}_{total} = \frac{1}{\lambda_{total}} = \frac{1}{3 \times 10^{-6}} = 333 \text{ thousand hours}$$

Double normalled contacts:
Number of contacts in each path, $n = 3$,

$$\lambda_{path} = n\lambda_{contact} = 3 \times 10^{-6} \text{ failures per hour}$$

$$\text{MTTF}_{path} = \frac{1}{\lambda_{total}} = \frac{1}{3 \times 10^{-6}} = 333 \text{ thousand hours}$$

$$\text{MTTF}_{overall} = \frac{1}{\lambda_1} + \frac{1}{\lambda_2} - \frac{1}{\lambda_1 + \lambda_2}$$

$$\text{MTTF}_{overall} = \frac{1}{3 \times 10^{-6}} + \frac{1}{3 \times 10^{-6}} - \frac{1}{3 \times 10^{-6} + 3 \times 10^{-6}}$$

$$\text{MTTF}_{overall} = 3.33 \times 10^{5} + 3.33 \times 10^{5} - 1.67 \times 10^{5}$$

$$\text{MTTF}_{overall} = 6.50 \times 10^{5} = 650 \text{ thousand hours}$$

In this case the paralleling of the contacts has nearly doubled the MTTF for the signal path. In a patch bay which might have hundreds of these connections this is significant. However, this analysis applies only to the through signal path. In fact any fault will alter the behaviour of the patchbay because it will convert the double normalled patchbay socket into a single normalled one. Thus the operator would see its behaviour alter and this could be considered as a form of soft failure.

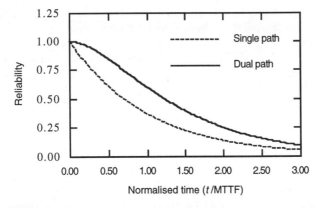

Fig. 7.12 Variation of reliability versus time for single and dual path systems.

The reliability can also no longer be predicted from a simple exponential equation because there are other terms in it. In the above example:

$$R_{overall}(t) = e^{-\lambda t} + e^{-\lambda t} - e^{-(\lambda + \lambda)t}$$
$$R_{overall}(t) = 2e^{-\lambda t} - e^{-2\lambda t}$$

Figure 7.12 shows the variation of probability of failure as a function of λt for single and dual path systems. The above equation shows that there are two time constants involved in the reduction of reliability and if further redundant paths were involved there would be more. The implication of this is that the shape of the reliability curve as a function of time is altered and so might be even better than the simple use of the MTTF figure suggests. It is clear from Fig. 7.12 that the shape of the reliability curve is different for the two systems. In particular the dual path system stays at a high reliability value for longer than a simple consideration of the MTTFs would indicate.

A similar analysis can be done for multi -path systems and this shows that the slope of the probability gets even faster. In fact the slope increases as the power of the number of paths in a similar manner to the order of a filter.

It is more revealing to look at the probability of failure for the two different systems as shown in Fig. 7.13. From this graph we can see that the probability of failure increases, as the time approaches the MTTF, more rapidly for the dual path system compared with the single path system. So in addition to the improvement to the MTTF the dual path system's reliability improves more rapidly below the MTTF compared with the single channel system.

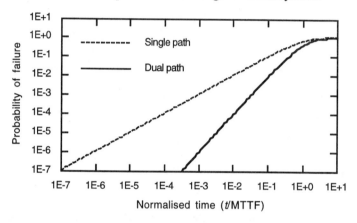

Fig. 7.13 Variation of of failure versus time for single and dual path systems.

As we have seen before, MTTF is a naive way of looking at reliability. What we are really interested in is the product lifetime, given a desired end-of-life reliability. From the above graph we can see that this can be considerably more than the ratios of the MTTFs for the single and dual path systems. We can calculate the product lifetime for a single path system, given a desired end-of-life reliability, from the reliability equation as follows.

$$R_{desired}(t) = e^{-\lambda t} \text{ or } \ln\left(R_{desired}(t)\right) = -\lambda t$$

$$t_{lifetime} = \frac{1}{\lambda} \ln\left(\frac{1}{R_{desired}(t)}\right) = \text{MTTF} \times \ln\left(\frac{1}{R_{desired}(t)}\right) \tag{7.7}$$

For the dual path system the equation is more complicated and ideally we would like to relate it to the MTTF of the single path. The reliability for a dual path system with identical paths is given by:

$$R_{desired}(t) = 2e^{-\lambda t} - e^{-2\lambda t}$$

Let $x = e^{-\lambda t}$ which gives:

$$R_{desired}(t) = 2x - x^2 \text{ or } x^2 - 2x + R_{desired}(t) = 0$$

This is a quadratic which can be solved to give:

$$x = \left(\frac{+2 \pm \sqrt{4 - 4R_{desired}(t)}}{2} \right) = 1 - \sqrt{1 - R_{desired}(t)}$$

The larger solution is ignored because x cannot be greater than one. The remaining solution is the value of $e^{-\lambda t}$ which would give the same value of $R_{desired}(t)$ in the dual path case as the single path one. Therefore it can be used to calculate the product lifetime for a dual path system, given a desired end-of-life reliability, in terms of the single path MTTF as follows.

This analysis can be extended to the n-path case, although it gets a bit tricky! The result for the n-path case is a further improvement in the lifetime to a given reliability in proportion to the number of paths. However, there is a law of diminishing returns, the corner gets sharper and the slope of the change in the probability of failure increases, so more paths are not necessarily better.

$$t_{lifetime} = \text{MTTF} \times \ln\left(\frac{1}{\left(1 - \sqrt{1 - R_{desired}(t)}\right)} \right)$$

From the above equation we can see that as we require more reliability at the end of the product life the gap between single and dual path systems increases.

Determine the $t_{lifetime}$ as a function of the MTTF for single and dual path systems to give an end-of-life reliability of 99%.

Worked Example 7.8

Single path system

$$t_{lifetime} = \text{MTTF} \times \ln\left(\frac{1}{R_{desired}(t)} \right)$$

$$t_{lifetime} = \text{MTTF} \times \ln\left(\frac{1}{0.99} \right) = \text{MTTF} \times 0.01$$

Dual path system

$$t_{lifetime} = \text{MTTF} \times \ln\left(\frac{1}{\left(1 - \sqrt{1 - R_{desired}(t)}\right)} \right)$$

$$t_{lifetime} = \text{MTTF} \times \ln\left(\frac{1}{\left(1 - \sqrt{1 - 0.99}\right)} \right) = \text{MTTF} \times 0.105$$

In this case the dual path system has just over 10 times the lifetime of a single path system for the same level of reliability at the end of the product life. This ratio becomes even greater as the required reliability increases and therefore redundancy is often a cost-effective way of improving reliability in systems which require a high degree of reliability. However, these systems will degrade more quickly than the single path system beyond the design lifetime. They also rely on the paths being wholly independent and this is often difficult to achieve in practice

Fault correction systems

Redundancy (and hence improved reliability) can be provided through fault detection and correction. There are many ways of doing this. In communications or digital systems an error-correcting code may be used to correct faults. CD-roms are made robust by this means, as are many computer systems. An alternative is to have three separate paths and vote on the outcome (Fig. 7.14). If only one path is faulty the voting ensures correctness. However, replication of paths requires more components and so more failures are likely. Also the faults may not be independent, leading to the majority of paths indicating a faulty result. (This condition is known as a common mode failure.)

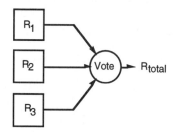

Fig. 7.14 Voting fault correction system.

So how does one calculate the reliability of a fault correction system? Consider the Poisson probability equation for a given number of failures occurring:

$$P_n(t) = \frac{(\lambda t)^n e^{-\lambda t}}{n!}$$

Where $P_n(t)$ is the probability that exactly n failures happen in the time period t and λ is the average number of failures per unit time.

Normally this equation is used with $n=0$ because that gives the probability of any failure occurring. However, if we have fault correction we will not have a failure unless there occur more failures than the fault correction circuitry can cope with. For example, if we can correct a single fault then we will have a failure only if two or more faults occur. So we can get the reliability by adding the probability of no faults occurring to the probability of one and only one fault occurring because the system will not fail in these circumstances. This can be expressed mathematically as:

Since $(\lambda t)^0 = 1$

$$R_{single\,fault\,correction}(t) = \frac{(\lambda t)^0 e^{-\lambda t}}{0!} + \frac{(\lambda t)^1 e^{-\lambda t}}{1!} = e^{-\lambda t} + \lambda t e^{-\lambda t} \qquad (7.8)$$

Equation (7.8) can be extended to cover fault correction systems which can handle M errors by summing the terms of the Poisson distribution up to M to give. the following equation for the reliability for multiple error correction.

$$R_{M\,fault\,correction}(t) = \sum_{n=0}^{M} \frac{(\lambda t)^n e^{-\lambda t}}{n!}$$

This equation is clearly a minor extension of the original term for reliability with just the addition of a term to cover the ability to cope with the correction of single failures.

Figure 7.15 shows the probability of failure, $(1 - R(t))$, for single fault correction system in comparison with dual path and zero correction system. Notice that the effect is similar to that of a dual path system and that again the MTTF increases by a small amount but that the reduction in failure probability is rapid for times shorter than the MTTF. This is because the single fault correction system also changes the shape of the reliability curve in a similar fashion to dual-path-systems, shown in Fig. 7.12. In fact it appears that single fault correction is better than the dual path system. This is because we have not allowed for the extra hardware required to provide the single fault correction, but we have allowed for it for the dual path system. This will reduce the reliability a little from that shown because λ will increase due to the extra hardware. However, whereas the dual path system typically requires twice the amount of hardware, the single fault correction system may be able to use less and so still show an improvement over the dual path system.

142

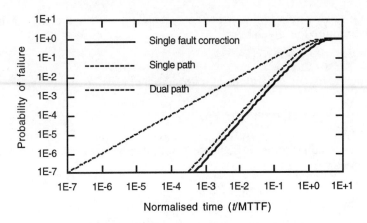

Fig. 7.15 Probability of failure for a single fault correction system.

Why does the single fault correction system give such improved reliability below the MTTF limit? Figure 7.16 shows a plot of the first two terms in the reliability equation and the total reliability. This figure shows that the effect of the single fault correction is to change the shape of the overall reliability graph. In particular, it extends it, because the ability to correct one fault is most useful as one approaches the MTTF and thus the composite effect is to extend the more reliable portion of the reliability curve. Note that the resulting shape is very similar to that achieved by the dual path system shown in Fig. 7.12.

As we have already seen what we are really interested in is the product lifetime given a desired end-of-life reliability. From the graph in Fig. 7.16 we can see that this can be considerably more than the ratios of the MTTFs for the zero and single fault correction systems. The product lifetime for a non fault correction system, given a desired end-of-life reliability is given by:

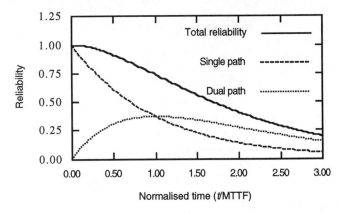

Fig. 7.16 Individual contributions to reliability in a fault correction system.

$$t_{lifetime} = \text{MTTF} \times \ln\left(\frac{1}{R_{desired}(t)}\right)$$

For the single fault correction system the equation is more complicated and ideally we would like to relate it to the non fault correction systems MTTF. The

143

reliability for a single fault correction system, ignoring the effect of the extra hardware required, is given by:

$$R_{desired}(t) = e^{-\lambda t} + \lambda t e^{-\lambda t} = e^{-\lambda t}(1 + \lambda t)$$

Taking the natural logarithms of both sides and rearranging gives:

$$\lambda t - \ln(1 + \lambda t) = \ln\left(\frac{1}{R_{desired}(t)}\right)$$

The above equation is difficult to simplify so let us expand $\ln(1 + \lambda t)$ as a Taylor series which gives:

$$\ln(1 + \lambda t) = \lambda t - \frac{(\lambda t)^2}{2} + \frac{(\lambda t)^3}{3} - \frac{(\lambda t)^4}{4} + \cdots \qquad \text{where } \lambda t < 1$$

This can be substituted into the left-hand side of the earlier equation to give:

$$\lambda t - \ln(1 + \lambda t) = \frac{(\lambda t)^2}{2} - \frac{(\lambda t)^3}{3} + \frac{(\lambda t)^4}{4} - \cdots \qquad \text{where } \lambda t < 1$$

If we are working at reasonably low values of λt then we can ignore all but the squared term; if $\lambda t < 0.2$ the error is less than 3%. This can be used to give an approximate equation for the lifetime of a single fault correcting system, given a desired end-of-life reliability. Substituting only the squared term gives:

$$\frac{(\lambda t)^2}{2} \approx \ln\left(\frac{1}{R_{desired}(t)}\right)$$

Which can be rearranged to give the lifetime as:

$$t_{lifetime} \approx \frac{\sqrt{2}}{\lambda}\sqrt{\ln\left(\frac{1}{R_{desired}(t)}\right)}$$

which can be expressed in terms of the MTTF as:

$$t_{lifetime} \approx \text{MTTF} \times \sqrt{2}\sqrt{\ln\left(\frac{1}{R_{desired}(t)}\right)}$$

From the above equation we can see that as we require more reliability at the end of the product life the gap between no fault correction and single fault correction systems increases.

Worked Example 7.9

Determine the $t_{lifetime}$ as a function of the MTTF for no fault correction and single fault correction systems given an end-of-life reliability of 0.99.

no fault correction

$$t_{lifetime} = \text{MTTF} \times \ln\left(\frac{1}{R_{desired}(t)}\right)$$

$$t_{lifetime} = \text{MTTF} \times \ln\left(\frac{1}{0.99}\right) = \text{MTTF} \times 0.01$$

single fault correction

$$t_{lifetime} \approx \text{MTTF} \times \sqrt{2} \sqrt{\ln\left(\frac{1}{R_{desired}(t)}\right)}$$

$$t_{lifetime} \approx \text{MTTF} \times 1.414 \times \sqrt{\ln\left(\frac{1}{0.99}\right)} \approx \text{MTTF} \times 0.142$$

So in this case the single fault correction system has just over 14 times the lifetime of a zero fault correction system, for the same level of reliability at the end of the product life. This ratio becomes even greater as the required reliability increases. This type of redundancy is often a much more cost-effective way of improving reliability in systems compared to simple replication. However, like the multiple path systems, these systems will degrade more quickly than the zero fault correction system beyond the design lifetime. Unlike the multiple path systems they do not require independent paths, although they can still suffer from common mode failure, for example, if the power supply fails. The above analysis also assumes that the extra hardware required for single fault correction does not reduce the MTTF over the zero fault correction system. In practice there is a reduction in the MTTF due to the extra hardware and this must be taken into account. However, even when this reduction is taken into account there are still substantial improvements in reliability over zero fault correction.

One still needs to take the extra hardware into account, so let us look at a real example of a single fault correction system, an error correcting memory system. The memory is 256Mbyte 16 bit words which is based on 4Mbyte×1 dynamic RAM chips with a reliability of between 0.2% to 0.05% per thousand hours. The fault correction system used is a Hamming error correcting code.

Calculate the time of operation, for an end-of-life reliability of 0.99, for the system with and without the error correction.

No error correction

$$\text{MTTF}_{memory} = \frac{1}{\lambda_{memory}} = \frac{1}{16 \times 64 \times 0.2\% / \text{khr}}$$

$$\text{MTTF}_{memory} = 488 \text{ hours}$$

$$t_{lifetime} = \text{MTTF}_{memory} \times \ln\left(\frac{1}{R_{desired}(t)}\right)$$

$$t_{lifetime} = \text{MTTF}_{memory} \times \ln\left(\frac{1}{0.99}\right) = 488 \text{ hours} \times 0.01 = 4.88 \text{ hours}$$

In order to calculate the lifetime for the error correcting memory we have to allow for the extra hardware required for the error correction which will reduce the MTTF.

Single error correction

$$\text{MTTF}_{memory} = \frac{1}{\lambda_{memory}} = \frac{1}{(16 + 5) \times 64 \times 0.2\% / \text{khr}}$$

Worked Example 7.10

Hamming code: This uses several parity checks on the data which are arranged such that, when a bit is read in error, the pattern of parity failures uniquely identifies the errors location. Therefore, in addition to the data bits, one must also store some check digits, which requires extra hardware. As the check digits might also be in error they must be checked as well. In order to identify which bit is in error we must be able to generate a binary number which can cover the appropriate number of bits and, in this example, five extra bits are required. The system can also detect, but not correct, double error digit errors and when this occurs the computer reports, and logs, a fault.

$$MTTF_{memory} = 372 \ \text{hours}$$

$$t_{lifetime} \approx MTTF_{memory} \times \sqrt{2} \sqrt{\ln\left(\frac{1}{R_{desired}(t)}\right)}$$

$$t_{lifetime} \approx MTTF_{memory} \times 1.414 \times \sqrt{\ln\left(\frac{1}{0.99}\right)} \approx 372 \times 0.142 \approx 53 \ \text{hours}$$

The lifetime of the error correcting memory has over 10 times the lifetime of the memory without correction despite the reduction in system MTTF due to the extra hardware.

As well as correcting errors the system also logs their occurrence. This enables the maintenance engineer to print out a fault log which identifies memory chips that fail more frequently and thus are compromising the system reliability because they are either dead or weak. These chips can then be replaced and so the system reliability will improve with time. The failure rate for the chips will gradually approach the best Figure of 0.05%/khr, as on is effectively weeding out the early failure region of the bathtub curve, which would give a lifetime of:

In the margin:

In order to do the same for a multi-bit memory chip one would have to use a different type of error correcting code. That is, a burst error correcting code which can handle multi-bit errors.

$$MTTF_{memory} = \frac{1}{\lambda_{memory}} = \frac{1}{(16+5) \times 64 \times 0.05\% / khr}$$

$$MTTF_{memory} = 1488 \ \text{hours}$$

$$t_{lifetime} \approx MTTF_{memory} \times \sqrt{2} \sqrt{\ln\left(\frac{1}{R_{desired}(t)}\right)}$$

$$t_{lifetime} \approx MTTF_{memory} \times 1.414 \times \sqrt{\ln\left(\frac{1}{0.99}\right)} \approx 1488 \times 0.142 \approx 211 \ \text{hours}$$

This example demonstrates a twofold advantage of fault correction in that not only does it keep the system running longer but it can also improve the maintenance program. Note however that as the system could correct only single errors one had to choose a memory structure which was more likely to have single bit errors. This is true for $Nk \times 1$ memory chips but it is not true for memory chip which are more than one bit wide.

Standby systems

Redundancy may also be provided by a standby system, which is switched in when a fault occurs (Fig. 7.17). It differs from the active parallel system in that the probability of failures are no longer independent; the standby system cannot fail before it operates and it does not operate until the main system fails. Its failure rate therefore depends on the main system and, because of this, the methods used so far do not apply. Instead we must consider the probability of failure of the system in several states together with the probabilities of transition between states.

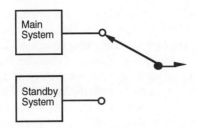

Fig. 7.17 A standby fault tolerant system.

There are four possible states in a standby system and these are as follows:

1. Both systems are failure free.

2. The main system has failed but the backup system is working.

3. The main system is working but the backup system has failed.

4. Both systems have failed.

There are also several possible transitions between these states which are:

• The main system fails and successfully switches to the backup.

• The backup system fails while active.

• The backup system fails while on standby.

• The main system fails and switches to the failed backup system.

• Both the main system and the switch fail.

• There are also transitions which allow for the possibility of the faulty systems being repaired

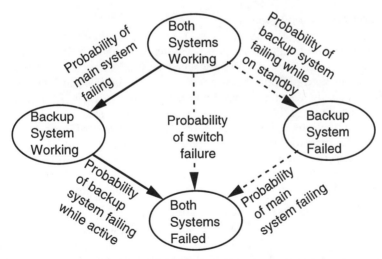

Fig. 7.18 State transition diagram for a standby system.

The four states and all the possible transitions except for repairs are shown in Fig. 7.18. The possibility of repair will put in additional reverse transitions between the states.

The details of this are beyond the scope of this book. More details can be found in *An Introduction to Reliability Engineering,* by E. E. Lewis, published by John Wiley & Sons (1987).

As we are dealing with a probabilistic state machine the most appropriate method of analysis is a Markov model. The details of this are beyond the scope of this book but it is interesting to compare the reliability of a standby system with that of a parallel redundancy system. Consider the situation where the failure rates of the main and standby systems are equal, and the failure rates of the backup system in standby and the switch are zero. Note, this is an optimistic scenario, but the failure rates for the backup system in standby and the switch should be lower than the operating system's failure rates in a well designed standby system.

Under these circumstances the reliability can be expressed by:

$$R(t)_{standby\ system} = (1 + \lambda t)e^{-\lambda t} \tag{7.9}$$

Note that reliability given by equation (7.9) for the standby system is the same as the single fault correction system's, equation (7.8). and so its performance is identical to the single error correction curve in Fig. 7.15.

However, equation (7.14) does not take into account the possibility of failure of the backup during standby, or the switch, and the reduction in the reliability due to the extra fault detection circuitry required. All of these effects will tend to erode the apparent advantage of standby over dual systems.

Note: Standby systems are not the only ones that result in failure rates which are not independent. Parallel systems in which the surviving systems have extra stress placed upon them will also have interacting failure rates, and so will also require the use of Markov models to predict their reliability. An example of such a system would be the parallel combination for two power transistors which normally share the power between them. If one of them fails then the remaining transistor is placed under greater stress and so its failure rate will increase.

The above discussion considered standby systems which were only switched on in the event of a failure in the main system, these are known as cold standby systems. They have the disadvantage that there will be a break in the system operation during the switch over period. Where this is unacceptable a hot standby system can be used, in which the standby system is switched on for the same amount of time as the main system, so that it is ready for immediate operation should the main system fail. Interestingly the reliability for a hot standby system, with the same failure rate as the main system, is identical to that of a dual path system providing one ignores the failure rate of the switch.

Time varying reliability calculations

So far we have assumed that the failure rate is constant as a function of time in our calculations. But we have already seen that this is true only in the constant failure rate of the traditional bathtub curve. If we know we are dealing with a situation which violates this assumption then we need to use a different approach which takes account of the temporal variation of failure rate.

In these situations a Poisson probability distribution of time to failure is inappropriate. Instead other distributions, which take account of the variation with respect to time, must be used. These distributions all require one or more additional parameters in order to model the time variation of failure rate. There are three distributions which are commonly used in this context and these are:

An example might be a car tyre or a video or audio tape recorder's head. In these situations the probability of a particular time to failure can be approximated reasonably accurately by a Gaussian distribution centred around the MTTF.

- **The Normal, (Gaussian) distribution**: This is useful when there is a well defined wearout time with a small variance. Typical situations where this occurs are when there is a constant wearout process, such as abrasion, so that each, hour of operation adds to the likelihood of failure. The equation for the probability of failure within a particular time interval is:

$$f(t) = \frac{1}{\sqrt{2\pi}\sigma}e^{\left(-\frac{(t-\mu)^2}{2\sigma^2}\right)} \tag{7.10}$$

This distribution needs two parameters, the mean and the standard deviation. From this equation the probability of failure can be derived by integrating equation (7.10) to get the cumulative density

$$F(t) = \Phi\left(\frac{t-\mu}{\sigma}\right)$$

where $\Phi\left(\dfrac{t-\mu}{\sigma}\right)$ = The normal cumulative density function

and hence the reliability from equation (7.1).

$$R(t) = 1 - \Phi\left(\frac{t-\mu}{\sigma}\right)$$

The failure rate can then be derived using the probability of a particular time to failure and the reliability using equations (7.3) or (7.4). Figure 7.19 shows the three distributions involved.

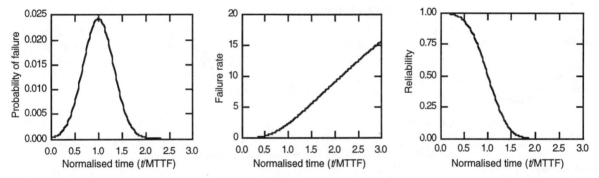

Fig. 7.19 Normal distributed probability of failure, failure rate, and reliability.

It is clear that this distribution has a rapidly increasing failure rate beyond the mean time to failure. Let us look at an example of how it might be used.

Calculate the lifetime of a video tape head for an end-of-life reliability of 90%. The MTTF of the video head is 2000 hours with a standard deviation of 400 hours.

Worked Example 7.11

We want the reliability $R(t) = 0.9$ This implies that the probability of failures, given by:

$$F(t) = 1 - R(t) = 0.1$$

But $F(t)$ is simply the cumulative distribution function of the probability of a particular time to failure. For the Normal distribution we can simply look this value up in a table of the Standard Normal Cumulative Distribution Function $\Phi(u)$.

This function has a value of 0.1 when $u = -1.28$. that is

$$\Phi(\mu - 1.28\sigma) = 0.1$$

Thus the lifetime for a reliability of 90% is given by:

$$\mu - 1.28\sigma = 2000\,\text{hours} - 1.28 \times 400\,\text{hours} = 1488\,\text{hours}$$

The Standard Normal Cumulative Distribution is the area under the Normal distribution plotted with respect to the parameter value and starting from minus infinity. It represents the proportion of a total population up to a particular value. For example, at the mean μ 50% of the population has been covered. A failure rate of 10% value for the Standard Normal Cumulative Distribution. This can be looked up in a table of the function which can be found in most books of standard tables.

149

One should therefore consider replacing the video head after about 1500 hours of use.

Note that the reliability drops rapidly after this point for example, at 1600 hours the reliability would be about 84% and at 1700 hours it would be about 77%. Equipment with this sort of reliability distribution must be regularly replaced and this sort of distribution is useful for developing effective maintenance schemes.

- **The Lognormal distribution**: This is a useful distribution when there is a known wearout time with a large variance. A typical example might be a semiconductor laser or microwave device operating under high stress or cases of metal fatigue. It can be argued that in these situations the failures are related to the product, rather than the sum, of the demands placed on the product. In these situations the time to failure distribution cannot be approximated accurately by a Gaussian distribution. Instead the Lognormal distribution provides a better fit.

- **The Wiebull distribution**: This distribution is the most widely used, and misused, distribution besides the exponential. The reason is simple, it can model a variety of, wearin, wearout and, as a special case, constant failure rate, curves. The Wiebull distribution assumes that the failure rate can be described by some form of power law.

Burn-in is a technique for improving the reliability of a device by operating it at the factory during the initial wearin period. The early failures are then weeded out and the product shipped has a failure rate nearer the base of the bathtub curve.

It is therefore possible to model, and so make predictions about, systems with failure rates which vary with time, for example during a burn-in period. However, care is needed because the chosen distribution makes some assumptions about the underlying system, and no one distribution models all the aspects of a products reliability as a function of time. For example, the normal distribution might model the wearout part of the curve well, but will not describe the constant failure rate or the wearin portions of a product's failure rate. In other words it is vital to be aware of the context of the application, in order to interpret the predictions made by the reliability calculations.

The impact of the environment and other external factors

There are more complex Weibull distributions which involve three parameters which have some utility in modelling failure rates which increase after some threshold time.

Time is not the only thing that affects the reliability of a component. In fact any form of environmental stress also affects the failure rate. These include voltage, heat, vibration, humidity, etc. Generally the effect of these stresses is to reduce the reliability, that is they increase the failure rate. Conversely reducing these stresses reduce the failure rate although one must be cautious. For example, high temperatures increase the failure rate and as one reduces the temperature the failure rate reduces. However, if one reduces the temperature too much the device will stop working, many semiconductor devices do not work well at extreme sub-zero temperatures. Clearly we need to take account of the environmental factors when calculating system reliabilities.

There are two main approaches to calculating reliability in the presence of environmental factors.

The 'Bible' for this method is, *MIL-HDBK-217, Military handbook: reliability prediction of electronic equipment*, published by the American Department of Defense.

- **The parts stress analysis method**: This is a method which uses extra multiplicative factors to modify a base failure rate, to allow for the effects of the environment, into an effective failure rate which takes them into account. This effective failure rate can then be used in place of the base failure rate in any subsequent reliability calculations. The effective failure rate, allowing for the impact of the operating environment, is therefore given by:

$$\lambda_{effective} = \lambda_{base} \times K_E \times K_Q \times K_T \times K_S \times \cdots \times K_N$$

where $\lambda_{effective}$ = Effective failure rate

λ_{base} = Base failure rate

K_E = Environmental factor

K_Q = Quality factor

K_T = Temperature factor

K_S = Electrical stress factor

$K_N = N_{th}$ Other factors dependent on the device

The environment factor, K_E, can vary from one for a benign environment to 690 for a extremely severe environment such as cannon launch! The other factors are also determined relative to the conditions for the base failure rate and depending on the value of the external factor might be less than or greater than one or even irrelevant. In addition to temperature and electrical stress other factor might take into account cyclic stress, such as regular temperature variation, complexity factors, external electromagnetic effects, etc. All of these factors are specific to the component type and so require the designer to look up many tables in order to determine the appropriate factors.

MIL-HDBK-217 contains innumerable tables covering most, but not all, imaginable electronic components. From argon ion lasers to variable wirewound resistors. It also contains equations as well as tables which relate failure rates to a cornucopia of reliability factors.

Worked Example 7.14

Table 7.2 Example spreadsheet reliability calculation

Component	Quantity	Failure rate (per 10^6hrs)	K_E	K_Q	Total failure rate (per 10^6hrs)	MTTF (hours)
Small signal transistor	8	0.0008	5.6	12	0.430	2325149
Power transistor	2	0.0400	5.6	12	5.376	186012
Resistor	23	0.0010	2.4	15	0.828	1207729
Capacitor	2	0.0010	1.9	7	0.027	37593985
Electrolytic capacitor	5	0.0250	2.4	10	3.000	333333
Potentiometer	1	0.0400	1.8	10	0.720	1388889
Connectors	2	0.0200	1.2	3.9	0.187	5341880
Soldered connections	97	0.0026	2.1	1	0.530	1888146
Complete amp:		11.10			MTTF=10.3years	90110

Use the parts stress analysis method to calculate the reliability of the audio amplifier that was analysed in Table 7.1. However, this time assume that low quality components are being used and that it is being operated in a fixed ground environment instead of an ideal one. Note that this would be a typical operation environment for such a product.

To apply the method one must look up all the relevant factors for the component types in MIL-HDBK-217, not a trivial task, and apply them to the components in turn. Table 7.2 shows an example spreadsheet calculation using the failure rates for the of components in the audio amplifier. Note that as well as including the component failure rates the reliability of the solder connections connecting the components has also been included.

The effect of the environment and quality factors is to reduce the MTTF by a factor of 20. One can also observe that the power transistors and electrolytic capacitors are now very large contributors to the failure rate.

Although the parts stress analysis is simple to apply, it suffers from the need to have tables of the multipliers for various values of the external factors. Furthermore these will be different for the different types components. This has several disadvantages. Firstly the tables might not exactly correspond to the situation that our product might operate under. Secondly they apply only to the constant failure rate regime whereas the external factors might also significantly enhance any wearout processes involved. Finally the tables are only available for existing components for which some reliability testing history is available. If a product involves recently developed components it is very difficult to use this method. These problems are addressed by the second method.

- **Physical or parametric modelling**: In this method we derive equations which relate the failure rate to the external factors. These equations might be related to some underlying physical model or they might be a parametric equation in which parameters are set to fit the observed behaviour. This has the advantage that one can derive the failure rate directly from the known values of the external factors and, If the model is a physical one, it is also possible to make predictions of the likely behaviour of new devices to the external factor. For example, a wide range of chemical and physical processes, such as corrosion of metals or diffusion in semiconductors, can be described by the rate of reaction or Arrhenius equation.

$$\text{Reaction rate} = Ae^{\left(\frac{-\Delta E}{kT}\right)}$$

where A = Scaling constant

ΔE = Activation energy (in eV)

k = Boltzmans constant (in eV)

T = Absolute temperature

This equation can be directly related to the failure rate by considering it to be a form of reaction which gives the following equation.

$$\lambda_{temp} = \lambda_0 e^{\left(\frac{-\Delta E}{kT}\right)}$$

where λ_{temp} = Failure rate at temperature T

and λ_0 = Failure rate at $T = \infty$

This equation can be used to provide a direct relationship between the reliability of the device and its temperature of operation. In addittion, with a knowledge of the thermal resistances, we can also calculate the effect of the power dissipation on the reliability as it to raises the temperature of the component. Typical values of ΔE for electronic devices are in the range $0.5eV \sim 1.5eV$. For a typical value of $\Delta E = 0.75eV$ this corresponds to a doubling of failure rate for every 10K rise in temperature. This means that such a device operating at $100°$ above ambient will have a failure rate of $2^{100/10} = 2^{10} \approx 1000$ times the rate at ambient temperatures. If the activation energy, ΔE, was doubled to $1.5eV$ the increase in the failure rate would only increase by of a factor of 32 in the same circumstances.

Calculate the effect of reducing the heatsink area, in order to save cost, on a power amplifier such that the power transistor operates at its maximum junction temperature of 125C instead of at 75C. The power transistor's $\Delta E = 0.75eV$ and its MTTF at 75C is 100 years.

Worked Example 7.15

The change in MTTF can be worked out by taking the ratio of the failure rate at the two temperatures.

$$\frac{MTTF_{125C}}{MTTF_{75C}} = \frac{\lambda_0 e^{\left(\frac{-\Delta E}{kT_{75C.}}\right)}}{\lambda_0 e^{\left(\frac{-\Delta E}{kT_{125C}}\right)}}$$

This equation can be simplified to give elevated temperature MTTF in terms of the temperature difference and the MTTF at the lower temperature to give:

Boltzmanns constant in eV is given by $k = \frac{1.38 \times 10^{-23}}{1.602 \times 10^{-19}} = 8.61 \times 10^{-5}$.

$$MTTF_{125C} = MTTF_{75C} e^{\left(\frac{-\Delta E}{k}\right)\left(\frac{1}{T_{75C.}} - \frac{1}{T_{125C}}\right)}$$

$$MTTF_{125C} = 100 \times e^{\left(\frac{-0.75eV}{8.61 \times 10^{-5}}\right)\left(\frac{1}{(273+75)} - \frac{1}{(273+125)}\right)} = 100 \times 0.043 = 4.3 \text{years}$$

Therefore reducing the size of the heatsink will reduce the MTTF, and hence the reliability, by about 23 times.

Another factor which has a functional relationship is the effect of voltage stress. This can be empirically modelled as a power law relationship given by:

$$\lambda_{voltage} = \lambda_{rated}\left(\frac{V_{operating}}{V_{rated}}\right)^{3 \sim 5} \qquad (7.11)$$

where $\lambda_{voltage}$ = Failure rate at the operating voltage
λ_{rated} = Failure rate at the rated voltage
λ_{rated} = Failure rate at the rated voltage
$V_{operating}$ = Operating voltage
V_{rated} = Rated voltage

Calculate the effect of choosing a 63 volt rated, instead of a 10 volt rated, electrolytic capacitor in a circuit with a supply voltage of 10volts. Assume that the exponent is 5 for this capacitor.

The power law varies between 3 and 5 in the literature. Again this equation can be used to provide an estimate of the effect of voltage stress. For example, operating a capacitor at double its voltage rating is going to increase the failure rate by a factor of between 9 and 32 relative to the reliability at the rated voltage, whereas operating it at half its rated voltage will result in the equivalent reduction in the failure rates. Note that many products fail because of reliability problems in the power supply due to under-rating the smoothing capacitor.

The operating voltage is 10 volts and the rated voltage is 63 volts. So, from equation (7.16) the failure rate is give by:

$$\lambda_{10v} = \lambda_{63v}\left(\frac{V_{10v}}{V_{63v}}\right)^5$$

Which gives:

$$\frac{\lambda_{10v}}{\lambda_{63v}} = \left(\frac{10}{63}\right)^5 = 1.0 \times 10^{-4}$$

So operating the capacitor at a reduced voltage reduces its failure rate by a factor of 10 000.

Another example of a specific environmental factor which can reduce the reliability of a product is electromagnetic radiation from other electronic products! This area of environmental threats to electronic equipment is known as electromagnetic compatibility (EMC) and is a specialist subject in its own right and forms an important part of electronic product design.

These parametric models are often used in conjunction with the parts stress analysis method more effectively to predict the effects of environmental and external factors. Note that the parts stress analysis method is more applicable to systems as opposed to components. This is because the multiplying factors represent statistical measures on systems with a mixture of components and technologies. Single components on the other hand are more affected by the precise nature of their individual context, for example how they mounted, and so their actual factors might vary wildly from the average ones.

Measuring reliability

If we are going to make use of reliability in our designs then we must have some way of measuring it. We require this for several reasons.

- We need to measure components and systems in order to obtain the necessary data for reliability calculations.

- We need to measure products in order to assure that they actually meet the required reliability specification.

- We also need to measure products to see if design and process changes are actually improving the quality and if the resulting improvement is worth the extra production cost.

Ungrouped data tests

The denominator in equation (7.12) is $N+1$ rather than N because the latter value would imply that the reliability is zero after the time of failure of the Nth unit. This is unlikely because if more units were tested then some of them would probably survive longer. It is reasonable to argue that, if the number of units under test were increased, the number of failures between each of the failure times up to the Nth failure would be approximately equal to the number of failures after that. This implies that the failures are distributed over $N+1$ rather than N intervals. Therefore a better estimate of the fraction of units which have not failed at a given time is obtained by using $N+1$ instead of N given the small number of units that are likely to be used in the test. As N gets bigger, the difference in results for the two different denominators becomes negligible.

The simplest way of measuring reliability, in the laboratory or factory, is to take a number of test units, run them until they all fail, and record their times of failure. This will result in a set of failure times $t_1, t_2, \ldots, t_i, \ldots, t_N$ This data can be used to estimate the reliability at t_i using the following equation which calculates the ratio of surviving units to the total number of units, N.

$$R_{estimated}(t_i) = \frac{N+1-i}{N+1} \qquad i = 0, 1, 2, \ldots, N \tag{7.12}$$

This is known as the ungrouped data approach because each failure is recorded individually.

Grouped data tests

Another simple way of measuring reliability, which is more applicable to field testing, is to is to start off with N units and record the number of failures over a set of time intervals until all the units have failed. Usually the length of the time intervals are fixed, for example, the number of failures each week. This information can then be used to provide a list of the number of surviving units at the end of each time period. That is, there is a set of times, $t_1, t_2, \ldots, t_i, \ldots, t_L$, and a set of the number of surviving units at those times, $n_1, n_2, \ldots, n_i, \ldots, n_L$. This is very similar to the earlier method except that the number of units which have not failed at time t_i is given by n_i instead of the index i. The equation for the estimated reliability from this sort of measurement is given by:

$$R_{estimated}(t_i) = \frac{n_i}{N} \qquad i = 0, 1, 2, \ldots, L \tag{7.13}$$

note $n_0 = N,$ because $t_0 = 0$

Because in this case there are possibly several failures per interval this is known as the grouped data approach. Data derived using equations (7.12) and (7.13) can be plotted to give graphs of estimated reliability as a function of time. However, often the failure rate, and the probability of failure within a certain time interval, are required. The first quantity is required for reliability calculations and the latter is required to observe the pattern of failure over the product life in order to obtain estimates of the wearin, operating, and wearout periods. This can be done using equations (7.2) and (7.4) to derive the necessary information from the data.

Unfortunately measuring the reliability using these direct approaches has several problems.

- **Measurement time**: Firstly we are dealing with a statistical measurement. This means that we can never measure the true value instead we can only obtain an estimate of the mean failure rates. The accuracy of this estimate is a function of the number of failure events which are observed. For example, we need to observe at least 90 failures in order to be able be 95% sure that the MTTF we have observed is within 25% of the true MTTF. Or to put it another way after we have observed 90 failures we can say that the MTTF has a 19 out of 20 chance of being X hours $\pm 25\%$. If we a dealing with a component whose MTTF is $\approx 10^8$ hours then we need to have $\approx 90 \times 10^8$ hours ≈ 1 million years of component testing time! This could be achieved by measuring 1 million components for about a year but that is likely to be too expensive. However, it is essential to get some measurements of reliability before the end of the product life.

- **Limited number of test devices**: In practice one can only measure a small number of the total number of components. This sampling can also introduce problems because one must ensure one has a representative sample of the set of components. It might also make the statistical interpretation of the results more difficult because the underlying statistics may assume that the test set is very large.

- **Incomplete tests**: The tests may not go on until all the units have failed or they might have incomplete data due to units being removed from the test because they have failed due to reasons other than reliability. For example, some car radios in a field trail might suddenly have to be removed from the test because they have been stolen! This is known as having censored data although it is possible modify the above methods in order to use it does reduce the accuracy of the measures.

The above reasons make it harder to use the direct approach in practice, although it is a very general method.

One solution is to use parametric methods, which rely on fitting a known PDF of the time to failure to model to the observed results of the test. The model can then be interpolated or extrapolated to make predictions about the reliability and failure rates. As an example consider applying the exponential distribution parametric model to the measurement of failure rate. The exponential distribution models constant failure rate systems and the reliability is given by:

$$R(t) = e^{-\lambda t}$$

Taking the logarithm gives:

$$\ln(R(t)) = -\lambda t$$

Which can be rewritten as:

$$\ln\left(\frac{1}{R(t)}\right) = \lambda t \tag{7.14}$$

Equation (7.14) describes an line of the form $y = mx$. So, by plotting the logarithm of the reciprocal of the reliability versus t, we should get a straight line passing through zero with a gradient equal to λ.

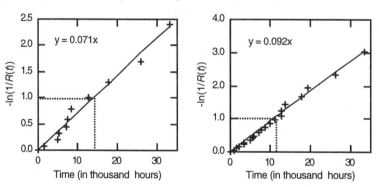

Fig. 7.20 Exponential plots of ungrouped failure data.

Figure 7.20 shows some measured reliability data plotted in this form. The first graph shows 10 points from this data, which was taken from a constant failure rate system. The second graph plots the same data but also includes an additional 10 data points. Both data sets are exponentially distributed and therefore form straight lines on the graph. By fitting a straight line to the data a straight line whose gradient estimates the MTTF can be obtained. However, because the line passes through zero the MTTF can also simply be read off the line, as it is the time at which the logarithm of the reciprocal of the reliability equals one. Note that the value measured is different in the two cases due the amount of data used. The graph with more data is closer to the true value of 10 000 hours.

A major advantage of analysing the data in this fashion is that the shape of the curve can be observed and therefore a check on whether the system has a constant failure rate can be performed.

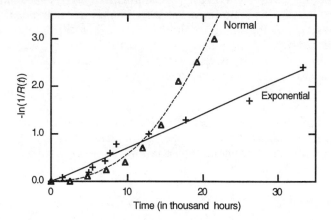

Fig. 7.21 Exponential plots of different probability of failure data.

As an example Fig. 7.21 plots two sets of data from two different failure distributions. One can see that although one set forms a straight line, the other does not. One set has a rising failure rate with time and on this type of graph it forms a curved line with the shape shown. If the failure rate had been falling with time the curve would have been in the opposite direction.

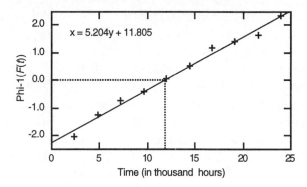

Fig. 7.22 Normal failure data versus time using the inverse normal CDF.

If a curved line is observed one can use other graphical techniques to develop the most appropriate model. In the previous example a normal distribution of failure rate is suspected. This means that the probability of failure is give by the normal cumulative density function.

$$F(t) = \Phi\left(\frac{t - \mu}{\sigma}\right)$$

If we take the inverse of the normal cumulative density function of $F(t)$ we get:

$$\Phi^{-1}(F(t)) = \left(\frac{1}{\sigma}\right)t - \left(\frac{\mu}{\sigma}\right)$$

(7.15)

Equation (7.20) is the equation of a straight line versus time with a slope given by $\frac{1}{\sigma}$ and an offset given by $\frac{\mu}{\sigma}$. Figure 7.22 shows the data which formed the curve in Fig. 7.21 plotted on using the normalised inverse cumulative density function versus time and one can see that a straight line is obtained. The MTTF can be found from the value of time which makes the normalised inverse cumulative density function equal to zero and the slope gives the standard deviation. From the graph one can see that the estimated MTTF is 11800 hours and the standard deviation is 5200 hours.

Even the parametric methods have problems due to the time involved. However, we can observe that what we need is a lower bound on the MTTF (or an upper bound on the failure rate). In such cases, although the component might be more reliable than is strictly necessary, it is possible to specify a number of test hours for which there should be no failures in order to be confident that an MTTF is greater than a specified value.

Accelerated testing

In accelerated testing the item under test is subjected to conditions which enhance the failure rates. This can take two forms.

- **Compressed life testing**: This method of acceleration is particularly applicable to mechanical components, or components with a significant wearout mechanism. In this method the components are operated under normal conditions but are subjected to more operations per unit time. For example, a switch or potentiometer might normally be used on average only every ten minutes whereas an accelerated life test would operate it perhaps once every six seconds. This would give a lifetime scaling of a 100 to 1 and so would allow data to be gathered more quickly. However, we must be careful not to introduce other artefacts into the measurement, for example, heat build-up due to the higher rate of operation, which could bias the result.

- **Stress testing**: In this method the component is operated under some form of environmental stress. The most popular is at temperatures above the normal operating conditions. Sometimes voltage stress is used, particularly for capacitors. In principle any stress factor which is easily measurable and which can be related to the components failure rates by some mathematical relationship. The method is popular because subjecting components to higher than normal temperatures is easy to do. It also has some physical justification because many failure processes are based on some form of reaction or diffusion process. The rates of both of these processes are exponentially related to the absolute temperature and therefore the failure rates caused by them are also affected in the same fashion. Again however one must be careful because there might be more than one failure mechanism with different levels of temperature sensitivities and therefore there is usually a limit to the maximum temperature that can be applied to the object under test.

The technique of transforming the cumulative failure, or the reliability, into a straight line is applicable to any of the distributions discussed. Thus one can also have lognormal and Weibull plots and these are useful for visualising the accuracy of the model as well as deriving estimates of the necessary parameters.

Another way is to carefully measure and analyse the components behaviour after testing to look for evidence of incipient failure. This is applicable to mechanical components which have significant wearout mechanisms which will tend to dominate the failure rate. However, in general one has to find ways of artificially increasing the failure rate so that a test can be done in a reasonable amount of time, this is known as accelerated testing.

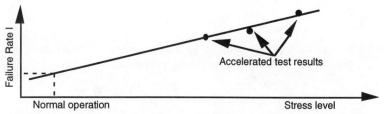

Fig. 7.23 Obtaining the failure rate from accelerated test results.

For example, the failure rate of a power transistor will increase as one increases the temperature but at some point one of the materials used in its construction might melt. As this is not a normal failure mechanism any failures due to meltdown failure would be misleading. Therefore one must be careful to chose the stress conditions carefully to avoid these spurious effects.

In order to make use of accelerated test procedures we must have some way of relating the accelerated results to the normal operating conditions. In the case of increased operating rates this is simply proportional to the time compression used in the test. So if the rate of operation is increased by a factor of 10 then the MTTF measured is scaled by the same proportion. However, in the case of stress testing the relationship between the measured and actual rates are not so simple. Instead one must have an equation which links the stress failure rate to the normal operating conditions. This is often achieved by performing several measurements at different levels of stress and then plotting the results, in a manner which results id an straight line. A straight line is then fitted to the data and extrapolated down to the normal levels of stress to predict the failure rate at normal operating conditions. Figure 7.23 shows the variation of failure rate as a function of stress level. This is appropriate for constant failure rate systems but is not appropriate for systems with time varying failure rates, such as wearout or wearin. In these situations it is better to plot the MTTF as a function of stress level.

As an example consider the using temperature stress to accelerate the failure rate.

Temperature stress testing

We have already seen that the failure rate as a function is given by the Arrhenius equation:

$$\lambda_{temp} = \lambda_0 e^{\left(\frac{\Delta E}{kT}\right)}$$

In order to be able to use this equation we need to know only the following:

λ_{temp} = Failure rate at temperature T

ΔE = Activation energy

This is because we are only interested in the ratio of the failure rates at two different temperatures. That is, we wish to find:

$$\frac{\lambda_{normal}}{\lambda_{accelerated}} = \frac{\lambda_0 e^{\left(\frac{-\Delta E}{kT_{normal}}\right)}}{\lambda_0 e^{\left(\frac{-\Delta E}{kT_{accelerated}}\right)}} = e^{\left(\frac{-\Delta E}{k}\left(\frac{1}{T_{normal}} - \frac{1}{T_{accelerated}}\right)\right)} \tag{7.16}$$

This ratio is independent of λ_0 and can be rearranged to give the normal failure rate as a function of the measured rate and the temperature difference to give:

159

$$\lambda_{normal.} = \lambda_{accelerated}e^{\left(\frac{-\Delta E}{k}\left(\frac{1}{T_{normal}} - \frac{1}{T_{accelerated}}\right)\right)}$$

The above equation can be used to derive the normal failure rate of the object under test, providing we know the following parameters:

$$\lambda_{accelerated} = \text{Failure rate at temperature } T_{accelerated}$$
$$\Delta E = \text{Activation energy in } eV$$

The straightforward way of measuring these parameters is to perform an accelerated life test at several elevated temperatures and then plot the logarithm of the failure rate against the reciprocal of temperature. This gives a straight line because the logarithm of the Arrhenius equation is of the form $y = mx + c$ as given by:

$$\ln\left(\lambda_{temp}\right) = \left(\frac{-\Delta E}{k}\right)\frac{1}{T} + \ln(\lambda_0)$$

The results of this is shown in Fig. 7.24.

Worked Example 7.19

Calculate the ΔE and MTTF, at 20C, of a component whose measured MTTF=574 hours at 200C and 82 hours at 250C.

From equation (7.21):

$$\frac{MTTF_{T_2}}{MTTF_{T_1}} = e^{\left(\frac{-\Delta E}{k}\left(\frac{1}{T_1} - \frac{1}{T_2}\right)\right)}$$

Taking logs gives:

$$\ln\left(\frac{MTTF_{T_2}}{MTTF_{T_1}}\right) = \left(\frac{-\Delta E}{k}\left(\frac{1}{T_1} - \frac{1}{T_2}\right)\right)$$

Which can be rearranged to give ΔE:

$$\Delta E = k\left(\frac{T_1 T_2}{T_2 - T_1}\right)\ln\left(\frac{MTTF_{T_1}}{MTTF_{T_2}}\right)$$

Now:

$$T_1 = 273 + 200 = 473K \text{ and } T_2 = 523K$$

Boltzmanns constant in eV is given by $k = \frac{1.38 \times 10^{-23}}{1.602 \times 10^{-19}} = 8.61 \times 10^{-5}$.

The activation can then be calculated using:

$$\Delta E = 8.61 \times 10^{-5} \times \left(\frac{473K \times 523K}{523K - 473K}\right)\ln\left(\frac{574 \text{ hours}}{87 \text{ hours}}\right) = 0.80eV$$

The MTTF at 20C is given by:

$$MTTF_{20C} = MTTF_{200C}e^{\left(\frac{-\Delta E}{k}\left(\frac{1}{473K} - \frac{1}{293K}\right)\right)}$$

Which gives:

$$MTTF_{20C} = 574 \times e^{\left(\frac{-0.80}{8.61 \times 10^{-5}} \times \left(\frac{1}{473K} - \frac{1}{293K}\right)\right)} = 1 \times 10^8 \text{ hours}$$

Clearly accelerated testing has benefits, although the above is an extreme example and one would normally have more than two points to work from. One would also want to check that the relationship was still valid at such high temperatures.

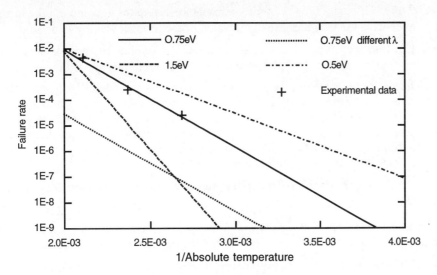

Fig. 7.24 Arrhenius plots for various failure rates and activation energies.

This technique can be applied to any form of stress testing, providing there is some equation, empirical or otherwise, to link the failure rates under stress to the normal operating conditions. Its limitations are as follows:

- It can give erroneous results if the underlying model is violated.

- It assumes a single, or dominant, failure process. For example, the Arrhenius model assumes that only one activation energy is controlling the failure rate. If several different activation energies are involved the results are erroneous.

- It relies on extrapolation and will tend to exaggerate any measurements inaccuracies .

It is often helpful to use the graphical techniques outlined earlier to derive the failure rates because deviations away from the model might be visible as changes in the shape of the failure probability versus time as the temperature of the test varies.

Providing these factors are taken into account stress testing is a highly useful way of obtaining reliability data.

Acceptance testing

Having designed, and produced, a reliable product how can a company test it to guarantee that it achieves its specified reliability? This is particularly important when the product is used in safety critical systems. Often in these situations there is an external reliability specification which the company is contracted to achieve. In other cases it is simply a useful part of the whole quality assurance and control process, because the overall reliability might be affected by the inevitable changes in the production process, for example, machinery changes due to wear and replacement.

However, as discussed earlier, there are several problems:

- **Measurement**: The reliability has to be estimated by taking a random subset of the production and testing them. Ideally as small a number as possible should be used as they contribute to loss in production yield.

- **Time**: The longer the reliability acceptance test takes to complete the more expensive the test, because of the value of the product waiting to be sold.

- **Confidence**: The measure is an estimate of the reliability and its accuracy depends on the number of components tested and the length of the test.

These problems are similar to those of measuring the reliability in first place and must be addressed if any form of acceptance test is to be practical. However, there is one important difference which makes the problem easier. This is because, unlike reliability testing, one is only interested in whether the product meets some threshold of reliability, as opposed to the actual level.

Stress testing can be used in two ways to assure reliability:

- It can be used to increase the failure rate and so reduce the time of the test.

- It can be also used to test the physical and electrical limits of the product.

In both of these cases though the number of units, and also the length of time, required for the test must be minimised. There are two aspects to consider:

- Minimising the time required to test that the products MTTF meets the specification.

- Minimising the number of units that must be tested to assure the reliability to a given confidence level.

The MTTF can be estimated from the following equation.

The $\chi^2(v)$ (chi squared) distribution is the distribution of v normalised squared deviations from the mean. It allows us to calculate confidence limits on the estimated mean using the value of deviation from the mean in the distribution which encompasses the required proportion of the population, for 90% confidence this is 90% of the population. In the case of reliability v is twice the number of failures that have occurred and the highest value of the MTTF for a given level of confidence (the lower confidence limit) can be calculated using the following equation.

$$MTTF_{estimate} = \frac{T}{n}$$

where $T = $ The total time of operation
$n = $ The number of failures

The confidence limits can be determined using the MTTF estimate and the number of failures by using the χ^2 (chi squared) distribution. In particular the lower confidence limits of the MTTF are of interest because this contains the smallest value of MTTF for a given confidence level. The confidence limits are dependent only on the number of failures and not on the length of time and are independent of the MTTF. The χ^2 distribution can be used to determine the accuracy of a MTTF estimate given a number of failures. However, the minimum length of time of failure free observation required to assure a given MTTF, to a particular confidence level, is of more interest for acceptance testing.

$$MTTF_{lower} = \frac{2T}{\chi^2_{conf}(2n)}$$

Where T is the total test time.

This can be achieved by examining the lower one sided confidence limit for one failure. The reason being that if a device was tested for a certain amount of time and without failure then the worst case would be that it failed immediately after the test. Therefore by looking at his confidence interval we can ascertain the length of time that a product under test must survive in order to set a lower bound on the MTTF. A typical confidence level is 90% and this results in a lower confidence limit of 0.43×MTTF for a single failure.

Worked Example 7.20

How long must a device be measured fault free for in order to be 90% confident that its MTTF is greater than 220 hours?

162

Lower confidence limit is:

$$L_{lower\,90\%} = 0.43 \times MTTF$$

therefore the measurement time must be greater than:

$$T_{measurement} \geq \frac{1}{0.43} \times MTTF_{desired} \geq 2.3 \times MTTF_{desired}$$

So for an MTTF of at least 220 hours with a confidence limit of 90% we must observe failure free operation in one device for at least:

$$T_{measurement} \geq 2.3 \times 220 \text{ hours} \geq 506 \text{ hours}$$

The value of $\chi^2_{conf}(2n)$ can be looked up in a book of statistical tables.

This is a pessimistic result as on has to assume that the device fails immediately the test is stopped and usually this will not be the case. In general it is better to stop the test when a certain number of devices have failed.

Although this gives us information about the lower bound on the MTTF, which is useful, it does not assure the quality of the whole batch. Also in many cases the specification is couched in terms of the reliability or the probability of failure.

Therefore we need to test more than one item of production and ideally for as short a time as possible. This can be done by using the binomial probability distribution to work out the probability of no failures after a number of trials, given a certain probability of failure, and can be expressed in terms of the confidence as:

$$F(t)_{max} = 1 - \left(1 - \text{Confidence}\right)^{\frac{1}{N}}$$

$F(t)_{max}$ is plotted versus N for various values of confidence in Fig. 7.25.

Figure 7.25 shows that if a low failure rate must be verified to a high confidence then a large number of units must be observed. However, the measurement time can be shorter because the units under test only have to operate up to their designed reliability life, which, can be a small fraction of the MTTF.

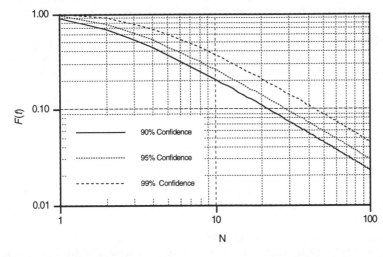

Fig. 7.25 Upper confidence limit on $F(t)$ as a function of units tested.

Calculate the number of units which must be tested with no failures to assure an end of product life reliability of 95% with a confidence limit of 90%.

Worked Example 7.21

163

From the equation the probability of observing no failures for a given reliability is given by:

$$P_{no\,failures}(t) = R(t)^N$$

The probability of no failures is equivalent to:

$$P_{no\,failures}(t) = \left(1 - P_{Confidence\,limit}\right) = R(t)^N$$

Taking logs of both sides gives:

$$\ln\left(1 - P_{Confidence\,limit}\right) = N\ln\left(R(t)\right)$$

Which can be rearranged to give N as:

$$N = \frac{\ln\left(1 - P_{Confidence\,limit}\right)}{\ln\left(R(t)\right)}$$

So the required number of units for the test is:

$$N = \frac{\ln(1 - 0.9)}{\ln(0.95)} = 45$$

Note: it is statistically possible for a unit to fail within this time period even though the product has a reliability of greater than 95%. If this happens the test must go on for longer. There are more sophisticated techniques such as sequential and binomial sampling acceptance methods, which make acceptance testing more efficient in such circumstances.

Therefore 45 units must be tested and none of them must fail for the duration of the product lifetime in order to be 90% confident of a reliability of better than 95%.

Reliability growth monitoring

In general the reliability of a new product is not constant with time. This is due to experience gained during development and production which results in improvement in reliability as the product goes through different versions. This is particularly true of software but is applicable to any product. Unfortunately this complicates the job of reliability prediction, because the reliability measurements might have taken place earlier on in the product development and therefore might now underestimate the actual product reliability. Therefore it is desirable to be able to monitor the evolution of a product's reliability throughout its lifetime for several reasons:

- to ensure that the reliability is improving or is at the very least static;

- to be able to predict the likely endpoint reliability of a product during its development on the basis of data gathered earlier;

- to monitor the effects of improvements in the product.

During development the product is often modified in the light of the failures that have already occurred. In this situation each time the prototype is changed it becomes a new unit and so its failures cannot be analysed simply as repeated failure of the same system. In this situation the reliability engineer has to use a different approach in order to be able to predict the likely reliability of the final system

'A Learning Curve Approach to Reliability Modelling,' by J. T. Duane, in the IEEE Transactions on Aerospace, volume 2, pp563-566 (1964).

A technique developed by Duane allows us to monitor the reliability growth of a product during development. He observed that if we plot the logarithm of the total number of failures per unit time up to a given operating time, based on all the prototypes, versus the logarithm of the total time of operation, then a straight line was obtained. This form of plot is known as a Duane chart.

The fact that they form straight lines on a log-log plot implies that there a power law relationship between the cumulative failure rate and the time of operation. These relationships are also applicable to the MTTF. Thus the MTTF to give the cumulative MTTF and instantaneous MTTF can be related to the total time of operation by:

$$MTTF_{cumulative} = e^{-c}T^{-m}$$

$$MTTF_{instantaneous} = \frac{1}{(m+1)}e^{-c}T^{-m}$$

The instantaneous MTTF can be further couched in terms of the cumulative MTTF, by substituting it into the equation for instantaneous MTTF, as:

$$MTTF_{instantaneous} = \frac{1}{(m+1)}MTTF_{cumulative} \qquad (7.17)$$

Equation (7.17) is interesting because it shows that, the instantaneous MTTF is related to the cumulative MTTF by a simple ratio. Figure 7.26 shows the MTTF form of the Duane chart. Because the instantaneous can be simply estimated from the cumulative MTTF, a Duane chart can also be used as a means of measuring reliability during the development of a product.

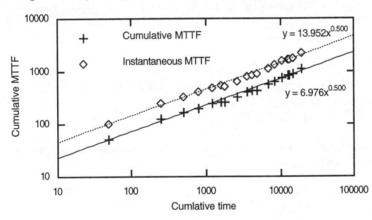

Fig. 7.26 Example Duane MTTF plot of reliability growth.

Typical values for the factor m, which determines the slope of the reliability growth, are around 0.5 for new technology components, although it can be less for established products. Therefore the cumulative reliability for new technologiestends to improve as the square root of time and the instantaneous MTTF therefore tends to be twice the value of the cumulative MTTF.

The failure rate of an electronic product with an embedded microcomputer is **Worked Example 7.22** dominated by the software. The cumulative MTTF of the prototype as a function of time is shown in Table 7.3. The product needs to have a minimum MTTF of one year and the launch date is in six months time. Should you be looking for another job?

Table 7.3 Prototype cumulative MTTF data

Cumulative Time	207	1035	2071	3313	4970
Cumulative MTTF	197	493	657	788	946

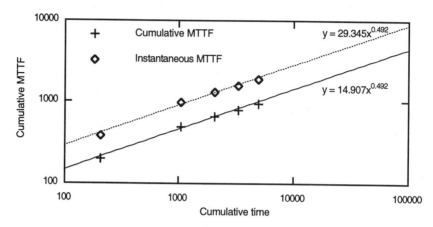

Fig. 7.27 Duane MTTF plot of Table 7.3 data.

One year is equivalent to 8766 hours therefore the instantaneous MTTF must equal 8766 hours. Plotting the data from Table 7.3 and curve fitting it, as shown in Fig. 7.27, gives the equation:

$$MTTF_{cumulative} = 14.9t_{cumulative}^{0.492}$$

Thus $m=0.492$ and therefore the instantaneous MTTF is given by:

$$MTTF_{instantaneous} = \frac{1}{(1-0.492)}14.9t_{cumulative}^{0.492} = 29.3t_{cumulative}^{0.492}$$

This equation can be rearranged to give the cumulative time, given a required instantaneous MTTF, as:

$$t_{cumulative} = \left[\left(\frac{1}{29.3}\right)MTTF_{instantaneous}\right]^{\frac{1}{0.492}}$$

So the cumulative development time required to achieve the required instantaneous MTTF of one year is:

$$t_{cumulative} = \left[\left(\frac{1}{29.3}\right)\times 8766 \text{ hours}\right]^{2.033} = 107742 \text{ hours}$$

The product has had 4970 cumulative hours of development so far so the extra cumulative time required is:

$$t_{required} = 107742 \text{ hours} - 4970 \text{ hours} = 102772 \text{ hours} = 11.72 \text{ years}$$

Unless 24 prototypes, or some other form of acceleration, can be used for development the deadline is not going to be met, start job hunting!

This method is useful but has limitations. At the end of the day it is just an empirical model and will not allow, for example, for an increase in failure rate after modification of the product. Reliability will not always grow for example, if all the design defects have been removed then there is no longer any room for reliability improvement. Also it might be prohibitively expensive to improve the reliability of the product.

166

Design considerations

Reliability affects all aspects of the design of an electronic product, in particular.

- **Specification**: The level of reliability must be decided at the specification stage, in particular both the level and nature of the reliability must be decided.

- **System design**: The level and nature of reliability required will affect the system design. For example, is the level required so high as to require some form of redundancy?

- **Detail design**: Some circuits are more reliable than others, some components might have failure modes which can be protected against; different physical arrangements are less likely to fail in a given context; some materials are more compatible than others, and components are less likely to fail in a lower stress environment.

- **Production and test**: The reliability of a product is often significantly affected by the quality of the production process. Semiconductor devices, for example, are much more reliable if they are manufactured in a clean environment with a minimum of electrical and physical stress.

- **Distribution and use**: Failures can result from poor packaging, storage and handling of a product during distribution. However, in many cases the product may not be obviously damaged, instead because the components have suffered stress outside their specification they are more unreliable. Also the user may mishandle the product, by connecting it up wrongly for example.

- **Design iteration**: Reliability must also be considered when bringing out the next version of a product. It is possible to have a latest version which is less reliable than the version it replaces! However, if information from the customer on the level, nature and context of the failures is gathered it can be incorporated into the design iteration process.

Clearly all these aspects require a combination of the modelling, analysis and measurement techniques discussed earlier and in many cases the approach taken will be very specific to the product and its market. However, there are a few general strategies that are broadly applicable over most products. These are as follows.

Setting reliability objectives

It is vital at the beginning of the design process to set the reliability specification for the product. In some cases such as safety critical systems this might be set externally however in many cases this is not so and one is left with a 'how long is a piece of string' problem. Clearly this will interact with the cost of providing a particular level of reliability. Therefore when setting the reliability objectives one must ascertain the following:

- **The reliability lifetime of the product**. That is, the length of time that a product must operate to a given reliability. This might be set in a variety of ways and there might be more than one reliability lifetime for a given product.

In the simplest case the product has only one reliability lifetime this is applicable to products which wearout, as customers expect to have to replace them. It might also be applicable to products which are short lived because they are replaced, or no longer used, by the customer because they have become out of date. Examples might be car tyres or trans-oceanic telephone cables. In these situations it is only necessary to set an end-of-life reliability specification, a typical value might be 90% at the end of the product life but this depends on cost and context.

However, for many products the situation is more complicated as there are several possible reliability lifetimes. In fact it might be difficult to specify a reasonable end of product life as the customer may want to keep using the product for as long as possible! In these situations it is the perception of the reliability that is important while maintaining the cost within reason. One possible approach is to use the guarantee periods as a means of setting the level. Thus there may be a high reliability specification for end of the main guarantee period reliability (say 99%), have a reduced specification for the end of the extended guarantee period (say 95%), and, possibly, a level at a reasonable product lifetime (say 90% after 10 years).

- **The confidence level required of the reliability lifetime**: This will affect the level of measurement required to assess whether the product meets a particular reliability level.

- **The customer's reliability versus time requirements**: For example, the customer may wish the product to continue working through a failure, or might not be too worried about a failure so long as it is repaired quickly, or may even expect to throw the product away after failure. These different contexts require different approaches to the reliability specification. In the first case the system must function long enough after a fault to allow repair. In the second the customer is happy so long as the faults do not happen too frequently or cause any damage. In the third once the product has failed another is purchased and reliability may affect the purchase choice at this point.

Once the required level of reliability has been set then the effect of the design options on the reliability can be ascertained. However, in many products there is a wide variety of failure rates and modes.

Failure budget

A useful way of looking at the problem is to take advantage of the fact that the individual failure rates add to give the overall effective failure rate. That is, according to equation (7.6):

$$\lambda_{total} = \lambda_1 + \lambda_2 + \lambda_3 + \cdots + \lambda_n$$

This can be used to give a failure rate budget where the end-of-life reliability specification is converted to an equivalent failure rate. This can then be used to give the design objective of not allowing the total failure rate to go into the red. This is highly useful in the early design stages as it can quickly show where the main focus for reliability effort must be concentrated. It can quickly show if the objective can be achieved at all. If just a few of the components exceed the maximum allowable failure rate then there is a problem, the reliability goal might not be achievable. It can also highlight where the design effort must be focused as there may be a dominant source of error in the system. This might be, for example, a mechanical component or a sub-system with a large number of components. In some cases one may have to consider ways of making the offending part more reliable, possibly by using some form of redundancy. In other cases there is no way of making the higher failure rate parts more reliable and therefore the rest of the parts will have to be more reliable in order to achieve the specification.

Using a failure budget, redesign the amplifier example so that it achieves and of **Worked Example 7.23** life reliability after five years of 90%.

Table 7.4 Initial failure budget calculations

Component	Quantity	Component failure rate (per 10^6 hrs)	K_E	K_Q	Total component failure rate (per 10^6 hrs)	Total failure rate	Failure rate budget
Capacitor	2	0.0010	1.9	7	0.027	0.03	2.38
Connectors	2	0.0200	1.2	3.9	0.187	0.21	2.19
Potentiometer	1	0.0400	1.8	5	0.360	0.57	1.83
Small signal transistor	8	0.0008	5.6	12	0.430	1.00	1.40
Soldered connections	97	0.0026	2.1	1	0.530	1.53	0.87
Resistor	23	0.0010	2.4	15	0.828	2.36	0.04
Electrolytic capacitor	5	0.0250	2.4	10	3.000	5.36	-2.96
Power transistor	2	0.0400	5.6	12	5.376	10.74	-8.33

		Total failure rate achieved			10.74	per 10^6 hrs	
		Failure rate desired			2.40	per 10^6 hrs	
		Desired MTTF			47.46 years		
		MTTF achieved			10.62 years		
		R(t)desired		90%	after 5 years		
		R(t) achieved		62.5%	after 5 years		

- Firstly, work out the required failure rate to achieve the end-of-life reliability using equation (7.12).

- Secondly, sort the failure rates for the components, or sub-systems, into order. This is most easily done on a spreadsheet as shown in Table 7.4. Using this table one can see that the dominant sources of failure are the power transistors and the electrolytic capacitors. This is due to using low quality components at their rated limits. However, even if these components were failure free the specification would still only just be met. In fact in order to meet the specification the quality of most of the components must be increased and their stresses must be reduced. One can also improve the reliability by using reflow soldering rather than hand soldering. Note that the environment rating cannot be altered because this is determined by the customer and out of designers control.

Table 7.5 Failure budget calculations for an improved design

Component	Quantity	Component failure rate (per 10^6 hrs)	K_E	K_Q	Total component failure rate (per 10^6 hrs)	Total failure rate	Failure rate budget
Capacitor	2	0.0010	1.9	7	0.027	0.03	2.38
Connectors	2	0.0200	1.2	3.9	0.187	0.21	2.19
Potentiometer	1	0.0400	1.8	5	0.360	0.57	1.83
Small signal transistor	8	0.0008	5.6	12	0.430	1.00	1.40
Soldered connections	97	0.0001	2.1	1	0.014	1.02	1.39
Resistor	23	0.0010	2.4	5	0.276	1.29	1.11
Electrolytic capacitor	5	0.0250	2.4	3	0.900	2.19	0.21
Power transistor	2	0.0010	5.6	6	0.067	2.26	0.14

Total failure rate achieved	2.26	per 10^6 hrs
Failure rate desired	2.40	per 10^6 hrs
Desired MTTF	47.46 years	
MTTF achieved	50.45 years	
R(t) desired	90%	after 5 years
R(t) achieved	90.6%	after 5 years

- Thirdly, make design improvements and assess their impact. This might well require several iterations. Table 7.5 shows the effect of using higher quality components and operating them at lower stress. In particular the power transistors had a higher rating and were mounted on a better heatsink. In addition the quality of the power transistors, the electrolytic capacitors, and the resistors were improved and reflow rather than hand soldering was used for the board assembly.

The resulting product just meets the reliability specification but at the cost of more expensive components. Note that one would have to work hard to double the reliability.

It is important to realise that the failure rate budget implies a constant failure rate which is often not true. However, it is possible to convert a time variable failure rate into an equivalent failure rate at the design life time and these can then be incorporated into the failure budget. The same technique can be also applied to redundant systems. However, this will only work at the design lifetime and the results cannot be used to predict the reliability at any other time.

Improving reliability

There are various ways in which the reliability of a product can be improved.

- **Redundancy**: Any of the redundancy approaches described earlier can be applied to a product with a consequent improvement in reliability. Even software can have redundancy applied to it. In many embedded systems this is essential.

- **Reduced stress operation**: If environmental stress increases the failure rate then conversely reducing it will reduce the failure rate. Therefore one way of improving the reliability is to ensure that the components are operated below their rated voltages and power dissipation. For example, if a capacitor is operated at half its rated voltage then, according to equation (7.16), its failure rate will be reduced by a factor of between 8 to 32 times over the rate at its rated voltage, depending on the value of the exponent in equation (7.16). Another form of hidden stress is the voltages components' experience during switch on and switch off. In many cases these can subject components to significant transient stresses which can cause a premature increase in failure rate.

  An example is the base emitter junction of a silicon transistor which has a reverse breakdown voltage of typically less than 5 volts. Normally this junction is forward biased and so this parameter is unimportant but during turn on it is possible for the junction to be reverse biased in excess of breakdown. The result is an increase in failure rate.

  Temperature is also an important factor in reliability as there is an exponential growth in failure rate with temperature. A reasonable rule of thumb for many electronic components is that the failure rate doubles for every 10C rise in temperature. Conversely it will drop by the same factor for every 10C reduction in temperature. Therefore ensuring that components run cool is an important objective for reliable systems. Note that it is the actual temperature of the device that is important and this is affected by the ambient temperature and environment, the power dissipated, and the devices thermal resistance to the ambient environment. In many modern LSI devices the power dissipation is very high, often close to the maximum package limit, and the addition of heatsinking and cooling can have a significant effect.

  Vibration and mechanical factors, such as forces on sockets, are also a source of failures. and therefore minimising vibration and stresses in connections during normal, or even abnormal, operation is helpful.

- **Burn in**: Another way of improving reliability is to assure that the components an system are working in the normal operating region of the bathtub curve. One way of achieving this is to operate the components and possibly the product for an initial period at the factory, usually under stress, in order accelerate the early failures and get the product into the flat part of the curve. However, although this can enhance the reliability, it has to be approached with caution. Firstly, many modern semiconductor devices are so carefully screened in production that there is little if any wearin period. In fact it has been suggested that the major sources of early failure now are due to electrical stresses due to electrostatic discharge suffered by the device during handling in the production process. In this case a burn in procedure would have little effect. Secondly, there is some evidence that burn in procedures can actually increase the failure rate because the stress applied actually induces failures in the devices.

In general it is better to design reliability in at the initial system specification and system design stages rather than leave it until the end of the product development stage.

Summary

In this chapter the way in which reliability affects the design process has been examined. In particular the need to take account of reliability goals at the beginning of the design process has been stressed. The basic concepts of failure analysis for series, parallel, fault correction, and standby systems have been discussed. Methods of analysing, measuring analysing and assuring reliability have also been shown. The chapter has also shown some design methods for designing to a particular reliability specification including the effects of external factors.

A major thrust of the chapter has been to show that simply assuming a constant failure rate, and looking at the MTTF is a naive, and often misleading, way of treating reliability. This is especially true in modern electronic products which are often a mixture of mechanical, electronic and software components.

Remember if you can keep your head when all about you are losing theirs, then maybe you've misjudged the situation.

However, there is one caveat on all of this analysis, one is dealing with statistical models to extrapolate likely behaviour of the systems. Therefore the predictions are crucially dependent on the quality of the underlying models and whether the assumptions that they are based on are satisfied in practice. As a final example it is pointless designing an ultra reliable car engine if the user does not realise that it needs to have oil put in it to assure its longevity.

Problems

7.1   A product has an MTTF of 33 years calculate its reliability after 10 years of operation .

7.2   Calculate the MTTF of a product consisting of 67 devices with an MTTF of 2×10^4 years and two components with an MTTF of 7×10^3 years.

7.3   Take a, small, electronic product and estimate its reliability under ideal conditions.

7.4   Calculate the MTTF of single versus parallel contacts in a switch, a single contact has a failure rate of 0.1% per 1000 hours.

7.5   Determine the $t_{lifetime}$ as a function of the MTTF for single and dual path systems to give an end-of-life reliability of 90%.

7.6 Determine the $t_{lifetime}$ as a function of the MTTF for no fault correction and single fault correction systems given an end-of-life reliability of 99.9%.

7.7 Calculate the lifetime of a DAT tape head for an end-of-life reliability of 90%. The MTTF of the video head is 4000 hours with a standard deviation of 800 hours.

7.8 Use the parts stress analysis method to calculate the reliability of the small, electronic product that was analysed earlier in problem 7.3. However, this time assume that low quality components are being used and that it is being operated in a fixed ground environment instead of an ideal one.

7.9 Calculate the effect of reducing the heatsink area, in order to save cost, on a power amplifier such that the power transistor operates at 100C instead of at 75C. The power transistors $\Delta E = 0.75eV$ and its MTTF at 75C is 100 years.

7.10 Calculate the effect of choosing a 20 volt rated, instead of a 10 volt rated, electrolytic capacitor in a circuit with a supply voltage of 10 volts. Assume that the exponent is five for this capacitor.

7.11 How long must a device be measured fault free for in order to be 95% confident that its MTTF is greater than 1000 hours?

7.12 Calculate the number of units which must be tested with no failures to assure an end of product life reliability of 99% with a confidence limit of 95%.

Design for manufacture 8

At the end of this chapter you will be able to:

- State the parts of manufacturing that are affected by product design
- Design a production process for a new product
- State what is involved in the make/buy manufacturing decision
- State how the learning curve impacts assembly
- Explain how poka-yoke improves assembly quality and throughput rate
- Describe the various electronic component packages and their effect on the printed circuit board assembly process
- Explain the difference between batch and flow production

The successful delivery of a product is dependant not only on the basic design meeting the technical requirement but also on the ability to produce it in a way that is financially acceptable to the organisation. Manufacture is, in itself, a very broad subject within which there is a multitude of specialist fields. This chapter aims to introduce the concept of designing with production in mind and to introduce some of the constraints and considerations that need to be borne in mind during the design and development of a new product.

What manufacturing involves

Under the umbrella of design for manufacture there are a number of aspects which will be specifically addressed. Table 8.1 summarises these aspects.

Table 8.1 Aspects of manufacture

- Design for Piecepart Fabrication
- Design for Purchase
- Design for Assembly
- Design for Test
- Design for Inspection
- Design for Maintenance and Service
- Design for Shipment

Before any product design and development can commence consideration must be given to who will produce the product. It is the target production facility which will have a pronounced impact on the processes that can be used to produce the product and the achieved unit production cost, production yield and product quality level. At the most basic decision level there are two options for production location, in-house or sub-contract.

In-house production is where the manufacturing part of the organisation will produce the product. If the organisation either doesn't have a production part or the product under development requires processes which are outside the in-house capability then the services of an external manufacturer can be used. In this case production is sub-contracted to a third party. It should be noted that the whole product need not be made in-house or by sub-contract, a combination of the two can be a cost-effective manufacturing strategy. It is common for organisations to have a level of in-house production capability that is developed to a level that confers a competitive advantage. Specialist tasks are then performed using sub-contract manufacturers.

Knowledge of the proposed production facility is necessary so that the product can be designed and developed in sympathy with the production capability. The production of any product can be broken down to a cascade of basic production stage building blocks. This basic building block is illustrated in Fig. 8.1.

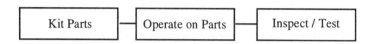

Fig. 8.1 Basic production building block.

The first stage is to 'kit the path', that is, to ensure all the parts required for the basic production operation are present ready for the operation to be performed. The second stage is to operate on the parts, this could be assembling them together, copying software from a master file to a disk or solid-state memory or machining a mechanical part from a solid ingot. The final stage is inspecting the output of the operation either visually or through some form of test.

The whole subject of design for manufacture will be developed through this chapter using the basic production building block of Fig. 8.1 such that it embraces the production aspects listed in Table 8.1. To illustrate the points being made a microprocessor-based programmable room thermostatic central heating controller will be used. The controller comprises a single printed circuit board mounted to the front half of a two part plastic case. The front half also has attached to it a plastic membrane keypad, used to select functions and programme the controller and some transparent legend areas illuminated by light emitting diodes mounted on the PCB to indicate the state of the product (central heating on or off and hot water on or off). The rear of the case is there to complete the housing and allow the controller to be screwed to a suitable wall. Each controller is packed in a bubble wrap plastic pouch with an instruction booklet and guarantee card inside a cardboard carton which is then shrink-wrap coated before being packed in larger, plain cardboard boxes for despatch to the distributors. For quality control purposes each product carries a label with a unique serial number.

The above description of the product serves as a useful starting point for the definition of a manufacturing process and for pointers for what is involved in the manufacturing process. Figure 8.2 shows the process as described.

The process depicted in Fig. 8.2 accurately describes the packing and supply part of production but is considerably more vague about the manufacture of the front case half. This would be typical of the definition of the product at the early stages of design and development. Marketing would have a strong view on the appearance of the product as it would be seen by the customer (the appearance of the product and of the packaging the customer will see) and a view on the means of getting the product to the end customer through the use of distributors and the supply chain. Marketing would also have an input on the overall product capability through market and/or customer surveys. It is the remainder of the detail of the production process that needs to be added to complete the picture.

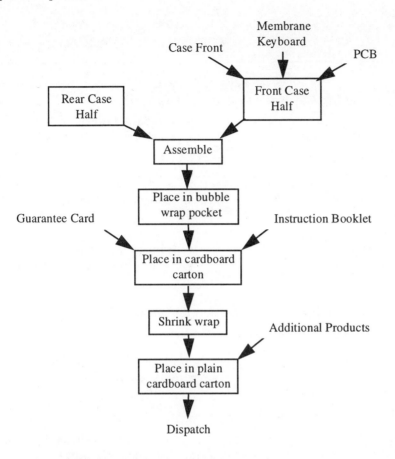

Fig. 8.2 Product manufacturing process.

The overall process of manufacture will be considered from start to finish as seen by a product, that is, starting with the purchase of raw materials. The development of Bill of Materials has already been introduced in chapter 4. The Bill of Materials is the final statement of what the product is in terms of constituent parts and required processes. The design and development process will identify a number of components and parts that will need to be purchased as raw materials for the product. These raw materials will be procured by the purchasing part of the organisation or fabricated within the machine shop part of the organisation.

Design for piecepart fabrication

Parts can be fabricated from a wide range of materials in many different ways. Table 8.2 lists the generic types of materials and Table 8.3 the generic methods of piecepart fabrication.

Each of the materials in Table 8.2 can be further broken down into groups of materials and composites until, ultimately, there are many different materials with different physical properties and characteristics that can be used to fabricate items. Some of the key physical characteristics and properties that are related to materials for electronic applications are shown in Table 8.4

Table 8.2 Generic types of materials

- Metals
- Plastics
- Woods
- Glass and Ceramics
- Paints and Varnishes

- Paper
- Foam
- Cotton and Linen
- Electronic Components

Table 8.3 Generic methods of fabricating pieceparts

- Machining from solid
- Cast, moulded or extruded

- Built by joining smaller pieces
- Built by electrochemical deposition

Table 8.4 Key physical characteristics and properties of materials

- Hardness
- Strength
- Thermal conductivity

- Electrical conductivity
- Environmental durability

In the same way the generic methods of fabricating parts shown in Table 8.3 can be broken down. For example, some of the methods of cutting parts from solid are shown in Table 8.5.

Table 8.5 Methods of machining parts from solid

- Turning
- Milling
- Etching
- Laser cutting
- Stamping

- Guillotining
- Drilling
- Paring
- Skimming

Even a superficial glance at the methods of machining and the types of materials available shows that not all materials can be machined by all the methods. Turning a slab of glass on a lathe, for example, is likely to result in shards of glass flying in all directions, that is assuming the entire slab does not completely shatter.

The hardness of materials affects the way they are machined and the skill and equipment required to perform the machining. The hardness of the materials also has a direct impact on how the equipment will survive the physical environment it is exposed to. The consequence of these is that there is scope for a design trade-off between environmental suitability and manufacturability.

Making parts by joining other parts together is simple when the parts lend themselves easily to being joined. Steel can be welded easily. Aluminium on the other hand, cannot be so easily welded and generally requires specialist equipment. The weight of these two materials is clearly different with aluminium frequently being used because of its light weight. A trade-off between user handling and ease of manufacture emerges.

To acquire and maintain a manufacturing operation capable of producing everything the product design and development process could require a very significant capital outlay, significant ongoing maintenance costs and the retention of skilled specialists in the more unusual fabrication methods. Unless the volume of production is such that these skilled specialists and the capital assets they require are fully utilised, there will be a cost penalty to the organisation. A more economically realistic strategy is to develop only skills which can be acquired and used cost-effectively and sub-contract everything else. Few organisations, for example, possess a dip bath brazing capability, one of the methods by which aluminium can be brazed. However there are a small number of sub-contractors that specialise in the technique and offer a first class service with very competent technical support. These sub-contractors can afford to maintain and develop capability on the combined production throughput requirement of all the main producers they service.

With the vast choice of different materials available and the wide range of fabrication methods there is scope to produce pieceparts in a very large number of different ways. For any organisation, with a limited manufacturing capability, the design and development process can have a pronounced impact on the ease of manufacture of the pieceparts. The design and development could, for example, make it impossible for the in-house capability to produce any of the required pieceparts. Equally, by designing in sympathy with the in-house production capability a product could be wholly manufacturable in-house, even when the organisation has a limited manufacturing capability.

Requiring parts to be fabricated by sub-contract instead of by in-house manufacture has a number of organisational implications, as summarised in Table 8.6

Table 8.6 Implications of sub-contracting piecepart fabrication

---

- cost
- effect on capital assets
- effect on workforce

- quality
- availability

Of these implications, cost can be more easily and quickly compared. The sub-contract cost, plus any administrative and purchasing overheads can be compared with the BOM cost (the total cost of producing the part including labour, materials and overheads). The two resulting numbers can be directly compared to see which is the lower.

A piecepart can be purchased from a sub-contractor for £13.00 each or manufactured in-house from raw materials costing £5.00 in 35 minutes. The **Worked Example 8.1** direct labour rate is £8.50 and the labour overhead £12.50 both per hour. There is a 15% purchasing overhead on all purchases. From a purely financial point of view should the organisation make or buy the part?

Cost to buy the part:	Sub-contract cost	£13.00
	Purchasing overhead	15.0%
	Total cost to buy part	£13.00 (1 + 0.15) = £ 14.95

Cost to fabricate:	Raw material cost	£3.50
	Purchasing overhead	15%
	Total material cost	£ 4.03
	Labour hours	35/60 = 0.58
	Direct labour rate	£8.50
	Direct labour cost	£4.93
	Labour overheads	£12.50
	Labour overhead cost	£7.25
	Total labour rate	£21.00
	Total labour cost	£12.18
	Total cost to make part	£16.21

At first sight buying the part wins. It is £1.33 cheaper than in-house manufacture. However there are other considerations. Purchasing the parts actually costs £13.00, the remaining £1.95 being a contribution towards the organisation's overheads. Manufacturing in-house costs £3.50 in materials and £4.93 in direct labour, that is £8.43, the remaining £7.78 being a contribution towards overheads. Whilst purchasing the part from a sub-contractor appears to be the cheapest, manufacturing the parts recovers more overheads. This is an interesting quirk of the absorption costing system and one which can distort the make / buy decision making process.

This approach to costing forms the basis of the make or buy decision but is not the whole story. It has ignored implications such as:

- effect on capital assets
- effect on workforce
- quality
- availability.

Effect on capital assets

A simple cost comparison assumes the existing capital assets are capable of producing the part consistently to the required standard and that there is sufficient spare capacity in the machine to allow all the parts to be produced as and when required. Over-use of a machine can result in an increase in the required level of maintenance or can reduce life expectancy. An example of the unearthing of hidden costs.

Effect on workforce

A workforce that sees an increasing volume of work being sub-contracted may feel threatened and fear for their future. Equally the sub-contract of all the more challenging jobs may be seen as a threat to internal development and the personal growth of the employees. Striking the right balance is one of the more difficult challenges in modern management.

Quality

The quality of work produced in-house should be easier to control than that produced by a sub-contractor. The feed-back path is shorter and contact more easily made. Having said that, in organisations that suffer poor internal communications and co-operation (often the larger, older and more bureaucratic organisations) the situation can be the reverse with a better responsiveness being offered by sub-contractors.

Unless there is a very close working relationship with sub-contractors, quality issues are normally resolved through rejection of the parts by the organisation's quality department back to the sub-contractors' quality department for resolution. In some cases this can result in delays whilst responsibility and corrective actions are negotiated. All such delays jeopardise availability.

Availability

Parts fabricated in-house have the potential for the greatest availability. Changes in the demand for a product alter the demand for piece parts. A repaid increase in product demand might be easier to accommodate where control of labour and machinery are both internal. Overtime, for example, can be used to make up shortfalls. If overall capacity is exceeded, the organisation has all the facts to make priority decisions between products or to authorise round the clock working. In the case of sub-contracted parts manufacture, the available capacity may be being used to service the demands of other organisations over which priority cannot be always be exercised. In such situations availability will be affected.

There are no golden rules to the buy/make decision. Decisions must be made on a case by case basis, using all the relevant facts and taking all considerations and potential implications into account.

In addition to the impact design and development has on whether the piece-parts can be fabricated using the in-house capability, there is also an impact on how easy parts are to fabricate. Consider the simple box shown in Fig. 8.3. It is an aluminium box, machined from solid, suitable for a microwave integrated circuit. The circuit board, in this case, an alumina substrate, is attached with conductive adhesive to the bottom of the box with connectors put in from the outside. A flat lid with a sealing gasket is used to seal it.

The box, as drawn, is extremely difficult to make and would be expensive for two reasons.

1. The internal aperture, the part that needs to be milled out, has square corners. Milling or router bits are circular, with the result that square corners cannot be produced by milling, at least not from vertically above. The square corners would need to be broached after the milling process, possibly requiring a special broaching tool.

2. The holes used to attach the lid are shown with flat bottoms. Flat-bottomed holes can be achieved but are considerably more expensive than the shape that results when an ordinary drill bit is used to produce a hole.

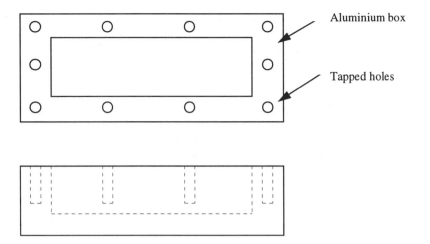

Fig. 8.3   Microwave integrated circuit housing.

In the above example there is no genuine reason why the corners need to be square or the holes flat bottomed.   Two simple design modifications would remove the problems and make the housing much cheaper to produce.   Figure 8.4 shows the necessary changes.

It is fair to say that any competent mechanical designer would foresee these problems at the design stage, assuming, of course, there is clear and effective communications between the electronic and mechanical designers.   The above illustration shows where the design can impact the cost and ease of producing a piecepart.   The example is a very simple piecepart with the potential of two quite expensive and unnecessary problems.   More complex parts such as moulded or cast parts have considerably more scope to make them impossible to produce.

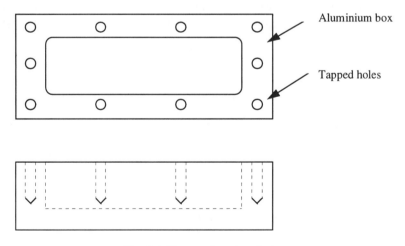

Fig. 8.4 Cheaper housing design.

To make a plastic part by injection moulding requires a mould half shaped to reflect the internal surface of the part and a second to reflect the outer surface. The two mould halves are then brought together with a gap between the surfaces equal to the material thickness required in the part.   Molten plastic is then injected to fill the cavity, the plastic and mould are cooled, separated and the part removed. Once the mould halves have been made and samples from them approved as acceptable, pieceparts can be manufactured with consistent quality and very quickly. Raw materials are low cost which makes the final parts very economical. The process cost per component is small.

To enable parts to be fabricated by injection moulding, the part and mould designs must be such that the molten plastic will flow, completely and evenly to fill the cavity and that the mould can be separated after the plastic has cooled. These considerations require a lot of thought to be given to the siting of the cavity fill locations and the provision of small exit holes to ensure even consistent fill. Ensuring that the mould halves will separate requires the pieceparts to have shape features that lie only in the direction of mould separation. This can pose problems where flanges or lips are required. More complex injection tools can be made by using more than two parts to the mould tool. These more complex tools are more expensive and take longer to develop. The design of mould tools is a specialist skill and is best carried out in conjunction with the piecepart manufacturer.

Design for purchase

It may seem obvious that, if the parts for a prototype can be obtained, the parts needed to manufacture a quantity of the same product can also be obtained. Simplistically this is true. In reality there is much more to purchasing. Purchasing is the creation and mutual agreement of a contract from a buyer to a supplier for a given quantity of a given item at a stated time, for an agreed price, in a stated form and to an agreed quality standard.

Consider, as an example, the electronic components required in the programmable controller. Table 8.7 lists the components.

Table 8.7 Programmable controller electronic components

Component	Quantity
Microprocessor	1
EPROM	1
Interface and General Logic Integrated Circuits	3
Noise Suppression Capacitors	5
Resistors	12
Voltage Stabiliser Integrated Circuit	1
Smoothing Capacitor	1
Tantalum Capacitors	3
Relays	2
Driver Transistors	2

Components to produce design prototypes are likely to be purchased from general purpose distributor specialising in a very wide range of components supplied at very short notice. Such sources usually carry a price premium resulting from the service they provide. If quantities in the thousands off are required, this price premium can put the product at a competitive disadvantage.

For such quantities it would be normal to purchase components directly from the manufacturer or a bulk distributor. The drawback of such a purchasing strategy is that many more purchasing contracts are required.

Larger organisations, manufacturing a range of products, can have many hundreds or even thousands of supplies from whom they obtain parts. This becomes organisationally very difficult to manage, requiring a significant management structure and consequential overhead costs. To ensure quality of parts it is very common for the buyer organisation to quality-assess each supplier and each prospective supplier. Supplier assessment is a sometimes lengthy and costly process which needs to be taken into account in the product design and development process. To manage the whole purchasing system, many organisations have an approved supplier list or a preferred component list with a quality procedure to add a new component or supplier to the list.

To illustrate the impact on design and development, consider the programmable controller components. The organisation has an established and comprehensive preferred component and approved supplier list. All the components required are available except for the EPROM which is a new memory device just launched by a memory manufacturer. To introduce this new device will require a supplier audit and their addition to the approved supplier list. This process requires several visits to the supplier, the answering of a questionnaire and approval by a quality panel. The whole process normally takes approximately six months.

For the project team to be able to use this new component in the design, time must be allowed for this company process to take place and would need to be incorporated into the project plan to ensure it is completed in time for production

Two further purchasing considerations are component obsolescence and component availability. Component manufacturers periodically redesign components and their processes and make older products, or new products that prove difficult to manufacturer cost effectively, obsolete. If a component specified for a product goes obsolete during the production life an alternative will need to be found and suitability verified. This can involve a significant amount of work on the part of the design and development team. In a similar way the procurement of parts from a supplier who, for any reason, cannot continue to supply, will result in the need for product redesign work.

The only effective measures that can be taken to avoid costly redesigns is by working closely with suppliers. Advanced warning of component obsolesces are usually given or can be sought on a periodic basis. Impending obsolescence can be dealt with by the purchase of sufficient parts to complete the predicted manufacturing volume or for sufficient parts to cover the time required to search and verify an alternative.

Purchased parts physically enter the organisation and end up at the 'production building block' stage that uses them. The block stage will require a certain volume of parts to allow the required number of assembled parts to be made.

This volume, and the way in which the parts are to be used, also affects purchasing. There are two basic methods of manufacture, batch or flow. In batch production a quantity of the product is manufactured on a production line that is configured for the manufacture of the particular product. An example might be the manufacture of Personal Locator Beacons in which beacons are made in batches of 100. When the batch of 100 is complete the line may lie idle before an instruction is issued to manufacture the next batch, or may be configured to be able to manufacture an alternative product. In flow production a line is dedicated to the manufacture of a particular product. Products are made on the line continuously.

The purchasing requirements of these two methods of manufacturing are very different. In batch production, parts may be purchased in quantities equal to the batch size. Alternatively, purchasing may obtain parts for a number of batches and take advantage of any bulk purchasing discounts. Purchasing is aligned to the batch nature of the product and is made on a periodic basis as and when required. In flow production the product is continuously being made so there is a continuous need for parts to feed the line. Purchasing for flow production is usually in the form of a bulk order which is delivered by the supplier small volumes at a time.

To illustrate the purchase of parts for flow production, consider a television production line which is making 100 televisions a day. Purchasing may commit an order for six months' worth of parts, gaining them considerable bulk discount benefits. The purchasing contract requires the supplier to deliver a weeks' worth of parts by 10.00 am every Monday morning. This delivery clause ensures that production can proceed at the desired rate but that the manufacturer does not have to hold huge stocks of the parts.

Design for assembly

The 'kitted' parts for an assembly process are usually turned into an assembled part by following a set sequence of operations. These operations are defined in a procedure document or a 'Works Instruction'. Figure 8.5 illustrates the basic assembly stage with all its inputs and outputs.

Kitting is the term used to describe the process of collecting together all the parts required to assemble an item.

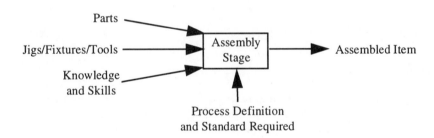

Fig. 8.5 Basic assembly stage.

Knowledge and skills

The assembly of a kit of parts, even to a defined process, can require special knowledge and skills which may need to be learned. Time will be required to be able to produce assembled items to the required quality standard in the required assembly time. It is unreasonable to expect any new assembly process to be able to be turned-on instantly at the required rate and quality. In reality, assemblers will become progressively more proficient with experience. This proficiency improvement can be illustrated graphically as the 'learning curve' effect as shown in Fig. 8.6.

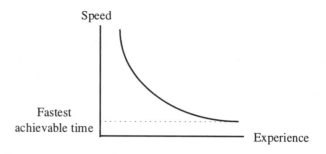

Fig. 8.6 The learning curve.

The time to which the learning curve tends is the fastest time that will be achievable given the parts and process as defined. Improvements in assembly time can be made only through a change in the parts or the process. The corollary of this is that the product design and development stage sets the fastest achievable time through the parts and the required process. There is scope in both of these 'inputs' to make the item easier or more difficult to assemble. Consider, for example, the assembly of the rear case half to the front case half in the programmable controller example. There are a number of different ways these two parts could be joined together. Three possible ways are shown in Table 8.8.

Table 8.8 Three possible ways of joining case halves

- Nuts and bolts
- Bolts into captive threaded inserts
- Plastic clips

To effect the join if the 'nuts and bolts' method is used requires the two halves to be mated together, bolts passed through the two halves, nuts added and tightened. To make the assembly easier a jig, such as that illustrated in Fig. 8.7, could be made such that the four nuts are first placed in holders in the base plate, the two case halves lowered between the guide posts and the bolts passed through from the front and tightened using a power torque screwdriver.

A similar, but slightly simpler jig could be used for the second method where bolts are screwed into captive threaded inserts. The third method requires the two halves to be offered together and snapped into place. This method requires no special jig.

A final consideration with this assembly is the orientation of the two case halves. If the case is rectangular in shape there are two joining orientations as shown in Fig. 8.8.

If the rear half and the fixing locations can be made symmetrical such that the two halves will mate irrespective of orientation, assembly time and risk of assembly errors will be reduced. If mating requires a certain orientation of the parts adding a key in one part and a slot in the other will ensure the parts can only go together the correct way. Figure 8.9 illustrates a key and slot arrangement.

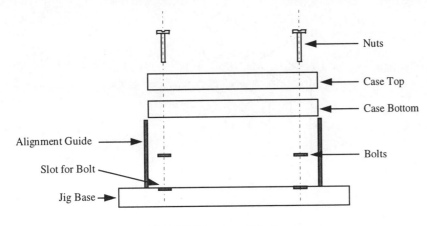

Fig. 8.7 Case assembly jig.

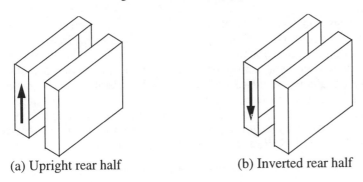

(a) Upright rear half   (b) Inverted rear half

Fig. 8.8 Case half joining orientations.

Given that the way pieceparts are designed can affect the ease with which they can be assembled, there is a direct link between design and the process part of the unit production cost. Further, the more complex the assembly the greater the risks of mistakes or poor quality. There is a clear need to design parts to be as easy to assemble as is reasonable. A sympathetic design and carefully thought through assembly jigs and fixtures can make significant differences to the cost of assembly.

The assembly fixture shown in Fig. 8.7 is very close to an example of a 'poka-yoke' jig.

Poka-yoke

Poka-yoke is a methodology conceived by Shiego Shingo for 'mistake proofing' or 'fool-proofing' of assembly operations. The basic principle of the methodology is that the assembly operation is immune to inadvertent mistakes. Inadvertent mistakes include omitting to assemble a part, incorrectly orientated parts, failing to make a connection between two parts correctly and so on.

Shiego Shingo, a Japanese quality guru, coined the term poka-yoke as the concept of designing a process to be error free.

With the poka-yoke methodology, manual or automated means can be used to ensure that everything is assembled correctly. It is important to remember that any jig or fixture required in any assembly stage will need to be designed, constructed and tested to verify correct operation. Each jig and fixture is, albeit, a mini project within the overall project. Each requires time, finance and resources.

187

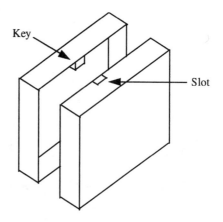

Fig. 8.9 Key and slot method of ensuring correct assembly orientation.

All such jigs and fixtures must be planned from the outset of the project to ensure the correct (and working) jigs and fixtures are in place in readiness for the start of product manufacture.

In the same way the assembly procedure or work instruction and statement of the required quality standard of the assembly operation need to be drafted, tested and produced to the company standard format. Note that there is a direct planning link between the procedure and the jig or fixture. Each needs the other during the verification stage. Both also need parts that are representative of the final build standard to allow verification to take place.

Worked Example 8.2

Resource limitations dictate that only one item can be designed at any one time and only one drawing can be produced at any one time. The design of pieceparts for a product is expected to take five working days and that two further days are required to draw the pieceparts and one day to produce the assembly drawing. Once the assembly drawing is complete, the assembly jig can be designed in two days and drawn in one. If it takes two weeks to make the pieceparts and one week to make the jig, produce a bar chart of the shortest overall time plan for this part of the overall process.

Figure 8.10 shows the shortest time plan given the above information.

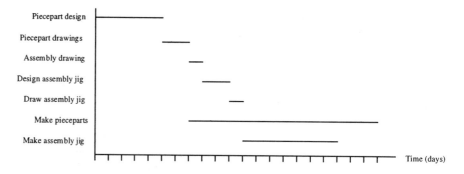

Fig. 8.10 Bar chart for pieceparts and assembly jig fabrication.

Design for assembly has so far focused on the assembly of mechanical parts. The other half of assembly is that of electronic components, especially the assembly onto printed circuit boards.

Design for PCB assembly

Components can be purchased in very many different packages. Table 8.9 shows just a few of the more common packages.

Table 8.9 A range of more common component packages

- Dual-In-Line (DIL) Integrated Circuits
- Single-In-Line (SIL)
- Axial
- Radial
- Chip (Surface Mount)
- Chip Carrier

The DIL is a standard for digital and analogue integrated circuits in which the connections to the integrated circuit are made via legs which are arranged in two parallel lines. The number of legs range from 6 to 40. The SIL package is similar to the DIL package except that the legs are arranged in a single line. In axial components there are typically only two legs, one at each end of the body of the component. Radial components also, typically have two legs but both are at the same end of the body. Chip components are the naked components without any connections. A block of ceramic with plated ends is the simplest example of a chip capacitor. Connection to the chip is made by connecting to the ends or, in the case of a semiconductor device, the connection pads, directly. Finally, a chip carrier is a base to which a chip component is attached to enable it more easily to be connected into a circuit. Typically only semiconductor chip devices are mounted on chip carriers.

The option of which package to use does have, in some cases, an impact on the performance of the circuit. At high frequencies the need to keep parasitic components to a minimum drives designers to select chip devices which can be bonded directly to tracks on the printed circuit board. High complexity circuits that need to be accommodated in a very small size provide a drive towards surface mounted components. Complex circuits or circuits that present problems as far as producing a printed circuit design, may require components to be mounted on both sides of the board. There are many different design considerations that impact the way components are laid out on the printed circuit board.

If all the components required in a circuit can be obtained in the same, or compatible, packages the entire printed circuit board can be assembled in one process stage if the board is single sided or two stages if double sided. A PCB assembly with so few stages would be very simple and cheap, in terms of process time, to assemble. In reality not all of the components can be obtained in compatible packages and a multi-stage assembly process results. Each component package requires a different piece of equipment to handle and mount them. The following is a brief description of what is involved in assembling the different packages.

Chip (surface mount)

Each component is picked out of a tray of similar components or extracted from a tape and rotated so that the component alignment is correct for the pads to which it is to be soldered. A small amount of glue is placed beneath where the chip is to be placed and the chip is placed on the board. Where components have a polarity such as polarised capacitors, diodes and transistors, device orientation also has to be allowed for. Modern surface mount machines will, once programmed, do all these functions very quickly. Once all the components are in place the whole board can be soldered to make the electrical connections. A typical surface mount placement is shown schematically in Fig. 8.11.

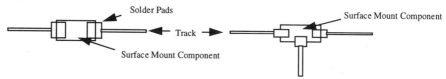

Fig. 8.11 Surface mounted component placements.

An advantage of surface mounted components is that, since both connections are made on one side of the board only and no through plated board connections are required, the cost of the bare board is lower and the board area directly under the chip component can be used for other tracks or components. There is, however, a disadvantage to this. Testing can be made significantly more difficult. This aspect is dealt with later in the chapter.

Axial and radial components

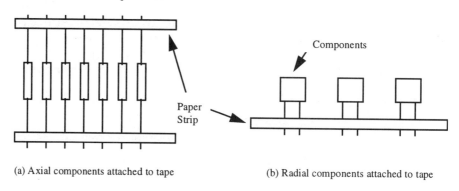

(a) Axial components attached to tape   (b) Radial components attached to tape

Fig. 8.12 Axial and radial component 'tapes'.

Axial and radial components are normally supplied to a placement machine on a 'tape' as depicted in Fig. 8.12.

The placement machine takes the first component, removes it from the tape, bends the legs as required for the mounting holes in the PCB, places the component in the correct location with correct orientation, cuts the excess leg length from the underside of the board and 'clinches' the legs over to prevent the component falling out of the board at a later stage. Figure 8.13 illustrates 'clinching'.

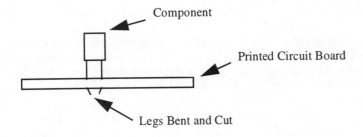

Fig. 8.13 Component leg 'clinching'.

To place components in the PCB in the shortest time possible, the placement part of the machine, the 'head', needs to move the shortest distance. If the board requires, for example, 10 resistors and 5 capacitors all in a single line, it would be quickest if the machine placed the first one, then the second one and so on down the line. If every component in the line were of the same value a reel of the component in question could be loaded onto the machine and assembly would follow. More frequently there will be different components in each position. Rather than have the assembly machine keep swapping reels, it is preferable to form a new component supply tape with the components in the correct sequence for optimum placement on the board. The machine used to produce this tape is called a 'sequencer'.

The 'sequencing' of components can be performed in advance of their being required by the printed circuit board population machine thereby optimising population process time.

DIL and SIL components

Single and line and dual 'in line' integrated circuits are usually supplied in tubes which are mounted vertically in a placement machine. The placement machine selects the desired tube, takes one integrated circuit from the tube, orientates it correctly for its target location, inserts it into the holes in the board and clinches the legs to prevent the component subsequently falling out of the board.

As with axial and radial components the fastest assembly is one requiring the lowest number of placement head movements.

With all of the component placement methods the design and the layout of the board can have a pronounced impact on the time taken and hence the cost of each stage. A component layout that is sympathetic to dual-in-line assembly would, for example place all of the ICs facing the same direction and all in a grid fashion across the board area. Components placed at complex angles may look attractive but may also result in a larger placement time and greater assembly process cost.

The number of different processes required to assemble any given PCB also affects the unit production cost. In chapter 4 the need to allow for machine set-up time in the total product cost was introduced, with one set-up cost being incurred for each process involved. There is also a need to inspect and, or test after each stage to ensure faults are detected early in the production process. These two considerations combine to suggest that the best strategy is to minimise the number of assembly stages. The number of stages is a designed-in feature, dictated relatively early in design and development of the product. It is another example of the production cost being defined well before production actually starts.

The final complexity of PCB assembly is soldering. It is important to ensure that, in multi-stage assembly components do not fall out between stages and that components soldered after one stage do not become unsoldered and move during a subsequent solder stage. One approach that can be taken to avoid this problem is to use solders with different melting temperatures for different stages. The first solder operation would use a higher melting point solder than the next. Overall the design of a complete PCB assembly process can be a complex operation in its own right.

Worked Example 8.3

Design a PCB assembly process for the temperature controller. The printed circuit board needs to be double sided. The components to be used have the following packages:

Processor and Glue Logic	DIL
Noise Suppression Capacitors	Chip
Resistors	Chip and axial
Large Capacitors	Radial

The following is one possible production process which places all surface mounted components first, followed by the larger axial, DIL and radial components. Note the methods used to secure the components between stages.

Step 1	Attach surface mount components
Step 2	Autoplace axial components
Step 3	Manually place DIL and radial components
Step 4	Solder whole board

Summary

In this chapter the need to consider design for manufacture has been considered. The chapter started by examining the different aspects of manufacture and what each involves. This establishes a framework for the remainder of the chapter which considers the aspects in turn.

Design for piecepart fabrication examines the effect of manufacturing on the organisations capital assets and where the best skills are. The choice of fabricating the part in-house or purchasing it from a sub-contractor is investigated paying due care to quality and availability issues.

Design for purchasing considers such issues as preferred components, obsolescence and preferred suppliers to establish a need to consider purchasing as an integral part of the product design and development process.

Once all the parts have been designed and purchased assembly can commence. The quality of the end product is not simply a function of the parts and the design. The skills of the assemblers and the attention paid to assembly jigs and fixtures can dramatically affect the achieved quality and throughput. The concept of error free assembly is examined as a tool for ensuring quality and ease of assembly.

Finally the special considerations of assembling printed circuit boards are addressed. Attention is specifically drawn to the overall assembly process which can, if poorly designed, introduce considerable cost to each product manufactured.

Overall the message of this chapter is that it is very easy to leave manufacturing considerations until after the initial design is complete. The result of such a strategy will be a very expensive unit production cost and the risk of poor throughput and poor quality. Production is the project stage that generates the profit to repay the product development and provide the funds for future growth. It is essential that this profit is maximised. The best way of achieving this is to involve manufacturing from the outset of a project.

Problems

8.1   A printed circuit board can be populated in-house or by a sub-contractor. The cost of the components for the board is £85.00 including the bare board. If it takes 20 minutes to populate the board using labour which has a direct cost of £9/hour, should the board be populated in-house or by the sub-contractor? The labour overhead is £15/hour, the purchasing overhead 12.5% and the sub-contractor quote for the fully populated board is £94.00.

What other considerations might be taken into account in the decision making process?

8.2   Design a poke-yoka jig for the assembly of a printed circuit board into the front half of a plastic product case such as that shown in Fig. 8.9. The printed circuit board is secured by four metal bolts. What suggestions would you make for reducing assembly time or cost?

8.3   Using the same product you analysed to answer problem 6.4, infer a manufacturing process for the product from what you can see.

8.4   Following on from problem 8.3, produce a printed circuit board assembly process chart.

Design for inspection and test 9

At the end of this chapter you will be able to:

- State the purpose of inspection and test in the assurance of product quality
- Explain the basic approaches to testing electronic products
- Design a test strategy for a new product
- Model and quantify the yield of a production process
- Quantify the impact that yield and rework has on product manufacturing cost

In chapter 8, on Design for Manufacture, it was noted that the successful delivery of a product is dependent not only on the basic design meeting the technical requirement but also on the ability to produce it in a way that is financially acceptable to the organisation. The production of any product can be broken down into a cascade of the basic production stage building blocks shown in Fig. 9.1. This chapter focuses on the output gate of this building block, that is, the inspection and/or test of the result of the 'operate on parts' activity.

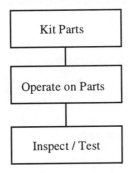

Fig. 9.1 Basic production building block.

The role of inspection and test

Inspection or test is a production operation designed to build, or establish, confidence that the previous stage or stages have produced a quality output. As such they are quality gates through which good outputs pass and which return bad outputs for corrective action. Figure 9.2 shows a more developed version of the basic building block to include this corrective action loop. In addition to verifying the integrity of the manufacturing operation, test is sometimes also required to align circuitry to a specific performance requirement. The economics of this approach are explored later in this chapter.

Where circuit alignment is required, a test operation cannot be avoided. However in cases where test is used purely for the verification of operation quality integrity there is scope to reduce the level of test, ultimately eliminating it altogether. To get to this stage there must be sufficient quality in the input components and in the operation itself. The development of the operation process itself and how feedback can be placed around operations to gain and maintain stability is explored in the chapter on quality.

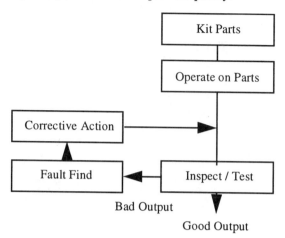

Fig. 9.2 Developed model of the basic production building block.

Given that the broad objective of quality assurance in production is to identify defective parts or assemblies, it makes economic sense to identify such defectives as early in the process as possible before they have accumulated significant added value. This calls for a very carefully-planned inspection and test strategy recognising at the same time that every test and inspection stage is a non-value-adding activity.

This section looks briefly at inspection and then in more detail at test by considering available test methods, the effective design of test strategies, process quality and how it impacts the test strategy, some general comments on design for test and finally production yield and the impact on product costs.

Inspection

Inspection is the mechanical quality gate. The output of the process operation is checked mechanically to see whether it conforms to the requirements. As with any quality gate, good product is passed and bad product is returned for repair or rework.

Inspection can be performed by either operator self-inspection or by the quality inspector. The self-inspection has the advantage that any defects found can be prevented in future by the operator modifying the way work is done to prevent a recurrence. Inspection by a quality inspector or other person will detect faults but will not have this rapid feedback. This issue is discussed in more detail in chapter 10.

A third option is for inspection to be carried out by the receiver of the output; in other words, the next person in line. All parts and assemblies are produced to drawings. The ultimate mechanical inspection is to measure every dimension specification and drawing for every part made. This is an expensive method of assuring quality when applied to every product; however, useful process information is gained by a very detailed inspection of a sample of the output.

An alternative method of inspecting a part is to focus on critical dimensions. The critical dimensions being those associated with the interfaces between the part and those to which it mates. A simple way of testing such dimensions is by using a 'go-no go' gauge.

A 'go-no go' gauge is a fixture shaped to reflect the part to which the manufactured object mates. For example, in a temperature controller unit, a 'go-no go' gauge can be fabricated to reflect the front facing half. The gauge would be very precisely made such that if a rear case half is mated with it, a new half that is on its maximum or minimum tolerance would just fit whereas one slightly out of tolerance would not fit. Any rear half mated with the 'go-no go' gauge can then be very easily checked. Any rear half that fits the gauge, passes and any that does not fit, fails.

A simple example of a 'go-no go' gauge for a circular rod would be a metal block with two adjacent holes, one hole would have a diameter precisely equal to the minimum tolerance and the other precisely equal to the maximum tolerance. Any rod sample that goes into the larger hole but not the smaller hole, passes any rod that either goes into the smaller hole or will not go into the larger hole, fails.

In all cases of mechanical inspection, a record of the results is usually kept for quality control purposes. Such records are normally kept by completing an inspection report, a sheet of paper on which the identification of the sample (serial number or other identification) and the result of the inspection is recorded.

In some cases special measuring equipment will be required for the inspection; for example surface flatness cannot be easily measured. On-line surface finish measuring equipment is normally in the province of a dedicated quality inspection area where it can be kept in a temperature and dust controlled environment. It would be unusual to need to verify the surface finish with every product produced, however, for specialist products it may be required and in such cases the cost of inspection would need to be more. Here again, if the need for a very precise surface flatness can be avoided in the design stage, the product can be made such that it was sympathetic to inspection requirements. In all cases the inspection to be carried out should be borne in mind during design and development. Critical dimensions (such as those associated with interfaces) should be highlighted on the drawings at the outset. The number of critical dimensions should be kept to a minimum.

Test methods

The basic approaches to testing electronic circuits are summarised in Table 9.1.

Table 9.1 Basic electronic test methods

• Continuity Check and Bare Board Test	• Functional Testing
• Component Testing	• System Testing
• In-circuit Testing	

The simplest test to perform is a continuity check, the check of whether an electrical path is present or absent. Continuity checks are used to verify the integrity of wiring looms and bare PCBs. In the case of a bare PCB, the board to be tested is offered up to a jig containing a series of spring loaded 'nails' that make contact with component connection pads or with the conductive area around a through plated hole or component hole as illustrated in Fig. 9.3.

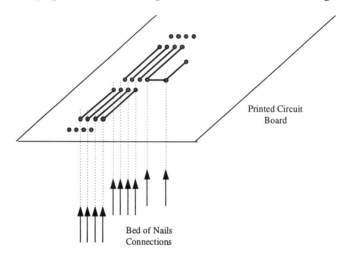

Fig. 9.3 Bare board 'bed-of-nails' continuity checker.

Table 9.2 Bare printed circuit board track testing

Path designed to be	Path measured to be	Normal or Fault	Possible causes
Present	Present	Normal	
Present	Absent	Fault	Design error Break in track Over etching Scratch
Absent	Present	Fault	Design error Solder bridge Under etching
Absent	Absent	Normal	

Each nail is connected through a switch matrix to a continuity checker. The switch matrix is computer controlled such that all required conductive paths are checked to verify tracks are intact and isolation exists between conductive paths that are not supposed to be connected. In this way checks can be made for four types of paths as summarised in Table 9.2.

The possible causes assume that the test equipment is functioning correctly. A constant and repetitive fault between board samples may indicate a test equipment fault such as a broken or bent 'nail' or broken wire in the test fixture.

Component testing

The most basic component tester is a hand-held electronic multimeter that will measure and indicate resistance. At the more sophisticated end is the tester into which can be plugged a complex application-specific integrated circuit (ASIC) which it will test against the results of known good devices or against the designed transfer functions of it. The objective of all component testers is to verify that a component in isolation from any circuit, is functioning to its particular specification.

Basically every electronic component that can be made can be tested. The most common components testable by a component tester are summarised in Table 9.3.

Table 9.3 The common component types testable using conventional component testers

• Resistors	• Diodes
• Capacitors	• Transistors
• Inductors	• Integrated circuits

More complex components such as Very Large Scale Integrated circuits (VLSIs) and Application Specific Integrated Circuits (ASICs) require either special test configurations or testers designed and built specifically for that component.

The complexity of the general purpose tester affects the level of test capability. For example, a standard multimeter will measure the resistance of a resistor. It will not measure the temperature coefficient. Knowledge of the tests performed by the component tester proposed to be used in the component verification operation is an important part of the design of a test strategy. If a particular design relies on a particular component parameter that is not tested by the component tester and very high quality cannot be assumed from delivered components, the parameter will need to be verified in some other way. An example of this would be the verification of the knee voltage of a Zener diode. A conventional diode tester may test for only forward and reverse conduction. A special test may need to be devised, or an alternative component tester used, if the knee voltage needs to be verified or selected for a specific value.

Complex components such as microprocessors present component test with an additional problem. The amount of internal circuitry and the number of different combinations of the various commands available, make such components almost impossible to test fully. The combinations can run to the multi-millions requiring huge amount of test time. A very uneconomic approach to testing. In practice it is normal to verify just that the basic operation of the device works by verifying that a few instruction cycles work.

Dedicated integrated circuits and programmed devices can be tested by applying a set of test vectors designed to simulate normal component operation. The test vectors would normally be derived from the design and development

A test vector is the name given to the binary levels applied to the inputs of a digital circuit. So, for example, if the digital test circuit comprised a single 2-input NAND gate, each input could be supplied with a '1' or a '0' resulting in four valid test vectors, namely '00', '01', '10' and '11'.

part of the process, another reason for test to be considered early in the product development process.

In circuit testing

The objective of in-circuit testing is to verify that individual components are functioning correctly as individual components when connected to others in a printed circuit board assembly. Table 9.4 lists the main defects that can be identified using in-circuit testing.

Table 9.4 Main defects detectable using ICT

• Short circuits	• Solder bridges between tracks
• Missing components	• Components wrongly orientated
• Failed components	• Components incorrectly placed
• Components out of tolerance	• Missing/defective jumper connectors

Functional testing

In functional testing parts of the circuitry on the PCB, or in the system, are powered as they normally would be when the board is inserted in the system itself. They are excited with signals that they would normally receive to simulate normal operating modes and loaded with normal operational loads. Provision can also be included to simulate fault conditions.

Functional testing enables parametric faults to be identified. Table 9.5 lists the more common faults. Where product design has not been performed correctly and completely, functional testing also identifies design defects and tolerance problems. It should be stressed that most of the parametric faults are indicators of a poor design. Design defects and tolerance problems are signs of inadequate design.

Table 9.5 The more common parametric faults

• Noise	• Speed-related
• Distortion	• Leakage
• Drift	

Consider the circuit shown in Fig. 9.4 as an example. The circuit comprises an input filter, amplifier, level shifter, analogue to digital converter and logic buffer.

Functional testing is the testing of each of these functional blocks in isolation or in combination with other functional blocks.

Worked Example 9.1

Table 9.6 shows the specification for the circuit shown in Fig. 9.4. Use the specification to devise a set of tests that will verify the correct operation of the circuit.

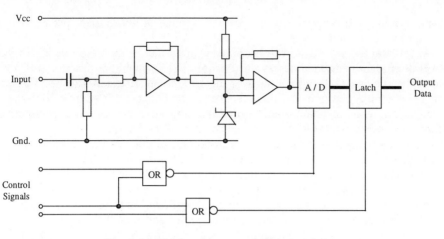

Fig. 9.4 Mixed analogues and digital circuit.

Table 9.6 Circuit specification

Input signal:	
Amplitude	2mV peak/peak
Frequency	10Hz to 15kHz
Input Frequency Cut-off	15kHz
Amplifier gain	1000
Zener Voltage	2.5V
A / D input voltage range	0.5V to 4.5V
A/ D quantisation	8 bits

Table 9.7 shows one possible set of tests that will test each functional block in turn to verify correct operation. The tests performed on each functional block are not exhaustive but verify that the block is functioning correctly.

Table 9.7 Possible set of tests

Test Number	Test Description
1	Test input filter for cut-off frequency
2	Test amplifier for gain
3(a)	Test level shifter for reference voltage level
3(b)	and output level
4	Test A / D for conversion
5	Test control logic for operation
6	Test latch for operation

This example is a very simple one but serves to illustrate the way in which a system can be divided into functional blocks and tests devised for each block.

Input stimuli and output measures can be applied at appropriate points in the circuit to test particular parts of the circuit.

At this stage it should start to become apparent that, if the functionality of the overall product is divided across one or more PCBs, such that functional blocks are split, the ease with which parts of the circuit can be tested will be affected. If, for example, the gain-defining feedback components of the amplifier stage were on a separate board then before the stage can be tested representative feedback component(s) will need to be added into the circuit.

To test the circuit functionally it is important to understand the operation of each functional block and how it interacts with the surrounding blocks. The time at which most is known about the detail of each block is during design. It is at this stage that the testing of each should be specified. Recall the part of chapter 3, system design, which covers 'top-down' design and 'bottom-up' build. During design, the system is functionally partitioned with specifications being developed for each functional block. During the design of each block, consideration should be given to how it will be tested. The tests should be specified in a test document which is used not only to verify the block design but also as a basis for building the block into the overall product, the 'building' of the system.

The general form of any electronic functional block is as shown in Fig. 9.5.

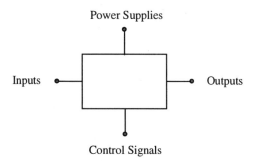

Fig. 9.5 General form of an electronic functional block.

A functional block might have a number of different modes of operation, each controlled by one or more control signals. For example, solid-state memory can be written to, or read from, using the same address and data lines depending on the states of a number of control lines. To verify fully the correct operation of a functional block all the different functional modes must be verified. This requires the tester to be able to take control over the control signals and put them into a state appropriate for the particular test. The circuit shown in Fig. 9.4 is such that the state of the logic ICs can be controlled easily by the tester. If, however, the control signals were connected to say, the output lines of a microprocessor which is also mounted on the same PCB, access and control over the lines might not be so straightforward. To test effectively the functional blocks might require special test code to be downloaded into the microprocessor or the microprocessor might need to be removed.

ATE - Automatic Test Equipment

Functional testing of PCBs is normally performed using a bed-of-nails fixture, as shown in Fig. 9.3, with the nails being connected through a suitable switch matrix, to a set of signal sources or measuring instruments. The whole test arrangement is controlled by a computer. Figure 9.6 shows the general ATE arrangement. Computer control makes the whole arrangement programmable and automatic. The general term for this is ATE.

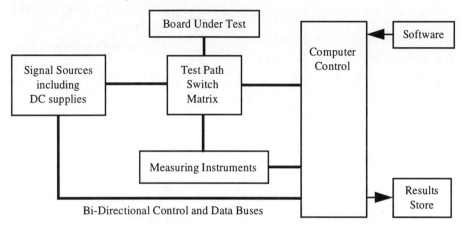

Fig. 9.6 General arrangement of functional ATE.

Using the set of tests devised in worked example 9.1, identify the measuring instruments and signal sources required to perform the tests required. Identify the number of test nodes and design the switch matrix required to produce an automatic tester for the circuit.

Worked Example 9.2

Table 9.7 shows the required test equipment and circuit nodes to allow the tests specified in Table 9.6 to be performed. The circuit nodes are shown in the annotated circuit diagram of Fig. 9.7.

Table 9.7 Test equipment requirement and connection nodes

| Test Number | Inputs | | | Outputs | |
	Signal	Node	Signal	Node
1	AC signal generator	a	AC voltmeter	b
2	AC signal generator	b	AC voltmeter	c
3(a)	none		DC voltmeter	d
3(b)	DC voltage	c	DC voltmeter	e
4	DC voltage	e	Logic analyser	f
5	DC voltage (3 off) (logic level)	h, j and k	DC voltmeter (logic level)	l and m
6	DC voltage DC voltage (3 off) (logic level)	e h, j and k	Logic analyser	g

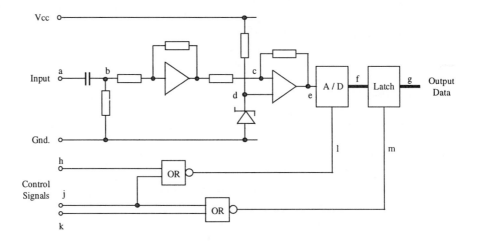

Fig. 9.7 Circuit diagram showing test nodes.

Given the test equipment and the nodes to which each piece of equipment must be connected, the switch matrix can be specified. Figure 9.8 shows the matrix for the specified set of tests.

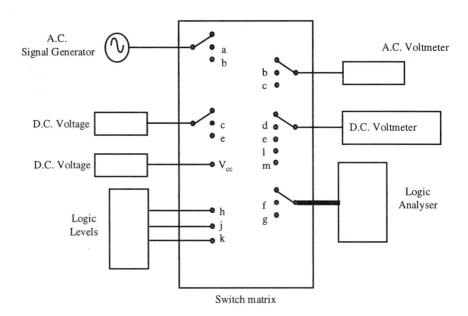

Fig. 9.8 Switch matrix design.

Note that each switch that routes a piece of test equipment to a set of nodes can also be routed to a blank node, that is, it can be isolated from the circuit. Assuming the switch matrix and all the pieces of test equipment are computer controllable, the entire arrangement forms a single piece of automatic test equipment.

Overall systems are frequently tested using ATE but not using a bed-of-nails fixture to access internal points. System testing, is by definition, the testing of the system by access only to its external interfaces. Special test connectors are usually made to connect the 'test path switch matrix' to the equipment under test interfaces. System test frequently requires operator intervention to put the equipment into various states and operate its controls to thoroughly exercise and verify correct operation.

The rigid rule of interfacing only to the external interfaces can be broken where necessary. Some equipment, especially those employing 'build in test' capabilities, will include circuitry which cannot be accessed from the external interfaces and which cannot therefore be verified. Access internally to force abnormal operation of the equipment is, therefore, necessary in such cases. Note that there is an additional cost associated with gaining access to the required internal points and of restoring the system to its fully closed state again afterwards.

As a final word on all the test methods described above it is worth briefly looking at Heisenberg's uncertainty principle which states:

> There is a principle of uncertainty as to the exact
> whereabouts of things on the atomic level which
> cannot be rendered exact due to the disturbances
> caused by the investigation itself.

This principle applies directly to electrical measurement. In all measurement cases the measuring instrument will interact with the circuit being tested and alter its performance. Even a simple AVO meter, when used to measure the voltage between two points in a circuit, will load the circuit (due to its internal resistance) and affect the voltage being measured. No instrument or measurement is completely immune from this and the best that can normally be achieved is that the interference is insignificant. The higher the frequency of the measurement the worse this situation gets. At microwave frequencies, that is, at alternating frequencies above a few hundred megahertz, high input impedance test equipment really becomes unrealistic. It is more usual to find test equipment with 50Ω or 75Ω input resistances. At these frequencies, no longer can test equipment simply be connected to a circuit without introducing a significant measurement uncertainty which must be taken into account when deciding whether a test result is indicating a pass or fail.

The design of effective test strategies

Having described the general approaches to testing, the next stage is to see how they can be employed to design an effective product test strategy.

The most complete approach to testing a product is to test every possible parameter at every possible opportunity. Assuming all the tests have been carefully designed and accurately performed, such an approach will guarantee to capture every fault at the earliest stage in the product's manufacturing cycle. The drawback of this all embracing test strategy is that it is very expensive. Every time a test has to be performed, the test must be set-up, the equipment under test connected to it, the test performed and the results recorded. If the cost of testing is directly attributed to the product, which it normally is, the unit manufacturing cost would be high and could make the product unsellable at an acceptable profit.

If, on the other hand, minimal testing is performed until the product is fully assembled, the failure rate may be excessively high. The cost of corrective action would certainly be very high. Figure 9.9 shows the generally accepted way the cost of test builds up through the manufacturing process.

An effective test strategy is one that identifies faults as early in the productive cycle as possible whilst maintaining an acceptable process yield and test and repair cost. The key additional inputs to this decision-making process are test equipment capability, process quality and component quality.

The ability of the test equipment to find faults is limited by the design of the circuitry being tested, by the sources and measuring instruments available and by the skill of the test equipment programmer. With modern 'bus-controllable' test equipment, special signal sources and measuring instruments can be linked into the tester usually to overcome the test equipment limitation.

The circuit design and the test software are best dealt with by the two teams working together during the circuit design phase. In this way many of the testability problems, addressed later in this chapter, can be overcome quickly and cheaply. Allowing designers to produce a design which is then passed to a test design engineer may lead to untestable circuits and the need for redesigns. An expensive solution to the testability problem.

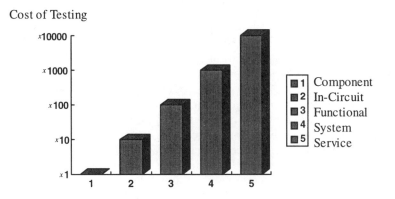

Fig. 9.9 Test cost build-up in production.

Functional testing identifies good and bad products. In the event of a failure being detected a repair is required. Figure 9.10 shows the general product flow cycle for failed items.

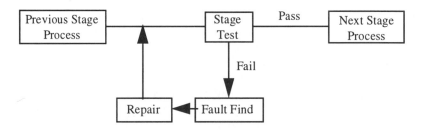

Fig. 9.10 General stage test and repair cycle.

The effectiveness of a test stage not only means the ability to identify good and bad products but embraces the ability to identify the specific defect or defects causing the failure. The fault finding part of the test cycle can be very complex. In the case of a circuit with many integrated functional blocks, many of which may have a number of different operational modes, the number of possible failure modes and effects can be very large. There are techniques such as Failure Modes and Effects Analysis (FMEA) or Fault Tree Analysis (FTA) which can be used to identify systematically failure mechanisms and their causes and thereby help to solve the fault diagnosis problem.

FMEA - Failure Mode and Effects Analysis.

FTA - Fault Tree Analysis.

Each identified failure can, through ATE programming, be automatically tested for in the event of a given functional block failure being identified. The drawback of this approach is the cost of programming all the failure mechanisms, some of which may never be experienced in the product's entire manufacturing life. This is, of course, only known with hindsight.

Figure 9.11 shows the general form of a test flow chart which includes fault diagnostics. The programming complexity of the test software rises dramatically with the complexity of the fault finding tests. As can be seen, for every test there can be a number of different fault finding tests depending on the different modes of operation of the circuit and of the complexity of the circuit being tested by each test. During the manufacturing life of the product some of these fault finding branches will, as has been said before, never be executed.

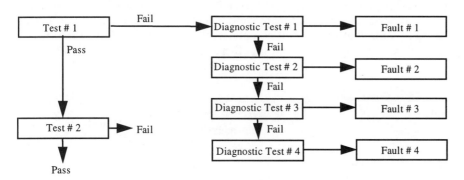

Fig. 9.11 Test flow chart with fault diagnostic branches.

An alternative strategy is to take failed boards back to in-circuit test first and then pass them to trained fault finders who could then spend time, perhaps in conjunction with an ATE, to identify the failure. The amount of time worth spending on the repair of a product or sub-assembly also has cost implications. If the value of the item, at the stage a failure is encountered is £C_f and the labour rate of a repairer is £C_r per hour as soon as C_f / C_r hours have been spent trying to find the fault the cost of building a new item, from scratch, has been incurred.

If a PCB costs £15.00 to build and test and the labour rate (including overheads) for a fault finder is £25.00 / hour, how long can the repairer spend trying to find the fault before it is cheaper to produce a new PCB?

Worked Example 9.3

$$Time = \frac{C_f}{C_r} = \frac{15}{25} = 0.6 hr = 36 \min$$

This monetary value equation becomes less important if there is difficulty in making additional items because of either parts availability or the time it would take. However, in the case of the continuous production of low value items it may prove economical to scrap the failures rather then waste time trying to find and correct faults.

The real issue in the test process is, therefore, one of quality. It is quality and the view on quality that will have the most pronounced impact on the test strategy.

Process quality and the test strategy

The need for the inspection and test quality gate is to identify defects introduced by the process itself. If the process can be made fault free, testing of every product would not be needed. Consider as an example the PCB assembly process depicted in Fig. 9.12

There are two types of faults possible in the assembled PCB, those due to defective parts (components or board) and those introduced by the assembly process. If it were known that there were no defects in the inputs, the test stage need verify only that the correct components have been inserted in the correct place with correct orientation and that there are no short or open circuits. The functionality of the components would not need to be verified.

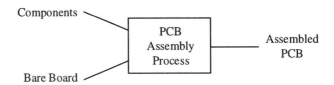

Fig. 9.12 PCB assembly process.

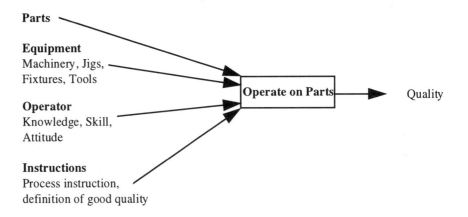

Fig. 9.13 Input factors to an activity.

Further, if there were sufficient confidence in the design that the risk of parametric defects was very low, only a very limited, if any, number of functional tests would be needed.

The confidence that raw materials (components and bare boards) are fault free can come from their being purchased only from sources that have an effective manufacturing and screening process. Confidence in the assembly process will only come from control over the quality influencing factors. Figure 9.13 shows all the inputs required to complete any activity. Poor quality in any one of these inputs will affect the quality of the activity output. All must be addressed if good quality is to be consistently achieved. The subject of quality control and assurance is explored in greater detail in chapter 10.

What are the input factors of the system test of a fully assembled personal stereo system? The system test is performed using manually operated test equipment on a fully packaged unit immediately before it is placed in its final packaging. Which of the factors could be altered to improve testing quality and whichcould be changed to improve product quality?

Worked Example 9.4

Using Fig. 9.13 as a framework, the following list summarises the input factors:

Parts	fully assembled player
Equipment	audio analyser, calibrated and fully functional
	source of music to test product
	headphone connector interface
	loudspeaker coupler
Operator	training
	testing skills
	attitude towards job and product
Instructions	test specification
	results sheet

The inputs that can be changed to improve the quality of the test stage are the operator and the instructions. The only input that can be changed to improve product quality is the product itself. This latter point is developed further in chapter 10.

When all the test stages have been identified and the appropriate test method for each decided, an overall test strategy can be defined. Figure 9.14 shows an example of such a strategy.

The impact of design on testability

The testability of a product, as has already been introduced, is affected by the way systems are partitioned. The physical placing of functional block boundaries and how well access is provided to inputs and outputs and the ability to put the functional block in the correct mode of operation are all design features. As a result, system partitioning that is sympathetic to test is essential for cost-effective product manufacture. In addition to the effect design has on the testability at system level, design also impacts the testability at the functional block level. Some functional blocks are inherently easier to test than others. In this section some of the practical problems of test will be considered and a basic testability checklist introduced.

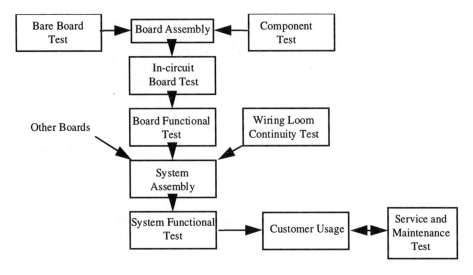

Fig. 9.14 Typical product test strategy.

Feedback and close loops

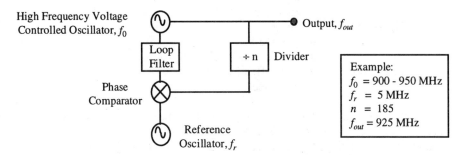

Fig. 9.15 Analogue feedback circuit.

Feedback is a common feature of both analogue and digital circuits. Figure 9.15 shows an example of an analogue feedback circuit in the form of a phase locked loop while Fig. 9.16 shows the outline of a logic feedback circuit.

In both these circuits it is not possible to test the functional blocks that make up the circuits on their own with the loops closed. The connection of the blocks is such that the output of any block influences, through the other blocks, its own input. The only solution to this, very common, test problem is to provide a means of breaking the loop. In the case of the phase locked loop this could be a removable link as shown in Fig. 9.17.

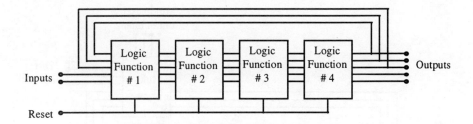

Fig. 9.16 Logic feedback circuit.

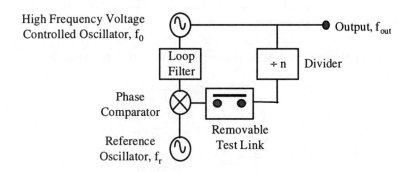

Fig. 9.17 Phase locked loop with removable link to open the loop.

The link requires operator intervention to open, test and then close the loop. Such intervention is acceptable where a small number of links are present, one in the case of the phase locked loop. In logic circuits however, whole bus connections (8, 16, or 32 wires) may well need to be isolated. In such cases it is preferable to introduce additional circuitry that will open the loop and allow the necessary circuit state control. Figure 9.18 shows how the circuit in Fig. 9.16 could be modified to make it testable.

Sequential logic

Another common testability problem occurs in sequential logic circuits where the circuit traverses a number of logic states in turn depending on the conditions of a number of inputs. Figure 9.19 shows an example of such a circuit.

The problem in this circuit arises through the absence of any control over the initialisation of the integrated circuits. The circuit cannot be put into a known start state from which successive states can be tested. In the example shown, simply removing the direct connection between the load and clear lines and VCC and allowing access to these lines may be sufficient to correct the problem.

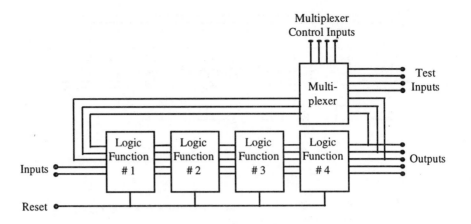

Fig. 9.18 Testable version of logic circuit with feedback.

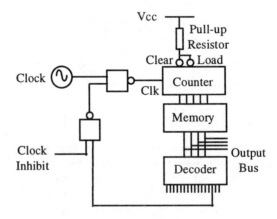

Fig. 9.19 Example of a sequential logic circuit.

General testability recommendations

Table 9.6 lists a few additional ways of making logic circuits more testable and forms the basis of a testability checklist.

Special problems with surface mount technology

The use of SMD's provides designers with a means of shrinking the product size or conversely increasing the functionality in a given physical space. With this advantage comes a serious disadvantage as far as test is concerned. Bed-of-nails board testing requires physical conductive areas with which to connect. The usual conductive pads used for surface mount components are just large enough for the components, adding extra pads for test probe connection reduces the area for components.

The only solution to this problem is to ensure the components are of high quality and the assembly process is high quality to avoid the need for in-circuit testing and go straight to functional test.

Table 9.6 A sample selection of logic testability recommendations

- Where logic signals that are edge sensitive, such as clock lines and flip-flop outputs, are interfaced with a board connector they should be buffered.
- Use IC sockets for complex integrated circuits wherever possible, i.e. microprocessors, UARTS, VLSI, ASICS, ROM- memory.
- Buffer any data buses that interface with a connector.
- De-couple every logic integrated circuit close to the integrated circuit.
- Do not leave unused logic pins open circuit; open circuit lines are prone to noise pickup.
- Use series current limiting resistors when using a logic gate to drive a transistor.
- Route test lines to spare pins on available connectors or to dedicated test connectors.

Process yield

No operation will produce perfect products all the time. Very high quality operations can come close to this ideal with defect rates in the few occasions per million of output. Zero, however, remains unachievable. The very fact that zero failures cannot be achieved means that, in complex processes involving a number of operations, there will be a financial loss to the organisation. Consider the production process shown in Fig. 9.14. Each test stage is the gate which identifies good and bad products. At each of these gates there will be a 'yield' where 'yield' is defined as the number of good products divided by the total number of products produced.

If the yield at each stage is y_i where i represents the stage reference number, for example as shown in Fig. 9.20, then an overall process yield model can be produced.

If 100 bare boards and 100 sets of components are supplied at the beginning of the process, the number of good bare boards at the output of the bare board test will be $100y_1$ (where y_1, the yield of process stage number one, is the decimal equivalent of the yield percentage, 0.95 for 95% for example). Similarly there will be $100y_2$ kits of components.

Since one bare board and one kit of parts is required to assemble one PCB the maximum number of boards that can be assembled will be the smaller of $100y_1$ and $100y_2$. The resulting number of assembled boards, $100y_b$, are subjected to an in-circuit test which has a yield of y_3. The number of good boards at this point becomes $(100y_b)y_3$ assuming that none of the failures are repaired and returned to the process. The assumption that all failures are put to one side will be assumed for the moment.

The next quality gate is board functional test with yield y_4. The number of good boards at the output of this gate is $100y_b y_3 y_4$ and so on. The resulting overall production to the customer, for the process shown in Fig. 9.20, ignoring service test and assuming no repairs, is called the 'first-time pass' yield and is given by:

$$Yield = y_6 y_f$$

where $\quad y_f$ = smaller of y_5 and $y_4.y_3.y_b$

and y_b = smaller of y_1 and y_2

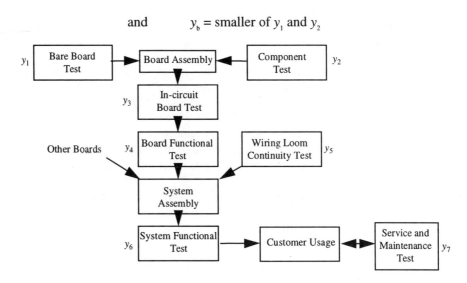

Fig. 9.20 Product test strategy with stage yields.

Worked Example 9.5

Given the yields of the production process steps shown in Fig. 9.20 as shown in Table 9.7 determine the overall first-pass yield. If the functional test yield could be improved to 95%, what impact would the change have on the overall first-pass yield?

Using the yield model developed above the percentage yield at each stage can be determined. Figure 9.21 shows the overall process model with stage yields shown. Where two constituent parts come together the combined yield is the smaller of the two constituent parts.

The first stage is board assembly which takes bare boards from bare board test (95% yield) and components from component test (95% yield). These two yields are the same so the combined yield is also 95%. The assembled boards are passed to in-circuit test which has an individual yield of 85%. Only 85% of the number of boards tested, 95% of the initial batch, will pass. The overall yield is therefore 0.95 x 0.85 = 0.81 or 81%.

Table 9.7 Process yields

Stage	Description	Yield
y1	Bare board test	95%
y2	Component test	95%
y3	In-circuit board test	85%
y4	Board functional test	85%
y5	Wiring loom continuity test	70%
y6	System functional test	95%

81% of the original batch of boards are passed to functional test, a stage with an individual yield of 85%. The number of good boards that emerge from functional test is therefore 85% of the 81% that entered the process, 0.85 x 0.81 = 0.69 or 69%.

These 69% are combined with wiring looms to make overall systems. The yield of wiring looms is 70%. Assuming the same number of wiring looms as original bare boards and kits of components, there will be 70% available for system assembly. The smaller of good functional boards and wiring looms is 69% so this number of overall systems can therefore be assembled.

System test has a yield of 95% which means 95% of the 69% will pass. The number of good systems and hence the overall first time pass rate will be 65%.

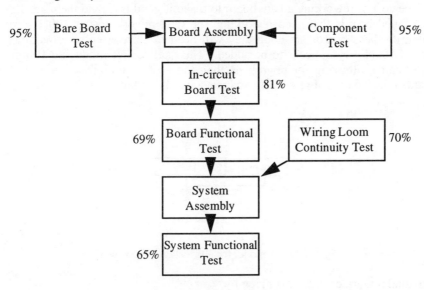

Fig. 9.21 Process yield model.

If the board functional test yield is improved to 95% the number of functionally working boards will increase to 77%. However, there are only 70% of the wiring looms available. The improvement to the overall process resulting from an improvement in the board functional test yield is therefore only 1%.

Having developed a yield model assuming all failed products are put to one side a very poor overall yield usually results. A more realistic scenario is for failed products to be reworked and returned to the main product stream. The production yield where all failures are reworked until they are good will be 100%. In such a case overall yield becomes meaningless and the overall cost becomes the critical measure.

BOM - Bill of Materials.

The overall cost of production can be introduced into the yield model by using information from the product Bill of Materials (BOM). The BOM is introduced in chapter 4. To introduce costs the value of each process needs to be attributable through the yield model. If, for example, the cost of the bare board in the above example is C_b and the cost of testing each bare board is C_{bt} the total cost of the bare boards at the end of test is $100(C_b + C_{bt})$. The yield at this stage is y_1 so the total number of good boards is $100y_1$. The effective cost,

$C_{b(eff)}$ of each good board is a total cost divided by the number of good boards. Equation for this is given below.

$$C_{b(eff)} = 100 \frac{(C_b + C_{bt})}{100 y_1} = \frac{(C_b + C_{bt})}{y_1}$$

This approach can be applied at each stage to produce an overall cost model for the overall product process and results in an effective cost for each good product. This approach again assumes that all failures are put to one side. To develop the model to allow for the return of reworked failed parts the cost of rework needs to be allowed for.

If the cost of reworking a bare board to make it good is C_r and there are $100(1 - y_i)$ failed boards that need reworking, the total rework cost is $100(1 - y_i)C_r$. To verify these boards are good they will need to be retested so an additional cost of $100(1 - y_i)C_{bt}$ needs to be added. The total cost of producing 100 good bare boards, allowing for rework, is then the cost of initially testing all 100 boards plus the cost of reworking and retesting all the failed boards, as shown in Fig. 9.22.

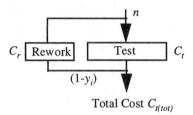

Fig. 9.22 Cost model for a test stage with rework.

The total rework cost, $C_{r(tot)}$ is given by:

$$C_{r(tot)} = C_r(1 - y_1)n$$

The total retest cost, $C_{tr(tot)}$ is given by:

$$C_{tr(tot)} = C_t(1 - y_1)n$$

The total cost of the rework, including retest, C_{rework}, is given by:

$$C_{rework} = (C_r + C_t)(1 - y_1)n$$

A spreadsheet is an ideal tool to create cost models of the type shown in this chapter. Hence the total cost, C_{total}, of producing n good products allowing for rework is given by:

$$C_{total} = nC_t + (C_r + C_t)(1 - y_1)n$$

The overall cost to produce a product allowing for reworking of failures at each stage can now be developed using this approach.

The final aspect of test to be considered is the impact adjustable and select-on-test, SOT, components have on the production process. Adjustable components include variable resistors, capacitors and inductors. They are typically used to enable the alignment of critical circuits to achieve a required performance in the presence of circuits with uncontrollable tolerances or component variability. Example of such circuits are radio receiver intermediate frequency amplifier chains and audio power amplifier output stages.

Select-on-test components serve a similar purpose except that, whereas an adjustable component is continuously variable, SOT involves the choice of a small number of fixed value components. The component value that yields an acceptable circuit performance is fitted to the product. The process involved, in either case, is as shown in Fig. 9.23.

It should be noted that a test engineer is involved in the make adjustment and measure performance loop. The tester is therefore occupied for the entire set-up period. This can be a very expensive production stage, often the most expensive stage in the entire test process. The avoidance of adjustable and SOT components is an essential design and development task if production cost is to be minimised.

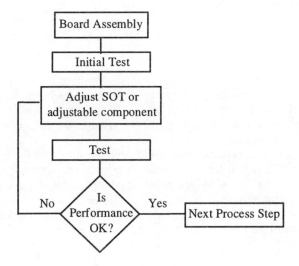

Fig. 9.23 Circuit alignment using adjustable or SOT components.

Summary

In this chapter the importance of the inspection and test quality gates of the production process have been examined. From the outset the importance of a well planned and constructed inspection and test strategies for new products cannot be overstated. The whole object of production is to make profit for the host organisation. Producing a product or parts of a product that will be expensive to inspect and test is a recipe for poor profitability. This chapter has examined the basic methods of testing electronic products from the simplest continuity checks to the most complex system testing. The approaches range from the most basic hand-held, manual test equipment to the sophisticated automatic test equipment. In all cases the basic fundamentals of design for test apply.

The general approach to designing effective test strategies is described along with a financial picture of the effect of getting the strategy wrong. Cost is then further explored through the development of an overall product process yield model. The financial impact of test and repair is included to make the model of practical use.

A number of common testability problem areas are introduced as a starting point for the development of a testability checklist. Checklists are an effective tool in the achievement of product development quality.

Any manufacture that sells products into the market without testing, unless there is very high confidence in the production process, or it is a very simple product such as an individual resistor, is taking a very great risk. Any manufacturer that tests every parameter of every product built and at every stage in the production process, has a very expensive product. These two scenarios clearly lie at opposite ends of the range of possible testing strategies. Neither is the best strategy in the general case. The optimal strategy lies somewhere in the middle. It is the role of the design and development team to find the optimal strategy for each new product and to ensure the design and development activities produce a product that fits this strategy. As with all the other 'Ilities, leaving design for test until the end is too late and will result in financial losses to the organisation.

Problems

9.1 Derive a cost model which allows for adjustable or SOT components.
9.2 The cost of producing an assembled product is £76.00 including £4.00 test. If the first time yield at test is 85% and the failed units are all reworked at an average cost of £12.00, what is the effective cost of each product to the organisation?
9.3 What signs of design for test could you see on a printed circuit board? For the product you have analysed to answer problem 6.4, which of the signs are evident? Can you infer anything about the testability of the printed circuit board?
9.4 Expand the possible set of test shown in Table 9.7 to produce a full test specification for the circuit shown in Fig. 9.4.

Quality in the design process $\quad$ 10

At the end of this chapter you will be able to:

- Take a product through the basic product development process
- Specify the differences between sequential and concurrent product development
- Specify the differences between product and process development
- Evaluate the risks associated with product development

We consider quality to be the glue which holds the product development process together. We do not agree with the popular notion that quality is the policeman of the company quality, nor do we subscribe to the view that a quality team is required to ensure quality. Both of these ideas are out of date and can be replaced with a much more effective way of ensuring quality. For product development to be really cost-effective and a generator of products that will provide the company with a sustainable competitive advantage, a very broad view of quality is needed. Quality must be introduced from day one of the product design and development process and be central to every activity and task undertaken. The aim of this chapter is to demonstrate how quality can be introduced to the product development process and used as a vehicle to make improvements, cut costs and improve productivity. These aims might sound grand and too good to be true; they are, however, based on the simple premise of 'do it once and do it right' and the use of a few tools.

The chapter starts with a definition of the frequently used terms relating to quality, in particular Quality Control and Quality Assurance.

Quality control

One possible definition of Quality Control is the inspection, analysis, and action applied to a process step to enable the overall quality of the product to be estimated and to determine what, if any, changes must be made to achieve or maintain the required level of control.

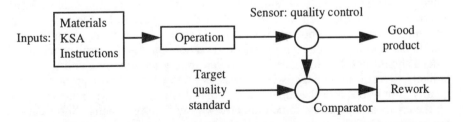

Fig. 10.1 Quality control as a process.

Quality Control is based on inspection, analysis and action. It is a process that starts after something has been done. Figure 10.1 shows Quality Control as a process in a control problem format.

There are a number of important points that result from the understanding of what Quality Control is. Firstly Quality Control is a post-event action, it occurs after the event, the activity or the process step. In this sense it is a reactive process. Consider as an illustration the following 'game'.

Look at the text in the box for about 15 seconds and count the number of f's.

> Finished files are the result of years of scientific study combined with the experience of many years

If this text is the output of the text-generating process step, who dictates the quality of the output? The answer is the person that did the generating. The 'doer' of the task. What you have done in counting the number of f's is to inspect somebody else's work and look to see if you could spot any errors. There are six f's in the text, it is the f's in the word 'of' that are most frequently missed.

In the case of the inspection of the real output of a process step, analysis and corrective action might well be required, these being the second and third parts of the Quality Control definition. In such cases the corrections may be made by the original 'doer' or by another person assigned the task of rework, possibly somebody trained in fault diagnosis. In the latter case the 'reworker' is not the 'doer'. Is there therefore any feedback around the control loop at all? Unless there is some form of feedback the answer is no, the system is operating open loop. The doer does not even know he or she is producing defective products and rework costs increase. Any significant amount of rework would trigger an oral, if not a written, communication thereby closing the loop. In this case the analysis and action parts of the definition would be applied and the process would again be bought under control.

NVA activities - non-value adding activities.

The final point worth drawing out of Quality Control is that, since it does not contribute to any output that is deemed to be good, it is a non-value adding activity. It catches only bad product and results in more value, in the form of labour hours and possibly material costs, being expended to make bad products good. The logical extension to this is that all Quality Control activities are non-value adding and should be stopped along with all other non-value adding activities. If this approach were to be adopted it is likely to lead to a decline in the reputation of the company, especially if Quality Control were identifying a significant number of bad products. In practice Quality Control cannot, and indeed should not, be eliminated. However, to rely entirely on Quality Control is likely to result in an expensive process and one which almost promotes poor quality simply because the 'doers' know that there is somebody who will pick up the errors and possibly somebody else who will correct them. Short cuts in the execution of the process, which make life easier for the 'doer', but may compromise quality, are encouraged. There has to be a better way of ensuring that good quality products go out of the door and the company has some profit at the end of the day. There is, and the answer lies in Quality Assurance.

A manager drafts a letter to another company. The letter is checked and corrections made by her secretary before the manager signs the letter ready for despatch. What are the non-value adding activities within this process?

Table 10.1 summarises exactly what happens in the process and separates the tasks into action, wait and transfer type of categories.

Table 10.1 Identifying non-value adding activities

Activity	Action	Transfer	Wait	NVA ?
Draft letter	✓			
Pass to secretary		✓		✓
Await typing			✓	✓
Type	✓			
Pass to manager for checking		✓		✓
Check	✓			✓
Pass to secretary		✓		✓
Await correcting			✓	✓
Correct	✓			✓
Pass to manager for signing		✓		✓
Sign	✓			
Pass to secretary for despatch		✓		✓
Await despatch			✓	✓
Despatch	✓			

The above process may seem laboured and perhaps old-fashioned, it is however, not unrealistic. The process serves to indicate the types of activities that take place and those which are non-value adding.

Quality assurance

In 1979, when the British Standard for Quality Assurance was produced, the definition for Quality Assurance was:

> The totality of features and characteristics of a
> Product or Service that bears on its ability to
> satisfy stated or implied needs.

The definition was drafted very carefully using specific words. The 'totality of features and characteristics' covers everything in the product or service as far as it relates to producing the desired end product. This includes meeting the basic specification, paying attention to all the 'Ilities', meeting documentation requirements, doing things to the agreed company procedures, and all the other factors that go together to form the broad product requirement. We saw, in chapter 3 the range of factors which need to be considered, and why they need to be considered, in preparing a complete product specification. The omission of any of the factors has the scope of resulting in confusion later in the design process and the need for rework to correct any design weaknesses that might result.

The definition goes on to bring in the 'ability to satisfy stated or implied needs'. This is usually taken to mean of the customer. But which customer? The traditional view of the customer is that it is the ultimate user of the product or recipient of the service provided. The end user customer is really only the last person in what can sometimes be, a long chain of people involved in the product or service. Consider for example, the designer of an interface card for a personal computer. The designer designs the board and perhaps goes as far as laying out the printed circuit board. Somebody else takes the layout information and manufactures the bare board; somebody else might take the component information and assemble the board; another person might take the assembled board and test it; yet another person might take the tested board and pack it together with manual or whatever ready for distribution to the ultimate customer. It is quite possible that the product might also be stored as finished goods stock for a while before being distributed. The packaged board is then sold through a distributor who sells it on to a shop for display and ultimate sale to the end user. Who is the customer in this chain? It is no longer adequate to say the end user, since everybody is the customer of the previous stage and each in turn is the supplier to the next stage.

It was Ishikawa who first recognised that the customer is the next stage in the process. Taking his definition and applying it in a general sense to a process step, the result is that each output of each step might have a different customer. Paperwork going to one person, information to another, hardware to a third and so on. Each next person in line is a customer and each deserves treatment as such.

Broadly then the customers can be divided into two groups, those internal to the organisation and those external to it. The boundary between these two groups cannot be generalised because it is very much dependant on the nature of the product or service, who the end customer is, and on the extent of the organisation.

Internal

Taking the internal customer to be any person within the organisation who receives any output from the process step in question there is scope for a large number of customers each with different needs and expectations. The definition of Quality Assurance includes the 'totality of features and characteristics'. To the internal customer this might cover drawings, reports, hardware, verbal communications, and so on. Everything related to the item in question.

Using this definition of customer, nothing within the organisation should ever be produced without a customer. What is more, the definition goes on to say that it is necessary to satisfy both the 'stated and implied' needs of the customer. Stated needs are relatively clear. They are written down or verbally communicated. Satisfying the expected needs is perhaps more difficult because they are much less tangible.

Consider, as an example, the internal process of supply and receipt of financial information used to manage a technical group. The information is produced by the finance department and issued to the technical managers. It is often the case that the information is produced automatically by a computerised system as a 'report' on spend for the period shown against budget with variances and over- or under-spend shown. A common practice is for every cost line item to be shown irrespective of value, including zeros. This can result in a

222

considerable amount of paper with a vast array of numbers. What is the objective of the output (of the financial department) and what is the impact on the customer (the technical manager)? The output is clearly to provide information to allow the technical managers to review progress and manage their area. The effect on the technical manager can be extremely demotivating. Pages of figures, many close to or actually zero, with the odd line of significant information. The result, another communication from the finance department that requires too much time to extract the information needed to be of real value. Filed! Is the customer-supplier relationship working? Well, perhaps it could be better. If the loop is closed and the information needs and expectations communicated a better information flow could result and satisfaction improved. Perhaps this example is a little cynical but it is cynicism borne from experience not imagination!

External

Recall that external customers are those who receive anything related to the product or service who are outside the organisation. This very broad ranging definition includes the end customer, naturally, plus all stages in the output logistics chain. But is that all? Here again the full extent of the external customers depends on the nature of the product or service being offered. It is possible, in the case of a car as the product for example, that the public at large are a potential customer because they could receive the benefit of an unsafe or dangerous product. Whilst some might argue that this is stretching the definition of customer too far, few would argue against the need to ensure the product or service offered is safe and as free of hazards as can reasonably be achieved. In chapter 3 the idea of 'reasonable user abuse' was introduced, customers have expectations that go beyond what might be stated.

An external group that merits special attention are the suppliers to the organisation. Suppliers are the providers of raw materials and parts to allow the organisation to make its products or offer its services. Suppliers are, however, also customers in that they need to receive information to enable them to produce their outputs to feed the organisation.

Figure 10.2 shows the traditional way organisations treat suppliers. A part is designed and drawn. The drawings are despatched to the customer for quoting. Quotes are received and considered, an order placed and finally parts are delivered. The parts are inspected at goods inwards inspection and accepted or rejected depending on their quality. This approach is very much the Quality Control approach to supplier dealings. The supplier is kept at arm's length until the part is designed and drawn. If the supplier has any comments on the drawings a meeting, or some other form of communication, will be arranged between the organisation's designers and the supplier's technical experts. If the comments are accepted the organisation will take the drawings away, modify them and supply a new, up-issued set for reconsideration. Ultimately, agreement will be reached allowing a sensible quotation to be produced. The time taken to go around this loop is project time. If the design and fabrication of the part is on the critical path of the project, all time taken iterating the drawings to be acceptable to both parties is time wasted. Remember any corrective actions are non-value adding tasks and hence only cost money, they add nothing. There is a better way to achieving the objective, that of an acceptable set of drawings from which a quotation can be raised. This better method is based on the Quality Assurance approach rather than the Quality Control one.

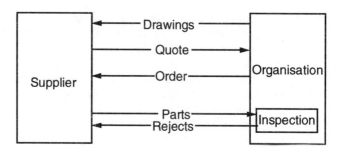

Fig. 10.2 Traditional sequence of events in dealing with suppliers.

The Quality Assurance approach is somewhat different. Given that the objective of Quality Assurance is to meet stated and implied needs, the Quality Assurance approach is based on supplier involvement throughout the process. If the supplier is invited to come and discuss the problem, that of the need to fabricate a part for the product, at the start of the design exercise, any comments the supplier has can be introduced straight away. The involvement gives the suppliers the opportunity to declare their needs and facilitates a negotiation on their achievement. There are a number of reasons why supplier involvement is not only healthy from a contract fulfilment point of view but also from a technical point of view. It is very likely that the supplier has 'expert' knowledge in the items being supplied. This knowledge, if bought into play at the design stage can save costly redesign and modifications downstream in the design process. The skills of the supplier can also be used, in most cases free of charge, for comments on ways of making the part easier, which will result in a lower part cost or higher part quality; or to add improvements that may make subsequent assembly easier and hence cheaper or of better quality.

In short where are the disadvantages of involving specific skills very early on in the design process? Clearly a degree of sensibility needs to be adopted in the involvement of suppliers. It would, for instance, be of little benefit in involving the supplier of a penny resistor at the design stage. The benefits of involving a tooled part manufacturer, perhaps a specially shaped case or casting, however, should not be underestimated. Advice on cost saving, ease of manufacture, strength, ease of handling or packaging, to name a few, can all result from advice from these free 'experts'.

The final, potential advantage of involving a supplier early is that they may be able to supply hardware or software appropriate for their process, that makes the relevant part of the design easier or more efficient. An example is the provision of dedicated design software for Application Specific Integrated Circuits. The chip manufacturer make their money through the supply of chips so they may supply the design software, or libraries for common computer aided design packages to enable better product designs with their chips.

ASIC - Application Specific Integrated Circuit.
An ASIC is an integrated circuit designed to carry out a specific function required by the company. It can contain analogue, digital circuitry or a combination of the two.

Quality assurance and customer needs

Given the broad introductory description of Quality Assurance, how can the quality of a product be assured? A step down this path is to aim to achieve customer satisfaction in the broad sense introduced above. Whilst this is easy to say it is less easy to achieve in practice and requires a significant initial and ongoing effort.

As we saw in chapter 2, the idea for a new product can come from a number of different sources. Since each source has a different range of customers there is a wide range of possible customers. Some products will be sold to the public at large, others to specific people or organisations. To complicate matters further, customers needs and expectations change. Consider for example, the personal computer market. In the space of a couple of years in the early 1990s, at the time when the IBM PC and its clones were based on the 486 microprocessor expectations in the memory, speed and storage capacity of the basic machine was increasing almost daily. The processor speed increased from the 25MHz version, very rapidly up to the 100MHz version. The internal RAM storage rose from 4Mbyte up to 16Mbyte and above. Hard disk storage capacity rose from the order of 100Mbyte to multi-hundreds and even into the Gbyte range. At the same time the range of peripherals that could be fitted started to increase. CD-ROM drives were commonplace as were sound cards, and so on.

The drive for increased power in PCs was coming, not only from the software suppliers, whose software was becoming more and more powerful, requiring more and more memory and power; but also from advertising. Big was seen as beautiful. A status symbol even. Owners boasted of the power and size of their PC and of the peripherals they had fitted.

What does this have to do with quality? The answer lies in what was happening to customer expectations during this time. Quite simply customer expectations were changing. Irrespective of whether the owner wanted to see rotating three dimensional solid model images of objects or full screen motion pictures or just to do relatively straightforward word-processing, the expectation of the hardware was rising. Kano offers a model for customer satisfaction based on the degree of achievement of customer expectations. Figure 10.3 shows the model.

The model tells us that there are three categories of performance related characteristics. The basic performance aspects are those that the customer will take for granted. Examples of basic requirements are, for a PC: that it works reliably without crashing; that it has a floppy drive to enable software to be loaded; and so on. If a PC manufacturer produces a PC that does not fully proved the customer with ALL of these basic performance aspects, the customer will be unhappy. As far as these characteristics are concerned the supplier can do no more than meet the requirements. He cannot gain customer satisfaction through them.

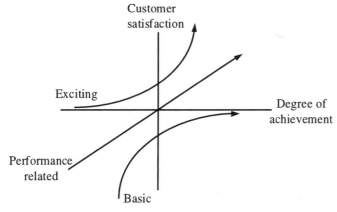

Fig. 10.3 The Kano model of customer satisfaction.

The second set of performance characteristics are the performance-related characteristics. The speed of the microprocessor; the amount of RAM storage; the size of the internal hard disk; and so on. In this category of characteristics the customer has a certain level of expectation and would be satisfied if the supplied PC meets that expectation. If performance is less then satisfaction will fall. However customer satisfaction can be won by supplying more than was expected.

The third category of characteristics are what Kano calls the 'wow' factors, the factors that immediately give customers satisfaction. The inclusion of a free CD-ROM; the inclusion of a voice recognition system; and so on. All these are exciting and novel and give the customer satisfaction in ownership.

The notion of customer satisfaction is a useful one for new product development in general. In the formation of a new product specification it is useful to try to define the current base level of customer expectation. Once established it needs to be monitored to ensure the product, as it is being developed, stays in tune to this base level and, hopefully, provides a few 'wow' factors as well.

Translating customer needs into specifications

One of the difficulties in building customer needs and expectations into product specifications lies in the language used. The customer, especially the general public, use terminology such as 'it needs to be quiet' or 'it should be soft to the touch'. The design and development team are more familiar with quantifiable terms such as dBA or surface roughness.

Quality functional deployment

QFD - Quality Functional Deployment was developed in Japan by Shigeru Mizuno and Yoji Akao in the late 1960s.

Quality functional deployment, QFD, is a methodology for translating customer needs into actions that can be taken throughout the organisation to assure the quality of the end product and to assure that the customer receives a product that fully meets their needs. At its simplest level it is a two stage process, the first stage being the translation of customer needs into product features and characteristics that can be monitored and controlled. The second stage is the deployment of activities required to assure that the required product quality is achieved.

The two stages of applying QFD are:

Stage 1	Step 1	State customer needs and expectations
	Step 2	Translate customer needs and expectations into product features and characteristics
Stage 2	Step 3	Translate product features and characteristics into required characteristics of parts
	Step 4	Translate product features and charcteristics into key process characteristics
	Step 5	Translate product features and characteristics into control methods

Step 1 is the analysis of the potential market and involves determining customer needs and expectations. To be of real value the needs and expectations must be ranked in order of importance. The usual technique for determining needs and expectations is through market surveys or sample questionnaires. Clearly, if the customer can be more specifically identified rather than simply as the general public, a more tailored and accurate set of needs and expectations can be obtained. As part of this step the competitive products can also be analysed to see how they satisfy customer needs and expectations. Competitive product analysis, the process of obtaining a competitive product and analysing its composition and methods used in construction, is a key tool in competitive analysis. An analysis of the competitive products can provide valuable information about any 'wow' factors being offered, the scope for future cost reductions, the scope for product development and so on.

Once the output of the customer and competitive product analyses are complete, the key factors that will determine the success of the product for the organisation can be determined. In the case of a new car for example, fuel economy and cost may be the two most important factors. These would be the key success factors.

Step 2 is the translation of customer needs and expectations into product characteristics and features. This translation will result in a set of relationships between needs and expectations and product features which are best described using a matrix in which customer needs form the rows and product features the columns, as shown in Fig. 10.4.

	Prod uct feature #1	Prod uct feature #2	Prod uct feature #3	Prod uct feature #4	....
Customer need or expectation #1	1		5		
Customer need or expectation #2		5			
Customer need or expectation #3					
Customer need or expectation #4					
....					

Fig. 10.4 Customer needs and product feature relationship matrix.

A hierarchical approach to both the needs and features can be adopted to help to clarify the overall picture. For example a set of needs could relate to product durability which would embrace case finish, labelling methodology, buttons, switches and so on. In each cell of the matrix a code representing the strength of the relationship would be entered. For example a '1'could be used to denote a strong relationship and a '5' no relationship at all. For example, there is a strong relationship between durability and case finish, resulting in a 1 in the appropriate cell, whereas there is only a loose relationship between durability and weight, resulting in perhaps a 4 or 5.

The relationship matrix can be extended to show the interrelationship between product features by adding a triangular section to the top of the matrix, as shown in Fig. 10.5.

Step 3 is the translation of product features and characteristics into features and characteristics of the parts or sub-assemblies that make up the product. This step can again be described in matrix form with the contents of each matrix cell representing the strength of the relationship. Figure 10.6 shows an example matrix for the ELT(S).

The final two steps in the QFD process are concerned with how the product will be made and how the delivery of the required customer needs and expectations can be assured. In step 4 the production processes that will be employed to produce the product are related to product features and characteristics, again through a matrix. As before the relationship between feature and process are shown by the contents of the corresponding cell. Figure 10.7 shows an example for the ELT(S).

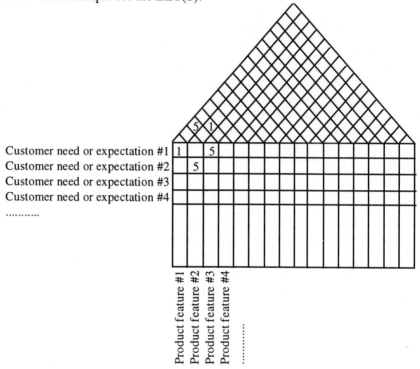

Fig. 10.5 Relationship matrix showing product feature interrelationships.

	Case body	Cast top	Antenna	Battery pack	Electronics pack	Switch mechanism
Robust case	1	1	5			4
Lightweight	1	1	2	1	2	2
Easy to activate						1
Immune to false activation					2	1
Reliable operation					1	2
Low cost	1	1	1	1	1	1
Meets statutory requirements	2	2	1	1	1	2

Fig. 10.6 Product to piecepart relationship matrix for the ELT(S).

Finally, in step 5 the control measures that can be employed to verify quality are determined. The control features can be added to the product feature to key process matrix as shown in Fig. 10.8.

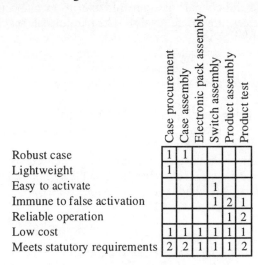

Fig. 10.7 Product feature to key process relationship matrix for the ELT(S).

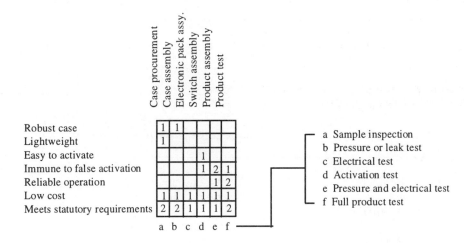

Fig. 10.8 The addition of control methods to the product/process matrix.

The most important point to note about QFD is that all five of the above stages should be planned before any design is carried out. That is to say the effort is put in up-front to build quality into the product and the process from the outset. QFD provides a means of making customer needs and expectations visible to all within the organisatiaon irrespective of what part they play in the overall process of product design, development and manufacture. Providing this visibility helps to ensure that all actions taken are orientated towards the goal of satisfying customer needs and expectations.

Assignment matrices

The second useful tool in the translation of customer needs into specifications is the physical and functional assignment matrix introduced in chapter 3. Assignment matrices are more useful when a formal specification for the product is available. They are used to map specification requirements onto product modules and functional blocks to ensure all aspects of the specification are addressed.

Assignment matrices are particularly useful when:

- the product is being developed to meet more than one set of standards as is often the case in a product being developed for an international or world-wide market;
- there are a number of different documents referenced by the main product specification, such as is the case in products that refer to British and European Standards in which one standard often references aspects of others.

Checklists

Checklists are a third method of building quality into the formation of a specification. In the absence of a supplied set of specifications, reference can be made to an organisational checklist of aspects that need to be included in the specification.

Worked Example 10.2

Produce a general checklist for aspects that should be included in a product specification.

With reference to the contents of the chapters in this book, the checklist shown in Table 10.2 can be drawn up

Table 10.2 Checklist of product characteristics for product specification

Product	Inputs, outputs, functional characteristics
Aesthetics	User controls, displays Power supply connections
Physical environment	Thermal, vibration, humidity, Contaminants, Survival, Electromagnetic compatibility
Packaging and labelling	Product packaging, product labelling, Quality labelling, transit packaging
Reliability	
Costs	Unit production cost
Production	Volume to be produced Maximum rate of production

Each line item can be expanded with additional details given in the appropriate chapter to further develop the checklist. The three approaches described in this section, Quality Functional Deployment, assignment matrices and design review checklists provide a choice of tool depending on the available information. Quality Functional Deployment is a general tool that is very appropriate where there are multiple customers whose needs and expectations are not well stated. Assignment matrices are useful where the specification is well stated and may be complicated by a multiplicity of documents that need to be addressed. Finally checklists are useful where no documents are available and where there is little guidance as to what should go into the specification.

Quality in the design process

The ability to manufacture a quality product in volume; for the product to meet customer needs and expectations and for the company to make a profit at the end of the process, requires a very effective product design and development process. This section considers some approaches that can be used to build quality into the system, thereby avoiding the need to inspect for it at the end.

Concurrent design

In chapter 1 the generic product development process was introduced. The process shown is essentially a cascade of stages through which the product must pass in being transformed from an idea to a manufacturable product. Whilst the activities are drawn as sequential it does not imply that they should be performed in sequence. Products that are developed by discrete groups of people with information being passed from one group to another as the project stage comes to an end is called over-the-wall development. One stage of the product is completed and passed over an organisational wall to the next group. The disadvantages of this approach are many and include:

- the unambiguous definition of what will be handed over;
- the need to gain agreement that the project has reached the stage that it is claimed to have reached;
- the establishment of a procedure for dealing with problems that arise after the handover.

For the reasons above, the over-the-wall approach is slow and problematic from a project managerial point of view and regularly requires design iterations to overcome shortcomings in the work of the previous stage.

A better approach, and the approach used throughout this book, is that of the involvement of all groups from the project outset. The name given to this approach is concurrent engineering or alternatively simultaneous engineering. The basis of this approach is that tasks are performed in parallel rather than in series. When the project team is formed at the beginning of the project, representatives of design and development are joined by representatives from production, finance, quality, marketing and sometimes human resources. This multi-disciplinary team has all the skills necessary to ensure that any design and development activity is carried out in such a way that every relevant aspect is addressed from the outset. For example, in the design of the printed circuit board for the ELT(S) the electronic designer was responsible for the circuit design and the selection of component values. The representative from production, in consultation with the purchasing department, assisted in the selection of the component packages and the supplier. In this way components were able to be purchased from the existing preferred suppliers and the component packages were compatible with the planned production process for the new product which had been agreed at the outset.

The production representative, in consultation with the company test engineers also injected test needs in the form of special test points once the circuit diagram was designed. The finance representative assisted in the creation of a developmental Bill of Materials and in the financial tracking of the project. The quality representative ensured that the components were of adequate quality and were appropriate for the environment the beacon was to be used in. The quality representative also chaired design reviews which were held periodically through the design and development phase. Finally the mechanical design representative was responsible for defining the shape and size of the printed circuit board to ensure that once populated it would slide into the beacon cases and that there would be sufficient clearance above the components and below the track side of the board.

In addition to their individual roles the team were responsible for carrying out a risk analysis, a reliability analysis and an assessment of the suitability of the product for its required environment.

Risk analysis

There are many risks associated with new product development. There is the risk that the product will prove to be unsafe for use by customers, there is the risk that the product will not sell and hence lose money and there is the risk that customers needs will have changed by the time the product development is complete and the product is launched. These and the many other risks need to be borne in mind as part of the product development process. The ELT(S) are a safety product. It is a radio transmitter and is activated in an emergency situation and it must work first time. The assessment of the risk of the product failing to operate and hence putting the carrier's life at risk was, therefore, of paramount importance. A very detailed Fault Tree Analysis was carried out on the product early in the design phase. The objective of the analysis was to identify the major failure or failures that could result in the product not working correctly when activated. These failures were analysed to the point where electronic or mechanical symptoms could be identified. The product documentation was then annotated with comments which specifically addressed these symptoms. FTA is explained below and the worked example illustrates how one of the annotations was arrived at.

Fault tree analysis

The objective of FTA is to identify all the product faults that will result in customer dissatisfaction or problems and analyse these problems from a product point of view. The types of customer problems as shown in Table 10.3.

Table 10.3 Types of customer problems

• death	• inconvenience
• serious physical injury	• serious annoyance
• injury	• annoyance
• serious inconvenience	• slight inconvenience

The problem types are laid out in Table 10.3 are in descending order of severity and in descending order of impact they may have, after the event, on the organisation.

The process followed in carrying out a fault tree analysis is shown in Table 10.4.

Table 10.4 Fault tree analysis process

Step 1	Identify the significant failures as seen by the customer
Step 2	Rank the failures in order of seriousness
Step 3	For each failure identify the possible causes within or associated with the product, including any fault conditions
Step 4	For each cause identify any steps that can be taken to eliminate or minimise risk of occurrence
Step 5	Annotate any appropriate product documentation with cause or risk reducing comments

A full fault tree analysis of a complex product can be a lengthy activity and will generate a significant number of failure mechanisms and their possible causes. It is important to note that, in addition to normal operation of the product, fault conditions should also be considered. However, in products that are for use in emergency situations or those used in critical fields such as medical electronics, a risk analysis, such as an FTA is highly recommended if not is made mandatory by the specific product requirements. The following worked example illustrates some of the findings of a fault tree analysis of the Survival Emergency Locator Transmitter.

Identify the failures appropriate to the bearer of an ELT(S).   **Worked Example 10.3**

The ELT(S), being a safety radio transmitter, must work, first time, once activated. The failures, as perceived by the bearer are ranked, in descending order of importance, in Table 10.5.

Table 10.5 ELT(S) failures in descending order of significance

- Beacon cannot be activated
- Beacon fails to operate once activated
- Beacon operates but only for very short time
- Beacon causes injury during activation
- Beacon operates but does not alert rescue system

The next stage in the FTA would be to take the most serious failure and look at the product to see what could cause the product to suffer this fault. A quick look at the concept of the product suggests a few possible causes: the antenna may be broken, the battery may be discharged; the switch may be defective; the electronics may have failed; and so on. In reality product experts from the electronic, mechanical and software (if appropriate) disciplines would be present at the analysis meeting to ensure the analysis is complete and considers fault conditions.

Fault tree analysis is a top-down approach to failure analysis in that the analysis starts at the top of the product structure, the product itself, and works downwards towards component level failures. The alternative approach to failure analysis if to work from the bottom of the product, namely the components, upwards. This approach is called Failure Mode and Effects Analysis (FMEA).

FMEA

FMEA - Failure Modes and Effects Analysis
FMECA - Failure Modes and Effects Criticality Analysis.

The objective of FMEA is to identify all the failure modes of the product and the effect each would have on the customer. When the analysis is confined to serious or critical failures such as those which would cause or would be likely to cause death or injury or would render the product useless it is called FMECA. One approach that can be used to carry out an FMEA is to analysis every component in the product, electrical and mechanical and all of its individual failure modes.

For example a resistor can fail in one of three ways: its value can change; it can become a short circuit or an open circuit. More complex components such as transistors and integrated circuits can fail in many different ways. The effect of each mode of failure of each component can be modelled and the effect on the overall product determined. This approach is complex and time consuming in a product of even reasonable complexity.

Design reviews

One of the ways of checking that the product development process is remaining on track to producing a top quality output is to hold periodic technical reviews of the project. Such reviews are referred to as 'design reviews'. Design reviews are typically held for one of three reasons:

- to approve a design;
- to agree a course of action between alternatives, or agree to do additional or alternative investigative tasks;
- authorise progression from one stage to another, or authorise a significant purchase or other resource request.

The objectives of design reviews are to review the quality of the task under review. Generally this will involve reviewing progress, in the form of achieved results, against the appropriate requirement specification. The British Standards Institute states that: 'It is necessary to set up a design review procedure whereby the design is scrutinised at a series of formal meetings.'

The guide goes onto identify some of the things that might be included such as the design concept; review of detail designs; review of prototype results and so on. For any project there should be a series of such design reviews built into the project plan from the outset, that serve as quality gates through which the design must pass before progressing.

Design reviews should consider, as a minimum, the aspects of the design and product as shown in Table 10.6

Table 10.6 Subjects to be addressed in a design review

- Critical review of the design requirement
- Critical review of the 'Illities
- Safety and Liability
- Target manufacturing cost
- Fit with production process

Design review checklists

Since design reviews appear regularly at specific points in the product development process, a general set of questionnaires can be produced to ensure all past problems and all anticipated problems are addressed. The checklists can be regularly updated to reflect changes in technology, product line or process used to develop products.

A good time for design reviews are at the end of process stages. For example at the end of prototype testing, or when the product specification is declared complete.

Produce the outline of a design review checklist for printed circuit board design and layout.

Worked Example 10.4

Questions can be produced in the following areas in relation to the design and labout of printed circuit boards:

- Board material
- Board profiling
- Components
- Connections to the board
- Decoupling capacitors
- Design for test

- Electrical considerations
- Environmental protection

- Layout design
- Mounting hole positions and clearance
- Quality control
- Soldering method
- Thermal design
- Tracking considerations (thinkness, spacing)
- Autoplacement or auto-assembly
- Labelling and general legends

Using the above set of headings, a fairly extensive checklist can be developed.

People

The most important resource of any organisation is its employees. The people who do the work. Top quality people need three characteristics:

- knowledge
- skill
- attitude.

235

Knowledge of the job to be completed or the principles underlying the job, skills appropriate to the task being undertaken and a positive attitude towards the work to be done. If any one of these three ingredients is missing efficiency or quality is likely to suffer.

For example, the absence of knowledge to perform a thermal analysis on the transmitter of the ELT(S) will mean the knowledge has to be obtained first, perhaps through training, perhaps through sitting reading books or the manufal of a computer program. Lack of the skills to solder the components into a printed circuit board could result in poor quality joints or no joints at all. Finally a poor attitude towards work will mean people do not have their hearts in the job and the work will suffer.

The factors that affect attitude are shown in Table 10.7.

Table 10.7 Attitude-influencing factors

- organisational culture
- perception of reward
- ease of task achievement
- esprit de corps
- degree of motivation
- perception of the task value.

The organisational culture can be one that generally supports employees, encourages freedom and teamworking or, at the other extreme, one that is highly authoritarian and directive towards the staff. The impact of the culture will affect how individuals feel towards the organisation and hence their attitude towards work asked of them. Similarly, if the rewards obtained are not perceived to be worth the effort then again a poor attitude will result. This latter point links in with how well-motivated the employee feels towards the organisation and towards the team, the esprit de corps and the perceived value of the task. Take for example the correction of a design fault. Correction of the fault is likely to be challenging and seen as being valuable. Completing the paperwork is less likely to be seen to be of such high value and may therefore be completed with less thoroughness.

Quality in production

The keys to good quality in production are:

- people
- product design
- raw materials
- procedures
- equipment.

People

People trained in the skills required to perform the tasks assigned to them; who have the right attitude towards work and knowledge of what their process involves; the quality expected of them; and the impact of their producing poor product.

Product

A product that has been designed to be compatible with existing production capability or for new capability which has been developed in parallel with the product development. The product should have addressed tolerance and yield issues and be fully fit for production and the end customer. It needs to be assemblable and testable at a cost that yields acceptable levels of profit given the forecast selling price.

Procedures

A set of procedures that enable the production process to be established and controlled such that quality work is performed at each and every stage. These procedures include a definition of each stage and a clear statement of the quality standard of the output.

Raw materials

Raw materials purchased to an appropriate quality standard from suppliers who will maintain the standard throughout the manufacturing time of the product.

Equipment

A set of production equipment, tool, jigs and fixtures, appropriate for the available production skills and the volume and volume rate of the planned production.

An important point to note in the above list is the absence of any effective Quality Control measures. The absence of such measures is intended. The thrust of this book has been to build quality into each stage so that only a minimal amount of non-value adding Quality Control is required. Clearly some Quality Control will be required but this should mainly be for product verification and process control purposes. The main aim of production should be to build quality into every activity so that the process produces product that works first time.

Summary

In this chapter the difference between Quality Control and Quality Assurance has been investigated, the Quality Control approach having been discarded in favour of the proactive, forward-thinking Quality Assurance. This chapter has considered quality, not as an essential part of the product development process but more as the glue to hold the process together and which, if applied correctly, will result in a well developed product in the shortest possible time.

Quality Assurance is considered by first addressing how customer needs can be integrated and used as the starting point of all activity within the product development process and production. Quality functional deployment is shown to be an important tool at this stage. As the product moves into the design and development phases, concurrent engineering is compared with the more conventional serial approach. Tools such as risk analysis, Failure Modes and Effects Analysis, Fault Tree Analysis, design reviews and design review checklists are all introduced as tools for use in building quality into the product. Finally the influences of quality in production are addressed.

Problems

10.1   What are the possible faults in a domestic central heating thermostatic controller as they affect the customer?

10.2   What are the failure modes of the general purpose NPN transistor such as the BC107?

10.3   What are the non-value adding activities in the traditional sequence of events in dealing with suppliers described in Fig. 10.2?

10.4   Create a design review checklist for the layout of a printed circuit board.

Summary

Designing new electronic products is a core aspect of the engineering discipline. In fact the word engineer is formed from the Latin word meaning genius or clever device. In the preceding chapters we have covered electronic product design from the perspective of the electronic designer. In particular we have covered the following areas:

- We have introduced the basic processes involved in the design of any electronic product and shown how to make the first important steps, correct ones.

- In the early stages, many aspects of electronic product design involve dealing with 'soft' information such as; how big, how much, what facilities, how reliable, etc. We have presented methods of rigorously handling this information so that the design process can be properly guided by a set of specifications which are as accurate as is possible given the fuzzy nature of some of the information available at that time. Most importantly, we have shown how to make use of the soft information in a way which vitally assists the design process.

- We have shown how to avoid jumping into detail too early and have shown how to take a top-down view of the product as a whole. System design at this level is not only effective, it is also time efficient and a spur to creativity as design alternatives, which may have significant impact on the ultimate utility of the product, can be explored here at a comparatively low cost.

- The analysis of the costs associated with product development and manufacture are also covered. This is an important aspect of the design process because the balance of the cost versus the specification is often the main factor in choosing between alternative design possibilities.

- It is pointless designing a product which cannot be produced, yet the success of production with real components is critically dependent on how sensitive the product is to the very real variation of component values. Tolerance design is an important aspect of the design. We have shown how you can analyse the tolerance sensitivity of the product. Furthermore we have shown that 100% production yield is not necessarily the optimum goal as regard minimising production cost. We have also shown how to centre the design as regards tolerances to achieve the maximum production yield.

- Electronic products must work in a variety of situations, from the benign to the hazardous. Designing the product with due attention to its likely operating environment is crucial to its long term success.

- The reliability of an electronic product is also an aspect of the design which is important. Setting the correct level of reliability has a significant effect on its overall cost. In safety-critical systems reliability is vital. We have shown how you can estimate, measure and assure the reliability of an electronic product. We also show how one can design a product to have a high reliability and how to monitor its reliability improvement during development so that you can predict its likely reliability during production.

- How to design products that can be made more easily and therefore more inexpensively. We have also shown how good design can also either reduce the need for production testing or make it easier and so further reduce the cost of production.

- The whole concept and application of quality as part of the design process has been covered. Quality is the glue that holds the design, manufacture and use process together.

The core philosophy of this book is that if you design an electronic product from the outset to take account of the needs of both the customer and production then it is more likely to be successful than if you do not. The design and implementation of electronic products that people can use and enjoy and that make a difference to life is surely the *raison d'être* of an electronic engineer and an integrated approach to it is not only sensible but essential. We also believe that to do so is not only at the heart of our discipline but is also intellectually challenging, emotionally satisfying, financially rewarding and generally fun! We hope that the knowledge you have gained through reading this book will help you to be able to approach electronic product design in this way and so be able to share our enthusiasm for this unique expression of the creativity of the human spirit.

Outline solutions

1.1 The basis of an answer should be that the development of such a new product would involve two of the three types of risk described in chapter 1. Technical risk in the ability to establish the display technology at an acceptable production cost and yield. Programme risk in the ability of the company to develop the product in a time appropriate for the customer or market. If the product is being developed as a race against other company's the risk of failing to develop on time could result in serious loss of sales.

1.2 The team would best comprise, as a minimum, representatives of the following functions: project manager; mechanical design; semiconductor design and processing; production; reliability; quality and purchasing.

1.3 Technical and physical requirements, approval requirements, quality, production, environment. safety, electromagnetic compatibility.

1.4 Main purposes are to demonstrate that the product can be manufactured, for type approval testing. Additional requirements may include market samples or advertising samples.

2.1 The specification should include three sections, customer requirements including the size and weight of the hand-held part of the product and the ease with which the controlling part of the product can be integrated into the existing domestic lighting system; a competitive aspect to ensure the product is competitive with other products or substitutes on the market; and a company requirement including production volume, rate, cost, etc.

2.2 The list should include EMC, medical devices, safety, maritime, etc.

2.3 The ways should include adding features, reducing costs to give better value for money, addressing a different set of customers through the addition of a games port, etc.

2.4 The checklist should include sinusoidal, random, resonance search, shock, bump and drop requirements. Included with each should be magnitude limits, frequency, number of incidences, etc.

2.5 An open ended question depending on the type of television, in general answer should include size, weight, colour, case material, position of controls (if any), position of loudspeaker(s), stand mounting points, etc.

3.1 The case rear and front, user interface and internal electronics pack with any required battery backup should be included.

3.2 At the top level the functional blocks could include the microcontroller, the user interface display and switches, the temperature sensor and power control blocks.

3.3 The functional specification should include details of all inputs and outputs including the power supply. There should be limits on all parameters. All controllable functions should be defined along with the range of control achievable.

3.4 The test and integration plan should take the product from discrete components at the input end through to deliverable, packaged, product at the other. Appropriate assembly and test or inspection stages should be included to ensure a good balance between the cost of testing and the need to catch faults as early in the process as possible.

3.5 Things to look for include: case structure, fabrication method and assembly method; number of printed circuit boards and the range of component types and hence assembly processes required to manufacture them; the number and complexity of internal wiring looms; the complexity of user interface assembly; product labelling strategy; product packaging and manual.

4.1 Activities should include development of the electronic circuit, the plastic housing, instruction manual, packaging.

4.2 Given:

C_{tot} = total cost
C_t = total manufacturing cost
C_{rw} = rework cost
C_{rt} = retest cost
y = yield
n = batch size

$$C_{tot} = n\left(C_t + \left(C_{rw} + C_{rt}\right)\left(1 - y\right)\right)$$

4.3 £294.12.

4.4 £616.45.

4.5 £593.30.

4.6 The net present value of the project is £526.54k. The project is therefore better than investing the money in the bank. The risk of the project and its impact on the organisation and workforce would need to be considered before making a real decision.

5.1 1149Hz, 1039Hz, 938Hz, 849Hz. The cutoff frequency is very sensitive to component values.

5.2 The yield is approximately 10%.

5.3 There are a range of RC combinations that give the same yield for any given resistor and capacitor tolerance.

6.1 Factors should include temperature, thermal shock, bump and solar radiation as a minimum.

6.2 Factors should include temperature, humidity and waterproofing as a minimum.

6.3 You may wish to contact an airline company or airline authority to find information to help you answer this question.

7.1 0.74.

7.2 275 years.

7.4 500 thousand hours versus 750 thousand hours.

7.5 0.105 x MTTF and 0.38 x MTTF.

7.6 0.001 x MTTF and 0.045 x MTTF.

7.7 2976 hours.

7.9 The MTTF becomes 18.7 years.

7.10 The failure rate is reduced by a factor of 32.

7.11 4 x MTTF or 4000 hours.

7.12 299.

8.1 The in-house cost is £103.55, the sub-contract cost is £105.75 making it cheaper to produce in-house. Other considerations include in-house capability, machine loading, skill requirements, etc.

8.3 Considerations in inferring the manufacturing process include the evenness of component placement, the number of different types of components used, printed circuit board legend, test points, connectors, components that need to be hand assembled, etc.

9.2 £78.40.

9.3 Marked test points, special test connectors, pads underneath surface mount components, etc.

10.1 It does not switch the central heating on or off. Part of the casing becomes live. It short circuits resulting in damage to another system component, and so on.

10.2 Open circuit base, collector or emitter; Short circuit between terminals; junction leakage or breakdown.

10.3 The largest source of non-value adding activities relate to rejects. Other sources include any negotiation about drawings and the detail contained on them plus the passing back and forth of paperwork.

10.4 Checks should inlcude positioning and orientation opf components, size of power and ground tracks, proximity of tracks carrying large signals or high frequency signalsd to one another, clearance between tracks and mounting points, position and form of labels required, legend, etc.

Index